# PROCESS FOR
# SYSTEM ARCHITECTURE
# AND REQUIREMENTS
# ENGINEERING

# PROCESS FOR SYSTEM ARCHITECTURE AND REQUIREMENTS ENGINEERING

**Derek Hatley   Peter Hruschka   Imtiaz Pirbhai**

Dorset House Publishing
353 West 12th Street
New York, NY  10014

Library of Congress Cataloging-in-Publication Data

Hatley, Derek J., 1934-
   Process for system architecture and requirements engineering / Derek Hatley, Peter
Hruschka, Imtiaz Pirbhai.
      p. cm.
   ISBN 0-932633-41-2 (pbk.)
   1. System design. 2. System analysis. I. Hruschka, Peter, 1951- II. Pirbhai, Imtiaz A.,
1953- III. Title.

QA76.9.S88 H3735 2000
005.1'2--dc21

                                                                                    00-060997

Cover Design:  David W. McClintock
Cover Graphic:  Detail from Figure 11.2
Cover Author Photographs:   Hatley photo: O'Connor-Rice Studios; Hruschka
      photo: James Robertson; Pirbhai photo: Stewart Auer.

Copyright © 2000 by Derek J. Hatley, Peter Hruschka, and Shams Pirbhai.  Published
by Dorset House Publishing Co., Inc., 353 West 12th Street, New York, NY  10014.

Distributed in the English language in Singapore, the Philippines, and Southeast Asia
by Alkem Company (S) Pte. Ltd., Singapore; in the English language in India,
Bangladesh, Sri Lanka, Nepal, and Mauritius by Prism Books Pvt., Ltd., Bangalore,
India; and in the English language in Japan by Toppan Co., Ltd., Tokyo, Japan.

Printed in the United States of America

Library of Congress Catalog Number: 00-060997

ISBN: 0-932633-41-2              12    11    10    9    8    7    6    5

## DEDICATION

*A wonderful friend and fine colleague of ours started this book:  He laid out the basic ideas and the structure, and developed some of the materials.  Then, suddenly and unexpectedly, and in the prime of his life, he passed away.  We miss him sorely.*

*We are grateful to his brother Shams for providing us with the original materials, and honored at being given the opportunity to complete the project.  It is not the same book it would have been had he completed it, but we hope it comes somewhere close to his expectations.*

*It is unusual to dedicate a book to one of its authors, but these are unusual and tragic circumstances.  So, we humbly dedicate* Process for System Architecture and Requirements Engineering *to the memory of a true visionary in the field of system development:*

Imtiaz Pirbhai.

# ACKNOWLEDGMENTS

We are deeply indebted to Kamal Hammoutene, Alan Hecht, Mark Maier, Vince Peterson, and Tanehiro Tatsuta for their painstaking reviews of the draft of this book and for their excellent comments and suggestions. The book is far better for their efforts.

We thank the editorial staff at Dorset House Publishing—Nuno Andrade, Debbie Carter, David Crohn, Wendy Eakin, Bob Hay, Mike Lumelsky, David McClintock, Matt McDonald, and Mike Richter—for the excruciating detail with which they examined, tore apart, and reconstructed our English. This, too, greatly improved the final product.

Finally, we thank the many participants in our seminars and workshops for their enthusiasm and for teaching us at least as much as we taught them.

# Contents

# Figures

# Part I
## Concepts

# Chapter 1
## Introduction

## 1.1 PURPOSE AND SCOPE

The overall purpose of this book is to present a broad approach to the effective development of systems, especially those involving multiple disciplines—as most systems do. We use a variety of practical, real-world case studies to illustrate the nature of systems and the system development process, and we include system models that can be used in the process.

The book builds on the methods and techniques originally described in *Strategies for Real-Time System Specification* [Hatley 88]. It is based on more than a decade of experience, our own and many others', in the practical application and teaching of the methods and techniques. When *Strategies* was written, we were working in the avionics engineering field, but since then, we have helped to introduce the methods, and have taught and facilitated their use, on a wide variety of projects, ranging from communications systems to biomedical systems, and from three-person projects to those of a hundred people and more.

The wide acceptance of the methods—which became known as the Hatley/Pirbhai methods—has been gratifying, but not all practitioners have used them correctly or effectively. There have been several changes over the years in the methods and their use, and several CASE (computer-aided system/software

3

engineering) tool developers have sought to automate the methods. Besides a few notable exceptions, most of these tools have fallen far short of doing the job adequately. Our goal, then, is to share the benefit of our experiences, good and bad, in the hope of improving the overall state of system development and the methods and tools that support it.

## 1.2 THE SYSTEM DEVELOPMENT PROCESS

Perhaps the most significant lesson we have learned since the publication of *Strategies* is that having a well-defined and effective system development process is necessary before any methods or tools can be effective. Accordingly, this book places a strong emphasis on the system development process, and what it means to use it. An important feature of our approach is that it applies equally well to all technologies, and thereby provides a common language for developers in widely differing disciplines. Another important feature is the coexistence of the requirements and architecture methods, and of the corresponding models they produce. Our approach keeps these two models separate, yet it fully records their ongoing and changing interrelationships. This feature is missing from virtually all other system and software development methods, and from most CASE tools, because most of them automate only the requirements model.

We are not alone in our focus on the system development process: It is also the focus of a great deal of work throughout the industry.

## 1.3 UNDERLYING PRINCIPLES

The specific techniques presented in this book are based upon general principles that we believe are fundamental to system development regardless of the particular techniques used. It is worth stating these principles right here, at the outset, to help you keep them firmly in mind as you progress through the book. We elaborate on them in later chapters, but here they are in summary:

- Every system below the level of the whole universe is a component of one or more larger systems. The larger systems are the context or environment in which the component system must work.
- Thus, systems comprise a layered set of subsystems below the layer with which we happen to be dealing, and a layered set of supersystems above that layer. This layered structure can be exploited both in representing systems and in defining the system development process.

- Most systems are members of multiple layered sets. The particular set or sets chosen to represent a system are determined by the viewpoint or viewpoints that are important for the particular system.
- Every system has a set of essential requirements, which meet the needs of the context or environment, without imposing any specific implementation, and a set of physical requirements, which reflect the architectural and design decisions made to satisfy the essential requirements.
- To carry out the essential requirements, and thereby to meet the needs of the environment, systems receive as inputs, produce as outputs, and process internally information and/or material and/or energy.

To achieve the dependability and flexibility needed in the development of complex systems, all of the system artifacts invoked by these principles must be represented separately, but with their relationships and interactions also represented. These artifacts include, at a minimum: the layered system structure and the relationships within it; the subsystems, the supersystems, and their relationships; the essential requirements, the physical requirements, and their relationships; the information, material, and energy that travel into and out of the sub- and supersystems; the processing of that information, material, and energy; and the links between the information, material, and energy, their processing, and the sub- and supersystems.

These, then, are the principles that we follow throughout this book.

## 1.4 WHAT'S IN A NAME?

When we wrote *Strategies*, we did not formally introduce a name for the methods it describes. As we mentioned earlier, practitioners in the industry eventually referred to them as the "Hatley/Pirbhai methods," or simply the "H/P methods." This presents us with a dilemma: First, many more people than the two original authors have now contributed to the methods, and at the very least the name should include that of the third author, Peter Hruschka; second, the methods themselves do not represent the entirety of *Strategies*, and they represent even less the entirety of this book. What we describe in both books is a *process* for which the methods provide support.

Our solution to this dilemma is to formally adopt separate names for the methods and for the process. Accepting the reality that the industry has de facto adopted a name for the methods, we will change that name to the "Hatley/Hruschka/Pirbhai" or "H/H/P" methods. For the process, the title of this book is about as good a description as we can think of: *Process for System Architecture and Requirements Engineering.* Its one flaw is its length, so we propose to use its acronym: *PSARE,* pronounced *sari,* as in the traditional southern Asian garment.

## 1.5 AUDIENCE FOR AND STRUCTURE OF THE BOOK

The intended audience for this book includes system managers, system architects, system engineers, and managers and engineers in all of the diverse engineering technologies, such as mechanical, electrical, electronic, hydraulic, chemical, manufacturing, computer hardware, and computer software. This book may also be used as a text for graduate courses in system engineering. It is intentional that no exercises are included: Practical examples from the students' own experiences are much better than "canned" exercises in a book. However, the case studies in Parts I and II can serve as exercises for students to study, critique, extend, and modify.

There are two main parts in this book:

- Part I: Concepts: An introduction to the system approach, to system models, to the system development process, and to the application of the models to the process. A hospital monitoring system is used as an illustrative case study.
- Part II: Case Study—Groundwater Analysis System: An in-depth look at the development of a highly multidisciplinary system.

These parts are followed by three important sections:

- Appendix: Changes, Improvements, and Misconceptions Since the Methods' Introduction: Summarizes changes, improvements, and misconceptions regarding the methods and their use since *Strategies for Real-Time System Specification* was written. This appendix should be particularly helpful to those who have already used the methods, and need a quick update on what is different about them in this book.

- Glossary: Definitions of words, phrases, acronyms, and abbreviations commonly used in system development using the Hatley/Hruschka/Pirbhai architecture and requirements methods.
- Bibliography: Useful references used throughout the book to point to other sources of information on specific topics.

All the chapters in Part I, and the case study in Part II, close with summaries. These can be used for a quick overview of the book before it is read in depth.

## 1.6 A PARTICIPATIVE CASE STUDY ON THE WEB

This book was to have included three case studies, and indeed we developed a third one, but we eventually decided not to include it. Instead, we offer it on the Web for the reasons discussed below.

While we were writing this book, software development went through some radical changes, most notably the adoption of object-oriented techniques, culminating in the integration of some of the most popular ones into the Unified Modeling Language (UML).

The third case study is of an automated airline quick-ticketing system (QTS) that is user-interface driven and very software-intensive. We consider the Web to be the right medium for this case study because the UML and other software notations are still changing, with new versions almost every year. Updating a book that frequently is not feasible.

The QTS model will demonstrate how our process of developing tightly linked architecture and requirements models can be used for software-intensive systems, and how to transition smoothly from our techniques at the system levels to the UML in software. Using the Web will allow you, the reader, to participate in the evolution of this and possibly other models as the system and software worlds change.

The Website is www.psare.com, and it includes a forum where those interested can discuss system and software issues, the methods, the QTS, and other systems and models as we develop them. We look forward to these virtual meetings with you, and we hope that this approach makes both the book and the third model more valuable to you.

## 1.7 A Caveat

One final introductory comment: Our commitment should be to developing quality systems that will satisfy the customers' needs. Very often, that end goal is missed. Methods and automated tools are only vehicles to reach that goal. Automated tools automate methods; the methods precede their automation. Our commitment should be first to the process of satisfying customer needs, then to the methods that facilitate that process, and finally to the tools that automate the selected methods. Even though we use automated tools to present the case studies here, please remember

> **Methods and automated tools are of no use without properly qualified people who are using a well-defined development process, and who are dedicated to satisfying customer needs.**

# Chapter 2
# What Is a System?

## 2.1 SYSTEM CHARACTERISTICS

We often hear and use terms such as "system," "system approach," and "system concept," but what do they mean, and how can an understanding of them help us develop better systems? To understand system problems and how to approach them, we must understand what a system is. In this chapter, we discuss these issues, and we establish which subset of the huge variety of systems is of interest to us.

### 2.1.1 Introduction to Systems

Attempts to define "system" usually end up encompassing just about everything in the universe. The problem is that the universe itself is a system, so is an atom, and so are most things in between. In the most general sense, a system is simply any organized set of components that work together in some defined way. We need to reduce the possibilities to just those systems that are of interest in our development work. But what are these interesting systems?

The biggest single distinction between systems in general and those that are of interest to us is that the latter are people-made systems. Most of what follows, then, is in reference to people-made systems, but much of it can be extrapolated to systems in general. First, we list some premises for a people-made system:

- It exists for some purpose or purposes that benefit people.
- It consists of components that fulfill its intended purpose through their interrelationships.
- Through exchanges of information and/or material and/or energy, it interacts with the environment in which it exists and operates.
- It must fit into its operating environment, which usually restricts its behavior.

System purpose ranges, for example, from the entire set of avionics functions for an aircraft to something as simple as the switching on and off of an electrical device. The components of a system can include: laws of physics, software, hardware, mathematical algorithms, or any other conceptual or physical entity. For the system to serve its intended purpose, all of these components must be well integrated.

These observations highlight the importance of the interactions between the system and its environment, and they suggest a definition:

> People-made system: An organized set of components that work together and with their environment to provide some perceived benefit for people.

Even though this definition narrows the field considerably, it still encompasses a vast array of systems: automobiles, cruise control systems, aircraft, bicycles, transportation systems, manufacturing plants, refrigerators, banking and insurance systems, computers, software systems, and many, many more. Later in this chapter, we consider system categorization by complexity, which supplements the definition above.

Note that the above definition of people-made systems does not preclude debate: What is an organized set? Who does the perceiving? Is the benefit for people real or imagined? Which particular people will benefit? Will anyone suffer? These are the debates that determine whether a system will be developed; they in no way detract from the validity of the definition itself.

To behave as a system, a group of components must serve a common purpose. An arbitrary grouping of sheet metal and rivets does not constitute an automobile, nor does an arbitrary grouping of hardware and software necessarily accomplish any desired purpose. Yet, this ad hoc approach to development seems to be the norm. Often, one of the first actions on a project is to split the project team into hardware, software, and other single-discipline groups. How did the project, a priori, decide on the hardware, software, and other partitioning?

Historically, systems have been considered just hardware or just software systems. The partitioning question becomes increasingly significant as systems evolve into hybrids of software and various types of hardware. In the past, for example, telephones and test instruments have principally been hardware systems, while information systems have principally been software systems. With modern advances in technology, these and almost all systems are evolving to include multiple hardware technologies and software, making it necessary to consider functional partitioning carefully.

A recent product advertisement stated: "Hardware does very little without software; software does nothing without hardware." We would add just one more statement: "Hardware and software do nothing without people." These may seem like truisms, but very often they are overlooked. When specifying systems, we must look at the whole system: software, all the hardware technologies, and the role of and benefit to people. This last item constitutes the purpose of the system. If it is overlooked, the system will not be useful and either will not be developed or, if developed, will not be used.

For the rest of this chapter—and indeed for the rest of the book—we focus only on the people-made systems we defined earlier. We discuss the characteristics of systems—behavior, structure, components, specification, and especially the process of development—and we give practical examples of how to fit together and represent all of these elements. We discuss what requirements are, where they come from, and how they are managed; how system architectures are developed; how requirements are allocated to architecture elements; how architecture elements are enhanced to serve the needs of new internal interfaces; and how to develop the complete system specification, from which the system can be built and tested.

## 2.1.2 System Hierarchies

The premise that every system must interact with its environment draws attention to the environment itself, and to the fact that it too is a system. Thus, every system is part of a larger system, from which we deduce: *Systems come in hierar-*

*chies.* Every system must find its place within its larger system, and the two systems must communicate via exchanges of information, material, or energy. Since the larger system constitutes the operating environment, it constrains the smaller system's usage, maintainability, and extensibility.

In this section and those that follow, we look further into the following properties of systems:

- Systems come in hierarchies.
- Systems at any one level of a hierarchy of systems may be considered independent peers, forming a network.
- All useful systems exhibit predictable, often cyclical, behavior.
- No system is error free.

These characteristics illustrate what we mean by a system concept—one of the terms with which we started this chapter: They consider a system as a whole, and address its overall characteristics rather than the characteristics of its individual components. Each of these characteristics is discussed below.

Figure 2.1 shows the most general view of the hierarchical nature of systems, starting with the whole universe, and proceeding, in this example, down to some automobile subsystems. The fact that systems come in hierarchies is important, since it allows us to focus on individual levels in our systems and subsystems, rather than to think of them as one big, insurmountable blob. There is no implication that a hierarchy represents a strict, top-down control structure. A given level of a hierarchy may control the level below (as in a management structure) or may be composed of it. The components at any one level can behave as a network interacting with each other as peers. We discuss this in Section 2.1.4 "System Networks."

Figure 2.2 shows a more detailed system hierarchy for several levels of an aircraft system. Both this hierarchy and the one in Figure 2.1 have composed-of relationships between the levels: Every system is a component in a higher-level system and is made up of component subsystems. These two perspectives can be described as the *context* perspective and the *content* perspective. In Figure 2.2, avionics is part of the *content* of the total system—the aircraft—which is the *context* for the avionics. The avionics consists of several levels of subsystem, which are *its* content. These perspectives provide a framework for the specifications that need to be written for a system. At every level of system specification, design decisions provide requirements for the component subsystems in levels below. We discuss layered models much more in Chapter 5.

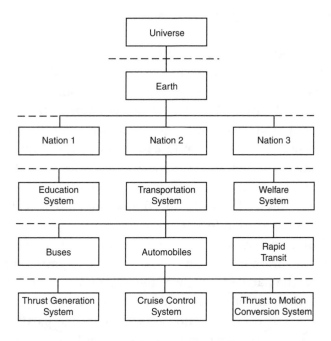

*Figure 2.1: Universal Hierarchy of Systems.*

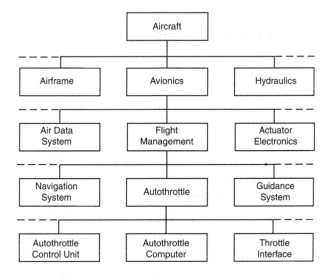

*Figure 2.2: Avionics Context and Content Hierarchy.*

### 2.1.3 Multiple Hierarchies

It is important to recognize that, in most cases, a given element in a hierarchy can also fit into numerous other hierarchies. The nature of a particular hierarchy depends on the criteria we use in selecting the partitioning from one layer to the next. For example, in Figure 2.1, the layer below Transportation System could be the one shown, or it could consist of Air Transportation, Water Transportation, and Ground Transportation, or it could consist of Private Transportation, Public Transportation, and Commercial Transportation. The layer illustrated in Figure 2.1 is partitioned according to vehicle type, the air/water/ground alternative according to transportation medium, and the private/public/commercial alternative according to transportation function.

So, which of these different partitionings (and any others we might think of) is correct? The answer is that they are all correct. The particular partitioning we choose depends on the particular view of the system we wish to take. The choice often depends on divisions of responsibility, or the actual physical structure of a system. In many cases, we might choose more than one partitioning for a single system: Whenever multiple partitionings are helpful in understanding the system, we should not hesitate to use them.

The idea of multiple hierarchies becomes particularly important when partitioning a system into hardware and software [Maier 98]. In this case, the hardware and software views can be very different. In the hardware view, the software is buried somewhere in the depths of the hardware; in the software view, the hardware is buried somewhere in the depths of the software. The two views could hardly be more different, yet both are correct. We discuss hardware/software partitioning further in Chapter 6.

### 2.1.4 System Networks

As stated earlier, the subsystems within a layer of the system hierarchy form a network of peers that interact and communicate with each other. Figure 2.3 illustrates this for the bottom layer of Figure 2.2. The three subsystems pass information (and, in general, material and energy) between each other and perform their respective tasks cooperatively, without any one having more importance or authority than another.

Both the hierarchical and network aspects of systems are important in system development, and both need to be specified and modeled.

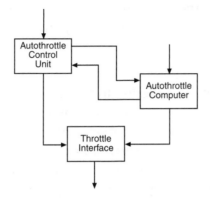

*Figure 2.3: A Subsystem Network.*

## 2.1.5 System Life Cycle and Errors

Figure 2.4 provides one of the justifications for taking a system approach. The figure shows that no matter how well-developed the system or how rigorous the testing, there will always be some residual errors, but the number of residual errors will be smaller in a well-structured system. The system approach, then, reduces errors during the operational life of the system and delays the time when the system "wears out" and exhibits an unacceptable error rate.

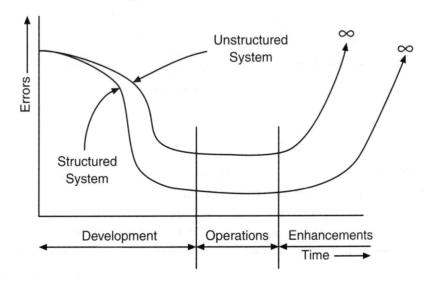

*Figure 2.4: System Errors.*

There is extensive data on the correlations between software practices and project performance in *Code Complete* [McConnell 93], particularly in its reference tables.

## 2.1.6 Order and Chaos

It is often said that society is suffering from information overload. That may or may not be true in general, but it surely is true in system development. In any given project, there is so much information that one wonders how it gets sorted and filtered to make it meaningful. The number of ways in which this information arrives can be overwhelming. The interactions during a project seem chaotic, as illustrated in the upper part of Figure 2.5. Everything seems to be going in every direction, and the hope is that it will all come together somehow. The information needs to be properly managed, and its appropriate role in the project established.

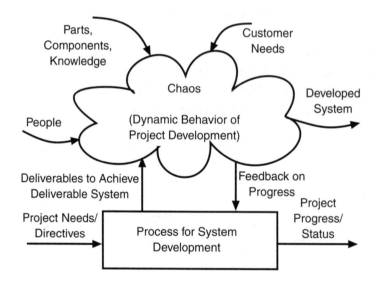

*Figure 2.5: Project Chaos and Order.*

A solution is suggested in the lower portion of Figure 2.5. Below the chaos is a Process for System Development that provides a framework for organizing the seemingly chaotic activities, ensuring that they contribute to the desired end. This is where the system approach is applied to organize the necessary development activities—a further justification for its use. Since modern systems are complex by nature, the development process too will be complex, but there is a big difference between complexity and chaos. For example, there might be several concurrent starting points; the development might take several routes at once; or there might be great flexibility in the way different parts of the project are conducted. If all of these things are part of an overriding strategy, they should all come together in a well-developed, deliverable system.

## 2.1.7 System Predictability

Despite the chaotic appearance of system development depicted in Figure 2.5, systems themselves have a predictable nature, which often manifests itself as cyclical or repeated behavior. This attribute allows us to specify and build systems successfully. Cyclical behavior does not necessarily imply exact repetitions, but it will have similar responses to repeated behavior in the environment, such as the steps in a chemical process or the take-off, cruise, and landing flight phases of an aircraft. Moreover, just as systems are hierarchical, their cyclical nature can be hierarchical, and the two can be related to each other: There are often major cycles associated with the system, and sub-cycles within major cycles that can be associated with either subsystems or sub-functions.

## 2.1.8 Dealing with Complexity

It is not hard to convince ourselves that we cannot process every possible combination and permutation of the information that is thrown at us. A single chess game, for example, has around $10^{120}$ possible sequences. We don't have numbers for the amount of information associated with a project: It is at least comparable to that of a chess game, but without all the nice prescribed moves. We need some way to filter the information into manageable chunks.

We can supplement our earlier definition of systems by categorizing them by complexity. Three major categories can be identified: simple systems, complex organized systems, and complex unorganized systems. Simple systems are those that always have the same response to a given stimulus, such as bicycles, hand-operated eggbeaters, lawn mowers, and door locks. Their overall behavior is the sum of the behaviors of their parts.

Complex organized systems are those that, though complex, can be analyzed, synthesized, and investigated using engineering techniques. Their responses to outside stimuli usually vary according to past and present circumstances, but they can be analyzed and described in engineering terms. Some examples are airplanes, automobiles, the national highway system, automated biomedical analysis systems, factory production lines, and communication systems. These systems have an inherent structure—hierarchical, networked, or some mixture of the two—that lends itself to organization and understandability.

Complex unorganized systems are those that are so complex that they can only be studied by averages, aggregates, and statistical methods. Examples are a country's economy, its political system, and the stock market. Only by studying trends and using other predictive methods can we understand such systems.

As with most categorizations, the boundaries between these categories are fuzzy, but this should not deter us from using them. These categories can help us decide early in a development which particular development techniques are appropriate.

Although the techniques described in this book can be used with all three categories of systems, we focus mostly on the complex organized category. Most engineering systems fall in this category, and the techniques suit them very well. In these systems, contrary to simple systems, the whole is *greater* than the sum of its parts. As the components of a complex organized system are assembled, their aggregate exhibits new properties that none of the individual components possessed. Rechtin and Maier [Rechtin 97] describe these as *emergent properties.* Another categorization—into primary and secondary features—is described in Pyle [Pyle 93].

## 2.2 VIEWS OF A SYSTEM

Based in part on the characteristics we have discussed already, systems can be viewed in several useful ways that will help us in analyzing and specifying them. The views are

>   *The Processing View,* how the system is partitioned between information, material, and energy processing,

>   *The Processor View,* whether the processing is automated or manual,

>   *The What/How View,* emphasizing the separation of requirements from architecture and design,

*The Level of Intelligence View*, whether each part of the system is a simple deterministic mechanism, or is adaptive to changing circumstances, and

*The Level of Activity View*, the separation of what the system stores (static) from what it does with what it stores (active).

Each of these is discussed in the following sections.

## 2.2.1 The Processing View

Using the third premise from Section 2.1.1, we can conclude that since systems exchange information, material, and energy with the environment, then they must process that information, material, and energy, and they must include processors to carry out this processing, as illustrated in Figure 2.6.

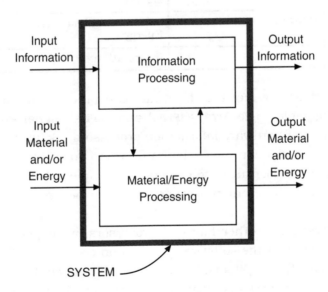

*Figure 2.6: System Processing.*

Each of the three types of processing requires its own processor or processors, as we discuss in the next section. Information processing is a major part of modern systems and, indeed, of modern life, but material and energy processing have been with us for much longer. Examples of materials processed are parts for assembly on a production line, the occupants carried by a vehicle, and fluids flowing through pipes and ducts. Examples of energy processed are torque on a drive shaft, a charge stored in a capacitor, and heat produced by an automobile engine used to heat the vehicle.

## 2.2.2 The Processor View

There are three types of processor that we normally encounter in systems: people, hardware, and software. Hardware processors are not restricted to electronic and electrical hardware; they also include mechanical, optical, hydraulic, pneumatic, and numerous other types of hardware. So, to which of the three processor types can be allocated the different types of processing?

| Type of Processor | Type of Processing |
|---|---|
| People | Information, Material, Energy |
| Hardware | Information, Material, Energy |
| Software | Information |

It is easy to overlook the fact that hardware can process information. Devices such as Programmable Logic Arrays (PLAs) and Digital Signal Processors (DSPs) are prime examples of hardware information processors. Software cannot process material or energy, but it can direct the hardware to do so. In any given system, not every kind of processor must be present. The same is true of the elements of a system hierarchy: Different processor types can be present in different elements.

Given the presence of other kinds of processors, what percentage of a total system specification does the software specification comprise? Obviously, no single number will satisfy all systems, but we can safely conclude that it is less than 100 percent. It might, perhaps, range anywhere from 20 percent to 80 percent, depending on the system, but the point is that the common practices of specifying only the software or minimizing the specification of the rest of the system are flawed.

Since people are such an integral part of a system and its environment, we must carefully account for manual processing in the system specification, and we must ensure that it is well integrated with the automated processing. These aspects of system specification are often overlooked or treated as an afterthought.

We have discussed the general question "What is a system?" but we face other questions when developing a specific system: "What is this particular system?"; "What is the context of this system?"; and, as illustrated in Figure 2.7, "Which is the true system?" In other words, is the system just the automated parts, or just the software, or is it the entire collection of hardware, software, and people? To do a good job of system development, we must choose this last alternative.

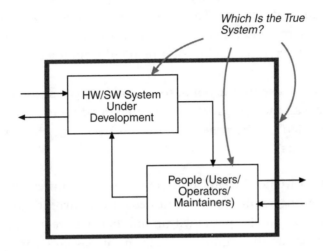

*Figure 2.7: Will the Real System Please Stand Up!*

By partitioning the system into its hardware and software too early, we may neglect some important factors that affect both, and we may neglect areas that should be performed manually. Hardware and software engineers tend to view their respective areas as the whole system, but it is best to define the system as the one the end user sees—the end product—including the automated and manual parts.

### 2.2.3 The *What/How* View

One of the most pervasive problems with system development has been the confusion between requirements and design—the *what* and the *how*. There are numerous difficulties surrounding this issue:

- What exactly *is* a requirement? Certainly, some requirements come from the customer, but what about those requirements we mentioned that arise as a result of design decisions?

- Early structured development approaches attempted to define requirements development as a completely separate and independent exercise, but requirements and design interact strongly throughout development.
- Quite apart from these close interactions, one of the most fundamental needs for sound system development—at least in requirements-driven systems (see Section 2.3.2)—is complete traceability between requirements and design. This has rarely been achieved in the past. Without it, there is no way to be sure that every requirement has been met, and that every piece of design resulted from a legitimate requirement.
- In spite of the close interactions, to conduct proper system testing, we need to have all the system requirements stated clearly and separately from the design. Otherwise, there is no basis on which to conduct "black box" tests.

It seems, then, that we need clear definitions of what requirements are; we need a means of representing requirements and design concurrently but separately; we need to record all traceability paths within and between requirements and design; and we need to separate the requirements from the design for use in testing.

All of this adds up to a need to represent the *what* and the *how* of systems completely and correctly, with all of their links in place, but separable when needed. Much of the rest of this book addresses how to achieve this and how it works in practice.

## 2.2.4 The Level of Intelligence View

Another way in which systems can be classified is

> *Mechanistic:* Systems that take a defined set of inputs and, through a fixed "transform process," produce a defined set of outputs, as illustrated in the inner region of Figure 2.8.

> *Adaptive:* Systems that have a mechanistic component but, by either monitoring their outputs or interacting with the environment, change their behavior, as illustrated in the outer region of Figure 2.8.

These classifications are in fact similar to the simple and the complex organized systems we discussed in Section 2.1.8, where we said that most systems we deal with are of the latter kind. Here we are recognizing that within these complex organized systems are subsystems in both classifications.

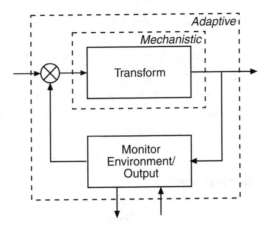

*Figure 2.8: System Classification.*

It is useful to characterize systems into these mechanistic and adaptive types in order to choose appropriate representation techniques. Adaptive systems need a means for monitoring the environment or themselves to determine their adaptations. Most of the systems we build or work with include elements having both of these characteristics, and recognizing them helps us to make appropriate choices in modeling and specifying these elements.

## 2.2.5 The Static/Dynamic View

Our final classification of systems is between their *static* and *dynamic* aspects. This is essentially a distinction between the stored information, material, and energy (herein referred to as *data*), and what the system does with them. Most systems are required to retain certain data in some kind of internal structure so that it can be retrieved and replenished readily. Although this data itself changes as needed, the structure in which it is retained remains static. When the system removes or reads data from the structure, it does so to process it in some way. This is the active aspect of the system.

Examples of static and dynamic system aspects include

- Parts (material) in a manufacturing stock room, which are always retained on the same racks and shelves (static), but are used and replaced as needed by the manufacturing process (dynamic).

- Voltages (energy) stored in an array of capacitors (static) that are read and summed to control the gain of an amplifier (dynamic).
- Account balances in a banking computer that are stored on disk (static), and updated whenever customer transactions occur (dynamic).

Especially when large amounts of data must be retained, the manner in which it is retained can have a major impact on system efficiency. A whole discipline of data and information modeling has been developed to deal with this issue, and while we do not cover this discipline in detail (that would be a whole separate book), we describe in later chapters how this type of modeling fits into our system development techniques.

## 2.3 SYSTEM REQUIREMENTS

No book on system development would be even remotely adequate without an in-depth look at requirements—where they come from, what they are, what their categories are, and what to do with them. This section provides that in-depth look into these topics.

### 2.3.1 The Sources of Requirements

It is vital to recognize that requirements do not come exclusively from the customer. Certainly, customer requirements are tremendously important, but requirements arrive from several other sources, and the system must meet them all to succeed. Broadly, requirements come from all the stakeholders in the system—everyone and everything having a vested interest in it: customers, users, managers, industry standards, the development process itself, and many others.

#### 2.3.1.1 Customers

By customer, we usually mean the person or organization that directly orders and pays for the system. Unfortunately, we often have little or no control over the form in which we receive customer requirements. They vary from a few notes on the back of an envelope—or even verbal instructions—to a thick stack of detailed documents that often exceeds the customer's real needs. Sometimes requirements reach the development team via an intermediary, such as a marketing department. Regardless of their form or the means by which they reach us, customer requirements usually require a lot of interpretation and clarification.

### 2.3.1.2 Users

Users are often different from customers. For example, a bank might be the customer, but the tellers and accountants that work for the bank are the end users. In other cases, such as that of commercial avionics systems, there is even more separation between customers and end users: The direct customer is an airframe manufacturer, its customer is an airline, and the end users are the airline pilots. Everyone in this chain can impose requirements on the system. It is often very difficult to obtain accurate information on end user needs—extensive market surveys may be required. In the case of airline pilots, they can be brought in to express their needs, and typically every one of them knows exactly what he or she wants—unfortunately, they all want something different! Regardless of these difficulties, the long-term success of the system can depend on how well it meets the needs of the end user.

### 2.3.1.3 Managers

Managers inevitably place resource constraints on system development; they might also insist that certain system, hardware, and software elements from previous projects be reused, and that stock electrical and mechanical components be used. Managers may also insist on commonality of design with other company products, and consideration of the needs of other customers besides the current one. Some of these demands might be of benefit to the customer, some might even be somewhat contrary to the customer's needs—but, regardless, management's requirements must be met.

### 2.3.1.4 Industry Standards

Most industries have standards, either self-imposed or government-imposed, to assure commonality, safety, reliability, and other characteristics of concern to the industry as a whole, and to the system's customers and users. Sometimes, the customer will state in the contract certain standards that must be met, but even without that direction, it is the system developers' responsibility to determine which standards apply to a particular system. Standards can have a major impact on system development.

### *2.3.1.5 The Development Process*

As we discuss in the next section, new requirements are added as a result of the development process itself. These requirements are often called developmental requirements, derived requirements, or enhancements. They arise as a result of architectural and design decisions: for example, to use a certain algorithm or interface to meet a higher-level requirement. These decisions then impose requirements on lower levels of the system structure. When the system is fully developed, there are usually far more developmental requirements than all other requirements combined.

### *2.3.1.6 Others*

There can be any number of additional stakeholders: maintainers, trainers, marketing people, and more. All have their particular needs of the system, and system engineers must identify them and ensure that their needs are valid, and if valid, met.

## 2.3.2 What Exactly Are Requirements, Anyway?

There has long been a complaint among system developers that customers and managers, instead of providing only "real" requirements, impose a lot of preconceived design on the system. The implication is that customers and management have no business dictating design. While there may be some grounds for this complaint, in the majority of cases it is not valid. Among the reasons that customers and managers place restrictions on the design are: the need to reuse previously developed items; the need for standard components to minimize stocks of spare parts; the need for commonality of function and interface with existing systems; and many others. These needs, then, are just as real as any other requirements; we refer to them here as *required constraints* or *design constraints*, and they are a very important part of the whole requirements set.

The "real" requirements referred to earlier are often known as *functional requirements* but, in accordance with requirements standards (MIL-STD-2167; DOD-STD-498), we prefer to call them *required capabilities*. Notice the subtle but important distinction between a required capability (a stated need that the system must fulfill) and an actual capability (a property of a developed system). Typically, the actual capability will be slightly better than the required capability so as to ensure compliance. A required capability describes something the system has to do; in the completed system, the actual capability is something that can be observed at the system outputs. It can be tested for conformance to the required capability.

Some typical statements of required capability are, "The system shall navigate the aircraft" and "The system shall calculate the current account balance" (here, we are following the US DOD approach—where rules prevail over grammar—of including "shall" in every requirements statement). However, these examples of required capabilities are incomplete: How accurately should the system navigate the aircraft? How fast and how often should the system calculate the current account balance? These questions lead us to the conclusion that a requirement is not complete unless its *required performance* is included—*how well* must the system do what it has to do. So, a statement of required performance is a necessary adjunct of a requirement. A prime requisite of a requirement is that it must be testable to ensure that the eventual system does indeed satisfy the requirement. A requirement without a performance statement is untestable, and therefore worthless.

It is worth asking: What is the difference between a required constraint and a performance requirement? Doesn't a performance requirement place a constraint on a required capability? The answer is that a performance requirement states how well a required capability must be carried out, regardless of how it is carried out; a required constraint places restrictions on how it is carried out—it directly limits the design choices. Perhaps the most telling point here is that required constraints also have performance requirements—"The system shall operate normally over the temperature range -20°C to +40°C" (a required constraint) "with no more than 1 failure in 2000 hours of continuous operation at the temperature extremes" (a performance requirement).

Thus, we have seen that, in general, there are three broad categories of requirements: required constraints, required capabilities, and performance requirements (which must be coupled with each of the others). The next section examines each of these categories in more detail and includes a model of their properties and relationships.

But before moving on, we have one last point to make on the relationship between requirements and system development. The point is best made by stating that not all systems are requirements-driven, at least, not driven by formal written requirements of the kind we have described so far [Rechtin 97]. As an example: A city is a people-made system, but (with a few notable exceptions) no one actually sits down and writes a set of requirements for a city, and then builds it. Rather, cities evolve over time, starting as small settlements exploiting favorable locations or natural resources, and growing as new facilities are added and more people decide to move in. It is most unlikely that the original settlers on Manhattan Island ever dreamed what their creation would grow into!

Similarly, consumer products are often driven much more by changing market forces than by any formal set of requirements.

How does all this affect our analysis of requirements? It simply tells us that not all systems start out with a formal set of requirements, but even so, the requirements that a system fulfills can be deduced from the form and function of the system itself. Ask residents of Manhattan what functions the city provides for them, and they will give you an impressive list. Do this for all the various stakeholders in the city, and you will have a pretty good set of requirements for Manhattan. This would be a useful exercise for city planners or for anyone considering starting a business in the city.

In summary, then, the fact that not all systems are requirements-driven does not diminish the value of analyzing requirements. Whether we carry out the analysis before or after the system exists, it still has great benefits.

## 2.3.3 A Model of Requirements

Figure 2.9 is a *class diagram* modeling the nature of requirements. We use this model throughout this section to describe requirements in great detail. We discuss class diagrams in depth in Chapter 4, but for now, we explain the notation only as needed to understand Figure 2.9. A class diagram is a static, nondirectional model, often used to define the requirements for a database. An important feature of the model is that every symbol is supported by a separate, detailed specification, not shown in Figure 2.9. A class diagram's static, nondirectional properties allow us to start our interpretation anywhere in a diagram, and to proceed in any direction. We choose to start with the Requirement entity class (a rectangle symbol). The description field of the specification for this entity class states

> A statement, in the format of the chosen method of requirements representation, describing one or more related characteristics that the system is required to have.

In the properties field of the specification are listed

> *Consistent*
> *Complete*
> *Correct*
> *Understandable*
> *Unambiguous*

These are the intrinsic properties needed of individual requirements. Other properties, such as traceability and prioritization, arise from relationships between requirements and with design artifacts, and may be added to the above list or captured in other parts of the modeling process.

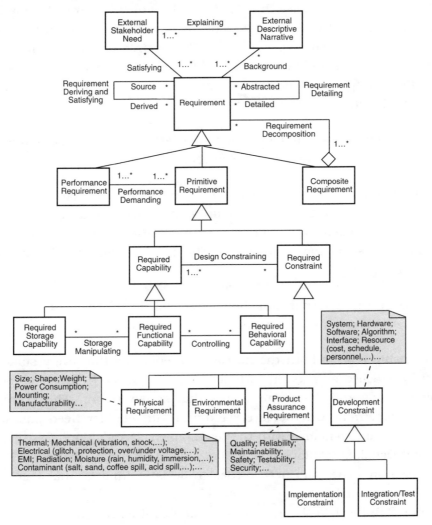

*Figure 2.9: A Class Diagram of Requirements.*

The attributes field of the specification states

*Unique identifier*

These three statements provide a concise description of what we mean by a requirement in its most general form. Note that to conform with the specified properties and attributes requires a good deal of requirement gathering and analysis. The entity model does not represent the activities needed to construct the entity classes it defines—that is done elsewhere (as we discuss later). Requirement, as defined in the entity model, is what we would expect to see in a fully prepared requirements specification. The source of these comprehensive requirements is represented by the External Stakeholder Need entity class, which has no defined properties, and its only attribute is a unique identifier. The description field of its specification states

> A statement, usually in conventional narrative form, of one or more related stakeholder needs that a system must fulfill.

This specification and the one for Requirement reflect the difference we described earlier between the way many external requirements arrive and the way we would prefer. The Requirement and External Stakeholder Need classes are linked by a relationship (a straight line): Satisfying. The specification for this relationship describes it as

> Identifies the External Stakeholder Need(s) that a given Requirement or group of Requirements entirely satisfies.

This relationship reflects both the necessity of ensuring that every stakeholder need is fully satisfied and the importance of tracing in both directions between stakeholder needs and the requirements that satisfy them. This traceability allows us to determine whether every External Stakeholder Need has, in fact, been accounted for; combined with the Requirement Deriving and Satisfying and Requirement Detailing relationships, it allows us to determine that every Requirement is based on some valid need or design decision (that is, that there are no spurious requirements).

In Figure 2.9, the 1 in the 1...* next to the Requirement entity class signifies mandatory participation of the External Stakeholder Need entity class—meaning that every External Stakeholder Need must participate in at least one Satisfying relationship. The * (which is short for 0...*) below the External Stakeholder Need entity class signifies optional (zero) participation: A requirement may or may not participate in a Satisfying relationship. This reflects the fact that some requirements are not directly based on an External Stakeholder Need (namely, the developmental requirements).

The asterisks above and below the Satisfying relationship indicate a many-to-many relationship in which a given External Stakeholder Need may be associated with any number of Requirements and a given Requirement may be based on any number of External Stakeholder Needs.

The description field of the specification for the External Descriptive Narrative entity class states

> Information, usually in conventional narrative form, that is useful for the developers of a system, but that does not actually state any needs or requirements. Typical information includes the reason the system is needed, the situations in which the system will be used, the types of users, and so on.

This kind of information is common in well-written specifications and gives the developers valuable insights into the system, beyond what the raw requirements provide. It is very significant that in Figure 2.9 this entity class is linked, via the Explaining and the Background relationships, both to the External Stakeholder Need entity class (with which it usually originates), and to the Requirement entity class. The message here is that when preparing a requirements specification, we should not discard this valuable information, even though it does not include actual requirements. Descriptive narratives should be carried over to the requirements specification.

In practice, External Descriptive Narrative is often completely intermingled with the External Stakeholder Need(s) it describes, and the two must be separated during requirements analysis.

The Requirement entity class in Figure 2.9 has two recursive relationships attached to it—Requirement Deriving And Satisfying and Requirement Detailing. Recursive relationships are shared by different instances of the same entity. The Requirement Deriving And Satisfying relationship links requirements derived through design decisions—as described in Section 2.3.3—with their source requirements. The Requirement Detailing relationship expresses the fact that requirements are often first stated in a general, abstract form, then restated in more detail. No design decisions are involved—the requirements in this relationship simply express the same thing at different levels of detail.

It is worth noting here that the particular class diagram of Figure 2.9 is not the only one that might represent requirements. For example, it would be possible to represent Derived Requirements as a separate entity—a subclass of Requirement—rather than lumping all requirements together in one entity class. Since we usually end up with a preponderance of derived requirements, it might be desirable to treat them separately; however, for our purposes of description, Figure 2.9 is satisfactory.

The narrative labels attached to a recursive relationship describe the roles that the two instances of the entity class play in that relationship. In the Requirement Deriving And Satisfying relationship, one or more requirements are the Source requirements from which the Derived requirements originate. All requirements are instances of the same entity, but it is important to know which are sources and which are derived. Note that in another instance of the relationship, a requirement that was derived can become a source (that is, there can be multiple layers of derivation). Likewise, in the Requirement Detailing relationship, one instance of Requirement is the Abstract statement from which any number of Detailed statements can arise.

Next consider the Primitive Requirement and the Performance Requirement entity classes. Since they must always occur together, as shown in Figure 2.9 by their mandatory participation in the Performance Demanding relationship, it is appropriate to consider them together here.

The description field for Primitive Requirement states

> A requirement statement containing enough detail for design decisions, expressible in the form of an indivisible sentence with a single verb acting on a single object.

Primitive Requirement has the same properties and attributes as the Requirement entity class. This idea of a fundamental, indivisible requirement statement is vital to the classification and management of requirements: Primitive requirements are the basic building blocks upon which our whole requirements specification is based.

The description field for Performance Requirement states

> A statement expressing how well the eventual system must conform with one or more Primitive Requirements. Typical performance measures are response time, repetition rate, and accuracy.

The description field for the Performance Demanding relationship states

> Identifies one or more Performance Requirements that apply to one or more Primitive Requirements.

So, how does all this look in a real specification?  Consider:

> The system shall calculate aircraft position at least once every 10 seconds with an accuracy of 15 meters.

This is a primitive requirement, complete with its performance requirements.  The basic required capability is, *The system shall calculate aircraft position;* the associated performance requirements are, *at least once every 10 seconds* and *with an accuracy of 15 meters.*  We are beginning to see how fine-grained the business of requirements analysis is.  A Requirement entity class is made up of primitive requirements that all relate to a particular feature or set of features of the system.  It is only at this primitive level that we can meaningfully sort and categorize the fundamental requirements of the system.

The grouping of primitive requirements into larger-scale requirements (and the breaking apart of the latter into the former) is called an aggregation/decomposition relationship, represented in Figure 2.9 by the diamond symbols above the composite Requirement entity class.  The entity class to which this diamond symbol is attached is the anchor point—the entity class that is an aggregate of the other entity classes.

The remainder of the class diagram in Figure 2.9 deals entirely with the categorization of primitive requirements.  First, they are subdivided into the two fundamental types that we discussed in the previous section: *required capability* and *required constraint.*  The description field for Required Capability states

> A Primitive Requirement for a system characteristic that can be observed at the outputs when the system is operating.

The description field for Required Constraint states

> A Primitive Requirement for a system characteristic that limits the design choices available to meet one or more of the Required Capabilities.

A sub/supertyping relationship links these last two entity classes with Primitive Requirement, shown in Figure 2.9 by the triangle attached to the Primitive Requirement entity class. Again, the attached entity class is the anchor point—in this case, the supertype entity class of which the other entities are subtypes. Sub/supertyping relationships are very common: They indicate *inheritance* of supertype attributes by the subtype. In other words, subtypes automatically possess all the attributes of the supertype, and may have additional attributes of their own. The relationship is often called an "is-a" relationship, because, for example, a required capability *is a* primitive requirement.

There is an additional relationship between the Required Capability and Required Constraint entity classes: Design Constraining. This indicates that a required constraint constrains the design of one or more required capabilities.

Required Capability is further divided into the following three subtypes, each with its description field statement:

- Required Functional Capability: A Required Capability that describes a function the system must perform, regardless of the conditions under which it must perform it.
- Required Behavioral Capability: A Required Capability that describes the required behavior of the system under specified external or internal conditions. In particular, it describes the conditions under which major sets of Required Functional Capabilities are active or inactive.
- Required Storage Capability: A Required Capability that identifies specific information, material, or energy that the system must be capable of storing for use by other Required Capabilities within the system.

This division between types of required capabilities is very significant with respect to the methods we describe later in this book. It is premature to discuss this division in detail here, but briefly, the original Structured Analysis methods simply ignored required behavioral capabilities, whereas the methods in this book (and some other contemporary methods) extend Structured Analysis specifically to deal with behavioral capabilities. When Required Storage Capabilities address information storage, then the representation of choice is often the class diagram—the representation we are walking through right now.

Required Functional Capability and Required Behavioral Capability are linked in Figure 2.9 by a further relationship—Controlling—whose meaning should be clear from the above description of Required Behavioral Capability. Required Storage Capability and Required Functional Capability are linked by a Storage Exchanging relationship, representing the fact that the stored information, material, or energy is there for the fulfillment of their various functional requirements.

In Figure 2.9, the Required Constraint entity class has the following subtypes: Physical Requirement, Environmental Requirement, Product Assurance Requirement, and Development Constraint. Each of these has next to it a list of typical, more-detailed classes of requirements that it may include. These lists are provided as suggestions only, and are open-ended; they tend to be very specific to particular companies, departments, projects, and so on, and it would be impossible to cover all these needs in a single book. In fact, if the entity model in Figure 2.9 were actually used in practice, each listed item would probably become a subtype of its associated entity.

The Development Constraint entity class is subtyped into Implementation Constraint and Integration/Test Constraint, in recognition of the fact that both of these aspects of system development have equal importance, and both can be subject to similar types of constraint.

Before proceeding further, perhaps we should ask: Why do we need to classify requirements in such fine detail? There are several answers. First, only when we have reached the level of detail indicated by the lists of subtypes shown on Figure 2.9 are we able to decide what attributes a particular requirement needs. The attributes of each of these subtypes are different: for example, those for reliability would be quite different from those for electrical glitch protection. Each company (or department, or project) needs to establish exactly what subtypes are needed, and what attributes those subtypes should have. These decisions will lead to organization-specific templates for the specification of each type of requirement.

Second, each of those detailed subtypes is likely to be the specialty of a different discipline, and therefore, in a large company, a different department. It is necessary to divide the requirements to a level of detail such that they can be assigned to the appropriate departments.

Third, with the easy availability of current computer technology, it is unquestionable that all project data, including requirements, should be kept in a database, with easy access by all project personnel (assuming proper read-only and write access controls). Since the class diagram representation is intended for database design, it lends itself to direct mapping into such a database.

Fourth, each subtype might require a different type of testing and test equipment. This is an example of how a well-structured requirements and design process can facilitate the testing process.

The need for detailed requirements categorization is discussed further in Chapter 5, and illustrated in the case study in Part II and on our Website, www.psare.com.

### 2.3.4 Quality

Why, you might ask, is a subsection on quality stuck here in a section on requirements? You might also have wondered why quality is not one of the attributes we listed in the requirements entity model, and why performance and quality are not the same thing. The answer to all these questions is that the term "quality," as it relates to system development, has taken on a special meaning. There is now an almost universal movement in industry to improve quality. This movement appears in numerous guises, but they all originate from the work of W. Edwards Deming [Deming 86] and the principles of Total Quality Management (TQM). In TQM, there is a very clear and simple definition of quality:

> Quality is conformance with requirements.

That statement is the whole basis of TQM. Some corollaries immediately arise from it:

- Requirements must be very well defined in order to assess quality.
- There must be a dependable way to determine that requirements are met (that is, requirements must be testable).
- An error is a failure to conform with requirements.
- Maximizing quality (as defined above) is synonymous with minimizing errors.
- The cost of quality is the cost of minimizing errors minus the cost saved by minimizing them—and the premise of TQM is that this difference is negative, hence the theme and the title of Philip B. Crosby's book *Quality Is Free* [Crosby 79].

This subsection on quality, then, is stuck here in a section on requirements because TQM is entirely dependent on good requirements definition and management; the reason we did not list quality in the requirements class diagram is that, based on the TQM definition, it pervades the whole diagram. Quality means conforming with every single requirement in the diagram. Performance is not the same as quality: It is a type of requirement against which quality is measured.

We will say no more about quality or TQM here (there are volumes of books and papers about these topics already), except that they are indeed very important. The principles of TQM, if properly applied, are very sound, and we believe that everything in this book can contribute toward the causes of quality and TQM.

## 2.3.5 Requirement Management and Analysis

There are six major activities involved in managing and analyzing requirements, all related to what we have seen in Figure 2.9: Requirement Gathering; Requirement Integrity Analysis; Requirement Feasibility Analysis; Requirement Detailing; Requirement Deriving; and Requirement Categorizing. The activities may be carried out concurrently, or sequentially, or by any mix of the two, but the end result is the complete population of the entity classes and relationships of the figure (or the database it represents). The activities are described in the following.

### 2.3.5.1 Requirement Gathering

The end result of requirement gathering is the population of the External Stakeholder Need and External Descriptive Narrative entity classes in Figure 2.9. Our discussion of the diverse nature of the sources and forms of external requirements informs us that requirement gathering is no simple task, and that it is extremely important (and surprisingly, it is often overlooked in the literature). Little could be worse than finding out late in a project that the needs of an important stakeholder had been overlooked. Requirement gathering, then, consists of identifying all the system stakeholders and obtaining from them their respective needs. As pointed out in [Rechtin 97], the system engineer should always be asking the question *why?* In other words, external requirements should not just be accepted at face value: The reason for each need should be questioned. Often, the stakeholders have only vague and ill-formed ideas of what their needs really are, or worse, they express their needs in the form of preconceived design solutions that might be far from ideal; raising these questions at an early stage can avoid a great deal of frustration later.

### 2.3.5.2 Requirement Integrity Analysis

The end result of requirement integrity analysis is the partial population of the Requirement entity class in Figure 2.9. Remember that the properties of this entity class are that it is consistent, complete, correct, understandable, and unambiguous. Typical External Stakeholder Need statements do not possess these properties: It is a major task to achieve them, involving examining the statements separately and together, and resolving everything that is inconsistent, incomplete, incorrect, and lacking in understandability. This activity involves considerable judgment, in particular regarding whether to go back to the source for resolution or whether to make an informed technical decision. A great deal of politics can be involved in these decisions. (Hint: If you don't want to hear the answer, don't ask the question!)

The Requirement entity class includes all the developmental requirements as well as those received from the external stakeholders. Developmental requirements need integrity analysis too, but developers have (or should have) more control over them.

### 2.3.5.3 Requirement Feasibility Analysis

Once a requirement or a set of requirements has been checked for integrity, it must be checked for feasibility. This is actually the first step in design, and it goes beyond the information contained in Figure 2.9. Checking for feasibility can range from simply recognizing that the requirement is well within the capabilities of the planned system, to generating several alternative system architectures and designs, performing trade-off studies of the alternatives, and even building prototypes. These activities are all well beyond the scope of this chapter, but we address them in the case studies, later in the book. In Figure 2.9, these activities apply a further screening to the Requirement entity class.

### 2.3.5.4 Requirement Detailing

Requirement detailing is the activity that corresponds to the Requirement Detailing relationship in Figure 2.9. It involves either identifying the links between abstract statements and their corresponding more detailed partners, or actually generating the abstract or more detailed statements. The questions being answered here are: Is this requirement expressed in sufficient detail to base a design on it? Is this requirement expressed at a high enough level of abstraction for someone to get a meaningful idea of what is intended? This activity goes hand in hand with ensuring the completeness and understandability properties of the Requirement entity class.

For example, an initial requirements specification might state that an automobile must be capable of accelerating from zero to sixty miles per hour in ten seconds. We might decide that we need to know the required acceleration from zero to twenty, twenty to thirty, and so on. These additional requirements statements do not change the original requirements, nor do they make any design decisions; they simply add detail to the original requirement.

### 2.3.5.5 Requirement Deriving

Requirement deriving is the activity associated with the relationship of the same name in Figure 2.9. This activity is very much a part of the architecture and design process. As we discussed earlier, derived requirements arise as a direct result of design decisions, and they are applied as requirements to entity classes (usually) in lower layers in the system structure. Derived requirements are further instances of the Requirement entity class in Figure 2.9, and can be identified by their associations within the Requirement Deriving relationship.

Again using the automobile acceleration example, we know that at some stage in designing the automobile, we must assign a certain total weight to the vehicle (a required constraint) and a certain torque/speed requirement to the power train (a required capability). We must ensure that the combination of total weight and torque/speed satisfies the acceleration requirements. This is a design consideration that requires major trade-off decisions involving many aspects of the vehicle design. Neither of the resulting derived requirements alone satisfies the original acceleration requirement, but each of them becomes a new requirement that must be met by the various affected components of the vehicle.

### 2.3.5.6 Requirement Categorizing

Finally, all instances of the Requirement entity class must be divided into their primitive elements, which then populate the Primitive Requirement entity class in Figure 2.9. These elements in turn must be categorized according to the subtypes chosen for a particular organization. They will then be mapped into the specification templates for each subtype, where the existence of all the required attributes is assured.

## 2.4 SYSTEM SUMMARY

In this chapter, we have seen the types of systems that are of interest to us, and we have seen how the systems approach allows us to deal with the complexity of modern systems in our system development work.

We have seen the hierarchical and network characteristics of systems, and how, even though there are no error-free systems, they can be made to work predictably and reliably.

We have seen that there are several system views, each of which illuminates a particular aspect of interest. This provides us with a set of simplified perspectives of the system, allowing us to separate our concerns and more easily manage system complexity.

Finally, we have noted the extreme importance of requirements in systems, and we have looked in depth at what requirements are, how they are categorized and related to each other, and what it takes to analyze and manage them.

# Chapter 3
## A Framework for Modeling Systems

## 3.1 A MODEL FRAMEWORK

In the preceding chapter, we discussed numerous facets of systems in the categories of general characteristics, views, and requirements.

We now focus on the development of such systems. In this chapter, we explore the role of models in system development and introduce a framework to organize the many different models created during the development process. This framework captures what we know about systems, including the properties discussed in Chapter 2.

The framework serves as a road map for the development process, providing a cue for *what* models to build and *how* to build them. It assists us in keeping all the models related and linked to each other. In the first sections that follow, we start with a discussion of models and their usefulness.

## 3.2 MODELS IN GENERAL

Most industries use models for purposes such as studying requirements for systems, examining feasibility and manufacturability, and determining how to build an actual system. In the computer hardware and software industry, models are used for some parts of the development process (usually for software requirements or design, or for hardware layout), but no techniques are widely used for modeling the *entire* system. Before discussing such modeling techniques, we discuss why models are useful.

## 3.2.1 Models Are Useful Abstractions

As Figure 3.1 shows, a model is an abstraction highlighting some aspects of real-world systems in order to depict those aspects more clearly. A model has an objective (the question we want it to answer) and a viewpoint (the point of view of one or more stakeholders: users, developers, and so on). Abstract models reduce the complexity of the real world to digestible chunks that are simpler to understand.

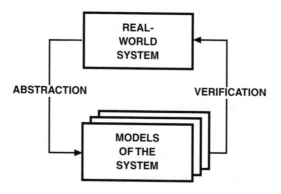

*Figure 3.1: The Role of a Model.*

On the other hand, abstract models are just representations, omitting some aspects of real-world systems, at least temporarily, but mapping what we hope to understand into a form that we can understand. Different types of models answer different types of questions about the system they represent, but even if we build a hundred different models, they could not answer every possible question about the system. That can only be done by the final system itself.

If we decide to build more than one model of a given system to investigate different aspects, then we should somehow organize these models according to their relationships to each other and to the system. This is why we need a framework.

## 3.2.2 Model Representations and Reuse

Before we discuss the framework for modeling systems, we expand on the idea of using models in two ways: First, models can be expressed using different notations; second, good models can be reused in different applications.

Though they appear very different from each other, Figures 3.2 through 3.5 can all represent the same scenario. Consider this description of a junior high school:

> Students enter school in seventh grade. Most of the students proceed to eighth grade, but some skip directly to ninth. Nobody graduates directly from eighth grade, but some leave school before graduating. The rest go on to ninth grade and then graduate.

In Figure 3.2, "The Bathtub Model"—adapted by permission from *General Principles of Systems Design* by Gerald M. Weinberg and Daniela Weinberg [Weinberg 88]—flows into and out of the various tubs can represent the flows of students into and out of grades. Tubs 1, 2, and 3 represent 7th, 8th, and 9th grades, respectively. S indicates the set of students entering school. P1 represents the students progressing to 8th grade. Q1 depicts the small number of students skipping 8th grade and going directly to 9th grade. P2 shows the normal progress from 8th to 9th grade. Q2 and Q3 show students leaving school without graduating. P3 represents the students graduating from 9th grade.

The Weinbergs use the bathtub model to explain the set of differential equations given here as Figure 3.3: Those equations can abstract the same junior high school situation in a different manner. N1, N2, and N3 either can represent the quantities of water in the three tubs or can indicate the number of students in three grades. N1' represents the rate of change of N1 over time, and so on.

Figure 3.4—a Structured Analysis data flow diagram—shows yet another representation of the bathtub model, and of the same real-world system.

Finally, Figure 3.5 gives the context diagram for Figure 3.4, once again representing the same real-world system, but in a more abstract form.

The models in Figures 3.2 through 3.5 also can show how models can be reused. The four models can be used to illustrate different applications, fitting the following description of a company's training program just as well as they fit the junior high school scenario, and just as well as they could fit many other similar scenarios.

Everyone joining Company X starts as an unskilled worker. The company's policy is to provide training and education for its employees. No one is allowed to work without some minimal vocational training that gets him or her into the semi-skilled labor pool. Those who have college degrees move to the skilled category, bypassing the semi-skilled pool. After five years in the semi-skilled category, workers automatically progress to the skilled pool. Eventually, employees either leave for better opportunities or retire.

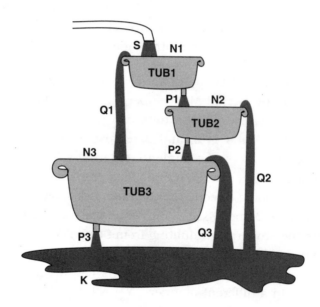

*Figure 3.2: The Bathtub Model.*

$$N1' = S - (P1 + Q1)$$
$$N2' = P1 - (P2 + Q2)$$
$$N3' = (Q1 + P2) - (P3 + Q3)$$

*Figure 3.3: Equations Representing the Bathtub Model.*

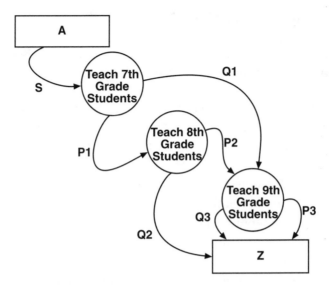

Figure 3.4:    *A Data Flow Diagram Representing the Bath-tub Model.*

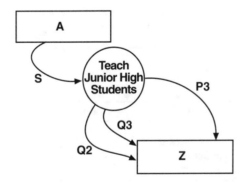

*Figure 3.5: A Context Diagram of the Model in Figure 3.4.*

## 3.3 EXPLOITING SYSTEM HIERARCHIES

In Sections 2.1.2 and 2.1.3, we explained that all real-world systems consist of subsystems, or—looking in the other direction—that every system is part of a larger system. In other words, systems come in hierarchies. Using these hierarchies is the first step in constructing our modeling framework.

### 3.3.1 Why Exploit Hierarchies?

Why do we want to exploit the idea of system hierarchies? Because we want to reduce complexity by not thinking about everything at once.

- At the highest level of a model, we establish the place of the system in its environment and define the broad objectives of the system and its relationships with that environment (for example, communication and physical linkage).
- Using these broad objectives, we proceed into the requirements and architecture of our system, remembering that it can be manual, auto-mated (by various technologies), or both. Creating an architecture for the system partitions it into subsystems that can themselves be con-sidered self-contained systems—similar to the top-level system. By iterating this partitioning procedure, as illustrated in Figure 3.6, we simplify the problem by treating each subsystem, sub-subsystem, and so on, as a system in its own right, with its external interconnections and interactions represented in the level above.

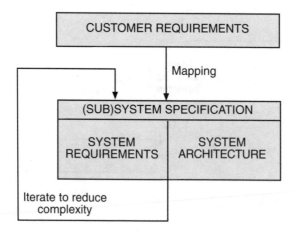

*Figure 3.6: Hierarchies to Reduce Complexity.*

### 3.3.2 What Are the Benefits and Pitfalls of Layered Systems?

There are many benefits in hierarchically organized systems and subsystems. Every layer of system definition supplies some of the requirements for the layer below. At the top, a firm link is established between the system and its environment. If we can stabilize the upper-level requirements and architecture early, the lower-level design can proceed much more effectively. We can anticipate high-risk subsystems and use prototyping to resolve those risks. Working on a certain level of abstraction helps us concentrate on that level and not get too detailed too fast.

One point needs to be strongly emphasized:

> System specification and development are not necessarily top-down processes.

Overlooking this heuristic can be a major pitfall. The fact that, for convenience, many of our descriptions of the process are presented top-down does not detract from this statement; neither does the top-down appearance of the figures. The top layers do not have to be complete before we can work on the lower layers; in some cases, it is appropriate to work upward from the lower layers. Think of development as a concurrent or iterative process—there is always some work going on in every layer.

The layered model results in a specification hierarchy and a representation of the requirements flows between layers. The process of filling in the framework and developing these models is discussed in Chapter 5, and illustrated in Part II.

Integration is key to developing the system: "The whole is greater than the sum of its parts." The systems we develop require that all of their components are integrated: software with software; hardware with hardware; software with hardware; automated with manual; and especially, system with environment. So, despite developing many separate models, we need subsystems linked to other subsystems, and layers linked to higher and lower layers. This is the purpose and benefit of the modeling framework.

### 3.3.3 How Many Models?

Many methods insist on building one large analysis model (as in Structured Analysis or entity-relationship modeling) and, separately, one large design model (as in Structured Design or in many object-oriented methods). We, too, use the "divide and conquer" approach in our framework, but we ensure that the sub-models are integrated.

How many models do we build, then? If we consider an integrated set of sub-models as a single model, then we build a model for the overall system and a model for each of its subsystems, sub-subsystems, and so on. Each of these models itself can contain numerous models of its own: models for requirements, design, architecture, information structures, interconnects, and many more. Good methods, and tools that automate them, will support all of these multifarious models and the links between them.

### 3.3.4 Where Do We Stop?

We have established that every system is part of a larger system. Looking in the other direction, How far down should we decompose a subsystem into further subsystems?

In larger systems, system developers will stop at the level where direct system responsibility ends, or where they have no constraints to impose internally to a subsystem. Then, specialists in those subsystems can decide whether to continue with the same process or to switch to some other approach that is specific to their discipline. For example,

- we decompose a multidisciplinary system into parts that are, say, mechanical or hydraulic, and pass those subsystems to the corresponding specialists
- in MIS, we often decompose until we can clearly differentiate between human activities (for example, clerks doing part of the work) and software activities (computer programs doing the remaining work)
- in embedded, real-time systems, we might decompose until we have a better understanding of the hardware/software split

A software subsystem can usually be decomposed into further subsystems, and an organizational subsystem can be organized as cooperating groups of further organizational subsystems. The techniques, methods, and tools for specialized subsystem development are often more mature and better automated than those used for overall system development. In this book, we do not discuss specialized hardware, software, or organizational methods, but instead refer to other publications on these topics.

On the other hand, we do not have to decompose every system into subsystems that comprise only one technology. Sometimes, the system levels stop where several related technologies are used in a single subsystem. For example, in a hydraulic subsystem with electromechanical valves, it would not make much sense to separate these two technologies, because they exist to support each other.

Figure 3.7 shows various alternatives for decomposing subsystems: The top-level decomposition separates a human subsystem from a purely mechanical subsystem and leaves a multi-technology subsystem to be further decomposed. On the next level, a software subsystem is further decomposed into two software subsystems. At the lowest level, we find a software subsystem, a human subsystem, and a subsystem that uses mixed technology but is treated as one unit.

In later chapters, we discuss more criteria to determine where to stop decomposing.

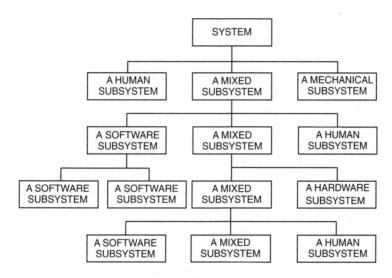

*Figure 3.7: Partitioning a System.*

## 3.4 EXPLOITING THE *WHAT/HOW* CLASSIFICATION

The next step in constructing our modeling framework is to use the *what/how* classification of systems that we discussed in Section 2.2.3. As you may have noticed in Figure 3.6, every specification consists of two parts: system requirements and system architecture. Both of these parts contain models. The system requirements model is a technology-independent model of the problem the system is to solve: It represents the *what*. The system architecture model is a technology-dependent model of the solution to the problem: It represents the *how*. These two models are created for the entire system and for every subsystem—hardware, software, human, or mixed technology—down to the lowest level.

## 3.4.1 Separation of *What* and *How*

The separation of the *what* and the *how* is extremely important for the following (and possibly other) reasons:

- It is often very useful to understand a problem (the *what)* independently of any particular solution (the *how).* (Conversely, there are situations where it is useful to develop a single architecture that will satisfy a whole class of problems.)
- Any given problem has many possible solutions. Selection of a particular solution (the *how)* is a trade-off process; we often need to make numerous different trade-offs while keeping the problem statement (the *what)* unchanged.
- The separation supports the generally recognized principle of separation of concerns, which means dealing with only one part of the system's complexity at a time. The requirements model (the *what)* only has to cope with essential problems; the architecture model (the *how)* has to cope with many constraints imposed by technology, organization, and so forth.
- Finally, seldom do we build systems totally from scratch. Most systems we build are either implementations using new technology (only changing the *how)* or the integration of several previous systems into a new system.

The separation of the *what* and the *how* gives us the power to reimplement the *what* using new technology, but it also gives us the power of reusability—not just for software or hardware, but for requirements as well. This is particularly important, because requirements are much more stable over much longer periods of time than technology [McMenamin 84].

In this book, we use the *what/how* classification for yet another important purpose. As we construct several different models later in the book, we would have to handle a lot of complexity at once if we addressed how to construct them at the same time as we addressed what to construct. So, we have split the following chapters using the *what/how* separation: Chapter 4 describes what models belong in our framework; Chapters 5 through 7, and all of Part II, describe how to develop these models.

As mentioned, Chapters 5 through 7 describe the *how* of constructing the models, but in Part II, we describe the *how* of applying these models to some real systems—from that perspective, Chapters 5 through 7 represent the *what!* This is analogous to the layered structure of systems, in which architectural or design decisions in one layer result in requirements in the layer below. This same principle applies to this book, which itself is a kind of system.

The purpose of Part II and of the on-line model is to exemplify what real projects must do—the *what,* the *how,* and also the *when.* The *when* refers to project planning and scheduling, including such issues as which tasks are conducted concurrently, and which sequentially. Throughout the 1970's and 1980's, simplistic process models like the waterfall model predominated. We know now that there are no simple solutions to project planning and scheduling. Rather, these are decisions that must be made for each project, by project management. It is the manager's job to observe the process, to watch and interpret the results of individual steps, to take into account many constraints, and based on all of that, to reconfigure dynamically the *what,* the *how,* and the *when* of the project.

## 3.4.2 The Architecture Template

Our modeling framework employs an extension of the *what/how* split to classify systems, subsystems, their components, and their activities according to a generic architecture template. Figure 3.8 shows that this architecture template classifies a system or subsystem into five categories:

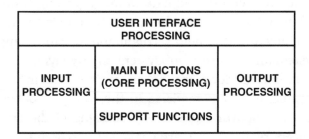

*Figure 3.8: The Architecture Template.*

1. The center region contains the main functions of the system: the core functional processing. Here, we model things that the system absolutely has to do, things that belong to the essence of the system, independent of any technology.

2. The top region hosts those parts of a system that interact with the users. It contains all subsystems, functions, and activities that make up the human-machine interface. It controls access to the system, and it accepts input from and prepares output for the human user, all in whatever forms are established with the user.

3. The left region contains the functions and subsystems that interface with other systems and subsystems to provide input for our system. It has to establish interconnections, request input, check it for acceptability, preprocess it, and perform many other input-related activities.

4. The right region provides similar resources for the output of our system to other systems. This includes establishing interconnection, converting output to the form needed for transfer, sending it, and so on.

5. The bottom region houses any functions or subsystems that provide support to the rest of the system to keep it running. These include self-test procedures, error logging, fault detection, and also maintenance functionality. This region is fundamentally different from the other outer regions: those regions deal with various kinds of interfaces between the system and its environment, whereas the bottom region deals with functions that support the system internally. The support functions might require additional inputs and outputs, but still, they are internal functions.

How do we use the architecture template in our modeling framework? As shown in Figure 3.9, the template mainly helps us with mapping between requirements (the *what)* and architecture (the *how).* This mapping can be applied on any level: for the overall system and for every subsystem on any layer.

From the requirements viewpoint, we augment or enhance the required functionality of the system (which is modeled in the core part of the template) with a ring of functionality supporting the core processing of the system. These augmented, or enhanced, requirements are packaged into architectural subsystems.

From the architecture viewpoint, the template provides an excellent starting point for building information-hiding subsystems [Parnas 71]. The center hides the essential functions, the top region hides the user-interface technology and behavior, the left and right regions hide input/output specifics, such as device characteristics and protocols, and the bottom region hides support functionality, such as service and maintenance modules, and many more. An alternative name for the template might be the information-hiding template.

Once we establish the functionality of the system and subsystems, we can easily categorize and extract the core requirements for future reuse.

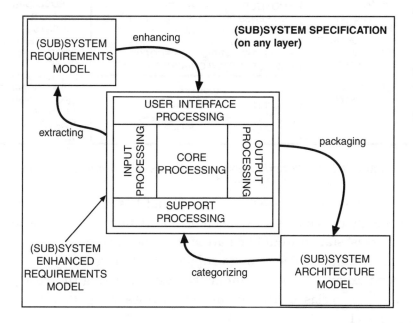

*Figure 3.9:*  *The Template Bridging Requirements and Architecture Models.*

## 3.4.3 Using the Architecture Template

In this section, we present two examples of using the architecture template to classify the functionality of systems. To demonstrate that it can be used on any layer of a system hierarchy and for any kind of application (automated or not), we start with an organizational system composed of automated and manual parts.

The template in Figure 3.10 illustrates the activities that are performed by nurses at their station in a hospital. We can divide the activities into the five categories. By doing so, if the procedures for helping visitors (in the user-interface part of the template) are changed, the rest of the system can remain unchanged. The same is true for changing the policy for checking stock supplies in the maintenance region, and for any changes involving just a single region of the template.

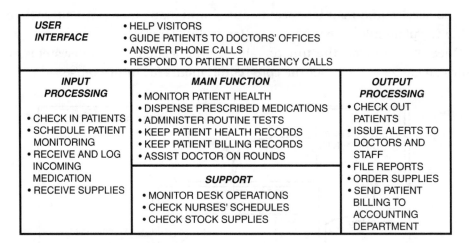

| USER INTERFACE | • HELP VISITORS<br>• GUIDE PATIENTS TO DOCTORS' OFFICES<br>• ANSWER PHONE CALLS<br>• RESPOND TO PATIENT EMERGENCY CALLS | |
|---|---|---|
| **INPUT PROCESSING**<br><br>• CHECK IN PATIENTS<br>• SCHEDULE PATIENT MONITORING<br>• RECEIVE AND LOG INCOMING MEDICATION<br>• RECEIVE SUPPLIES | **MAIN FUNCTION**<br>• MONITOR PATIENT HEALTH<br>• DISPENSE PRESCRIBED MEDICATIONS<br>• ADMINISTER ROUTINE TESTS<br>• KEEP PATIENT HEALTH RECORDS<br>• KEEP PATIENT BILLING RECORDS<br>• ASSIST DOCTOR ON ROUNDS<br><br>**SUPPORT**<br>• MONITOR DESK OPERATIONS<br>• CHECK NURSES' SCHEDULES<br>• CHECK STOCK SUPPLIES | **OUTPUT PROCESSING**<br>• CHECK OUT PATIENTS<br>• ISSUE ALERTS TO DOCTORS AND STAFF<br>• FILE REPORTS<br>• ORDER SUPPLIES<br>• SEND PATIENT BILLING TO ACCOUNTING DEPARTMENT |

*Figure 3.10: Classification of Activities in a Manual System.*

This nurses' station is a subsystem of an overall hospital system, for which we could also classify the activities. Depending on the purpose of the whole hospital model, the nurses' station would be part of the system core or may be considered part of the maintenance subsystem (to support the doctors).

The second example is of an automated system. Using the hospital application, we show how to classify the automated activities of a patient-monitoring system in Figure 3.11.

The architecture template is a very powerful modeling tool that we use repeatedly to classify system or subsystem activities. Not only can it be used to bridge the requirements/architecture models, it can be used very early in a project, before we even know the requirements or make decisions on the architecture, to discover topics to be treated in more detail later. It can also be used in distributing work among project members, allowing them to work concurrently.

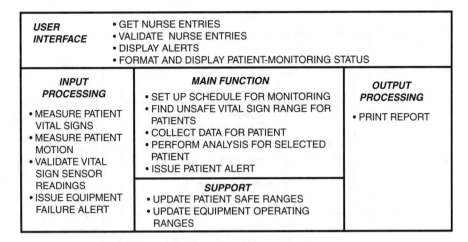

| USER INTERFACE | • GET NURSE ENTRIES • VALIDATE  NURSE ENTRIES • DISPLAY ALERTS • FORMAT AND DISPLAY PATIENT-MONITORING STATUS | | |
|---|---|---|---|
| **INPUT PROCESSING** • MEASURE PATIENT VITAL SIGNS • MEASURE PATIENT MOTION • VALIDATE VITAL SIGN SENSOR READINGS • ISSUE EQUIPMENT FAILURE ALERT | **MAIN FUNCTION** • SET UP SCHEDULE FOR MONITORING • FIND UNSAFE VITAL SIGN RANGE FOR PATIENTS • COLLECT DATA FOR PATIENT • PERFORM ANALYSIS FOR SELECTED PATIENT • ISSUE PATIENT ALERT | | **OUTPUT PROCESSING** • PRINT REPORT |
| | **SUPPORT** • UPDATE PATIENT SAFE RANGES • UPDATE EQUIPMENT OPERATING RANGES | | |

Figure 3.11:  *Classification of Activities in an Automated System.*

## 3.5 Exploiting the Information/Material/Energy Classification

The final step in constructing our modeling framework is to classify systems according to their information, material, and energy processing characteristics that we discussed in Section 2.2.1.

### 3.5.1 A Generic Subsystem Structure

In Chapter 2, we showed that everything a system does can be classified into material processing, energy processing, and information processing. Since material and energy processing are quite different from information processing, we can treat these two areas separately. If we combine this decision with the idea of categorization provided by the architecture template, we end up with the system partitioning shown in Figure 3.12, which divides the processing into finer classifications. These finer classifications become subsystems of the overall system. As Figure 3.12 shows, there are subsystems that do the two different types of processing, but the overall, or boundary, subsystem does both. Figure 3.13 explains more about the functions of the various subsystems.

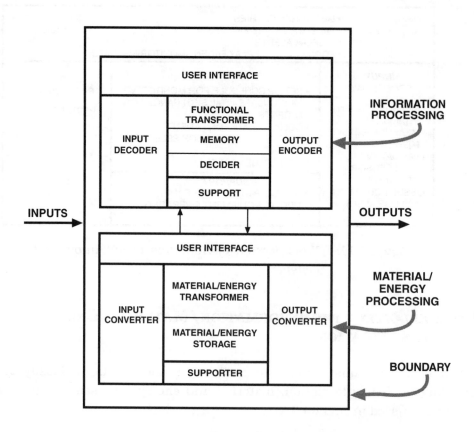

*Figure 3.12: Separating Material/Energy Processing from Information Processing.*

Note that there is no box in material/energy processing equivalent to the decider in information processing. With today's systems, the decision-making function is almost always an information processing function. Consequently, Figures 3.13 through 3.16 all have a blank entry in the material/energy processing side.

| Boundary: Subsystem(s) that form a barrier around a system, shielding it from its environment. ||
|---|---|
| **Information Processing Subsystems** | **Material/Energy Processing Subsystems** |
| **User Interface:** Subsystem(s) to allow information exchange with external human users. | **User Interface:** Subsystem(s) to allow material/energy exchange with external human users. |
| **Input Decoder:** Subsystem(s) to convert the coding of external information for internal use. | **Input Converter:** Subsystem(s) to transform material/energy from external to internal forms. |
| **Functional Transformer:** Subsystem(s) to transform input information into output information. | **Material/Energy Transformer:** Subsystem(s) to transform and associate material/energy inputs to outputs. |
| **Memory:** Subsystem(s) to retain for later use information, its relationships, and its organization. | **Material/Energy Storage:** Subsystem(s) to store material/energy for later use. |
| **Decider:** Subsystem(s) to control (for example, enable, inhibit, or trigger) functional transformers. | |
| **Output Encoder:** Subsystem(s) to convert the coding of internal information for external use. | **Output Converter:** Subsystem(s) to transform material/energy from internal to external forms. |
| **Support:** Subsystem(s) to support system monitoring, servicing, and reconfiguration. | **Supporter:** Subsystem(s) to enable maintenance, growth, and reconfiguration. |

*Figure 3.13:   Generic Description of Subsystem Responsibilities.*

## 3.5.2 Categories of a Deliverable System

For a deliverable system, product, or component, the categorization scheme introduced above can be a useful starting point for brainstorming the subsystems. Figure 3.14 makes the generic categories of Figure 3.13 specific to all deliverable systems, and Figure 3.15 makes them specific to a cruise control system.

Note that the categories in the generic template are applicable to many systems, although there are usually some that are not applicable to a specific system. Consider the generic categories a pattern for thinking about a system and its subsystems.

| **Boundary:** | |
|---|---|
| The external housing, casing, or such other exterior that shelters the system from its environment. | |
| **Information Processing Subsystems** | **Material/Energy Processing Subsystems** |
| **User Interface:** Data entry and display devices. | **User Interface:** Access mechanisms allowing operator insertion and extraction of physical items and electrical or mechanical energy. |
| **Input Decoder:** Processor(s) of information inputs from other systems, converting them, as needed, from their received formats to internal system formats. | **Input Converter:** Mechanism(s) for the physical manipulation of received physical items or energy into the orientation or form needed internally. |
| **Functional Transformer:** Input-to-output information conversion devices performing processes such as algorithms, functions, math equations, or string manipulations. | **Producer:** Electrical or mechanical devices that process received physical items or energy, and convert them into the desired product. For example, an automatic mechanism that receives component parts and assembles them into a finished product. |
| **Memory:** Device(s) that store, for later use, information from the operator, from other systems, or from the processes of this system retained, possibly with its relationships and organization. | **Storage:** Any part(s) of the system that store material or energy for later use, such as a storage room, a shelf, a battery, or a water reservoir. |
| **Decider:** Control processors by which information processing and resources are scheduled, and which establish the different states or modes of behavior of the system. | |
| **Output Encoder:** Processor(s) of information outputs to other systems, converting them, as needed, from their internal system formats to external formats. | **Output Converter:** Mechanisms for the physical manipulation of produced physical items or energy into the orientation or form needed externally. For example, the automatic packaging of manufactured products for shipment. |
| **Support:** Processors that perform tasks such as fault isolation, error handling, service monitoring, system reconfiguration, and graceful degradation. | **Supporter:** Access mechanisms for physical maintenance, growth, and reconfiguration. |

*Figure 3.14: A Template for Subsystems of a Deliverable, Human-Operated System.*

| Boundary: The box(es) that house the cruise control system to be installed into a car. | |
| --- | --- |
| Information Processing Subsystems | Material/Energy Processing Subsystems |
| **User Interface:** Subsystem to accept and interpret keyboard, switch inputs, and brake pedal action from the driver and to display cruise control status. | **User Interface:** N.A.: There is no direct material/energy exchange with drivers in this system. |
| **Input Decoder:** Device(s) and processor to convert shaft rotation into speed measurement. | **Input Converter:** N.A.: No material or (useful) energy is received by the cruise control system. |
| **Functional Transformer:** Processor that captures and maintains the desired speed, receives measured speed, and computes speed error. | **Producer:** Device that converts desired speed into physical motion to operate throttle. |
| **Memory:** Processor that retains desired speed and speed conversion factor(s). | **Storage:** N.A.: No material or energy is stored by the cruise control system. |
| **Decider:** The state machine that identifies the state of the cruise control—off, enabled, cruising, calibration, and so on. | |
| **Output Encoder:** Processor that converts speed error into desired throttle position. | **Output Converter:** Device that converts desired throttle position into throttle linkage motion. |
| **Support:** Processor that establishes the conversion factors for shaft rotation. | **Supporter:** The fail-safe mechanism on the throttle linkage. |

*Figure 3.15: Subsystems of a Cruise Control System.*

### 3.5.3 Categories of a People System

The systems we build reflect the organizations that build them. With this in mind, we can devise a categorization of organizational systems, such as of whole companies, departments, or groups of people cooperating to achieve a certain goal. Figure 3.16 maps the generic categories onto an organizational structure describing the various subsystems in such a context. Figure 3.17 shows categories specific to a garment factory. This kind of categorization helps to distinguish between value-adding functions and overhead functions in an organization: It can be used as a starting point for modeling business processes and identifying essential parts of them.

## 3.6 LAYERED MODELS: THE TRUTH AT LAST!

We discussed numerous characteristics and features of models in the previous sections, but we kept the important issue of layered models for the end of this chapter. In any discussion of systems, models of systems, or the process of building systems, the term "layer" plays an important role. Here, we explore several unique aspects of layers, and of the different relationships between layers, between elements in one layer, and between elements in different layers.

One purpose of this section is to dispel a couple of myths. First, there is the myth that all layered models fall into the category of functional decomposition or, worse yet, top-down functional decomposition. And second, that layered models are fundamentally incompatible with object orientation.

In the first pages of *Strategies for Real-Time System Specification*, we introduced a diagram titled, "The Total System Life Cycle," little realizing at the time just how significant it was. It showed various layers of the system modeling process and layers of specifications resulting from that process. We elaborate on that diagram in Figure 5.1 of this book, but for now, we discuss some of its implications. What we have realized since creating that diagram is that there is tremendous similarity between systems, system models, and the system development process. Layers are an important part of these similarities, but they are also the source of some confusion. There is not just one kind of relationship between layers or elements of layers: We can identify several basic relationships that keep recurring in different systems, system models, and in the development process.

| Boundary: | |
|---|---|
| Any protective enclosure for the organization or group: buildings, fences, walls, partitions, and so on. | |
| **Information Processing Subsystems** | **Material/Energy Processing Subsystems** |
| **User Interface:** | **User Interface:** |
| People responsible for determining market needs and communicating with potential customers. | The facilities that allow users to bring or receive goods (or energy) to or from the organization: receptionist; customer service department. |
| **Input Decoder:** | **Input Converter:** |
| Marketing and sales staff, program office, management in charge of market (customer) interface, legal department, language translators, cryptographers, technical and scientific researchers, and other interpreters of marketplace or technology. | Those who perform tasks such as receiving incoming materials, unpacking them, inspecting them, preparing them for internal use, and transferring them to the stock room or directly to manufacturing. Typically, the receiving department. |
| **Functional Transformer:** | **Producer:** |
| All persons or groups using information to produce new information: design engineers, product planners, information project teams, DP department, and so on. | All persons, groups, or machinery producing goods or services to be delivered to customers: factory production staff, assembly lines, nurses, and so on. |
| **Memory:** | **Storage:** |
| Filing department, bookkeeping/ accounting department, librarians, computers, file cabinets, secretaries. | Supply cabinets, equipment rooms, stock rooms, warehouse, holding areas, waiting areas. |
| **Decider:** | |
| Board of directors, company management committee, R & D board, project leaders, supervisors. | |
| **Output Encoder:** | **Output Converter:** |
| Marketing literature producers, document writers, users manual writers, publications department. | Shipping department, delivery people, installers. |
| **Support:** | **Supporter:** |
| Salary review committee, facilities design staff, payroll processing staff, project metrics measurement staff. | Janitors, cafeteria staff, accounting personnel, and so on. |

*Figure 3.16: A Template for an Organization That Builds Deliverable Systems.*

| Boundary: The building(s) that house the garment factory and its offices. | |
|---|---|
| **Information Processing Subsystems** | **Material/Energy Processing Subsystems** |
| **User Interface:** People who negotiate the designs and contracts with customers. | **User Interface:** Direct factory sales outlet, returns department. |
| **Input Decoder:** Purchase order processing, inventorying of received materials. | **Input Converter:** People unpacking received materials, repackaging them in a form that supports the production process; people from personnel department screening new hires. |
| **Functional Transformer:** Design department and equipment that transforms customer requests into actual designs to be manufactured. | **Producer:** Production line personnel and equipment that convert the received materials into finished garments according to the selected designs. |
| **Memory:** Storage of the designs, accounting records, shipping records, the employee records, and so on. | **Storage:** Supply cabinets, storage lockers, stock room, and so on. |
| **Decider:** Management that determines the production schedules, the factory plans, and the coordination of the factory floor. | |
| **Output Encoder:** People responsible for invoicing the customers, for waste disposal coordination, and so on. | **Output Converter:** The shipping department, delivery truck drivers, and so on. |
| **Support:** Customer accounting, payroll department, and so on. | **Supporter:** The facilities and maintenance crews who remove trash and keep the factory in operating condition. |

*Figure 3.17: Subsystems of a Garment Factory.*

Systems, models of systems, and the system development process share the following attributes:

- They are layered.
- The layers—once they are identified—form a structure that can be read and interpreted in any sequence: from the top layers to the lower layers, from right to left, from bottom to top, and so on. Moreover, the layers can be *developed* in any sequence: top to bottom, right to left, bottom to top, and so on, and the interpretation and development sequences are quite independent of each other.
- The number of elements per layer typically increases downward, giving the whole structure a pyramidal shape; but note that we sometimes have an independent structure of elements within one of the main layers. For such a structure, the basic statement of this paragraph is still true: The number of elements tends to increase downward.
- The elements forming the layered structure can be considered a set, either of activities or of entities. In any particular system, system model, or development project, these elements may be carried out or used in some prescribed sequence, concurrently, or in any combination of sequence and concurrency.
- Elements in the layers usually communicate and cooperate up, down, and sideways within and between layers. Communication and cooperation can be in the form of information, material, or energy, depending on the kind of system, model, or process in question. Some earlier models restricted the development process by asserting, for example, that all information flows vertically through the top layer, and that only information (not material or energy) can be communicated with the outside world. However, our model recognizes that information, material, and energy can all flow sideways to and from individual layers, and can all interact with the outside world.
- Every layer includes, deals with, or is associated with, some requirements, some architecture or design, some construction or implementation, and some integration and testing. Also, each layer usually requires planning, quality assurance, management, and other items, but we are not addressing these in this book.

An important conclusion for us is that layered models—for systems or as meta-models for system development processes—do not inherently imply any particular sequence. They represent a static structure (of a system, its development, the development process, or models of any and all of these) that can be populated in any convenient sequence that makes sense for the problem at hand. This point was beautifully made by Parnas—arguably the father of information-hiding structures—in [Parnas 86].

So, the layers and the elements in layers are nondirectional, but we are interested in their relationships. There are probably many types of relationships in layered models, but four of them are of special interest in system development: aggregation/decomposition, abstraction/detailing, supertype/subtype, and controlling/controlled. Let us look at each of these in detail, discussing properties of their relationships and examples from our methods and other well-known approaches.

### 3.6.1 Aggregation/Decomposition Relationship in Models

The architecture model, resulting from the architecture method, is an example of an aggregation/decomposition model. Such models characterize real physical elements, their sub-elements or parts, and their super-elements or assemblies. Elements in the higher layers actually consist of the elements in the lower layers, or conversely, elements in the lower layers are decompositions of those in the higher layers. The structure is also known as a whole/part structure [Coad 91] or a container/content structure: A given layer provides the container for the layer below, which is the content of the layer above. In entity-relationship modeling, entities can be linked by composed-of or consists-of relationships. In manufacturing terms, it is an assembly/subassembly/component structure. This type of structure is pervasive in engineering and in everyday life.

An aggregate actually involves more than just collecting sub-elements into a set. The sub-elements must also interface with each other, requiring linkages between them that may not be evident when they are considered separately. This is why we discuss enhancement of abstract requirements, using the architecture template, in our methods when the requirements are mapped into real physical modules.

We can better imagine aggregation/decomposition structures applied at the system levels, where physical hardware of various kinds is involved. For software, which does not have a physical form, it is not so clear. The trick is to imagine that software does have a physical form. A complete software program or assembly can be considered as an architecture module at the highest software layer; major subprograms it contains are modules in the next layer down; sub-subprograms or subroutines (if any) form a further layer, and so on. As we discuss elsewhere in this book, a transition can be made from an aggregation/decomposition model to an object-oriented representation by defining modules to be aggregate objects, as described, for example, in [Page-Jones 95, Section 4.2]. Once in the object-oriented domain, other structures may apply, depending on the particular object-oriented approach used.

To summarize the usage of this relationship: We build layers to show physical packaging of elements into larger groups or assemblies. In each layer, we can define physical interfaces between elements or between groups. The grouping forms a sort of fence around its elements, potentially protecting the visibility of the interior elements or regulating the access to them. In software development, we use terms like information hiding, scope, and visibility control to describe the nature of the aggregation/decomposition relationship.

## 3.6.2 Abstraction/Detailing Relationship in Models

When we use an abstraction/detailing relationship in models, the higher layers are simply more abstract expressions of the lower layers, or conversely, the lower layers are more detailed expressions of the higher layers. The most familiar example of this relationship occurs in Structured Analysis (SA), usually represented by data flow diagrams. (Note that the control model of the real-time extensions of SA does not use this relationship—see Section 3.6.4.) The process model part of the requirements model, being founded on SA, uses the abstraction/detailing relationship for processes and their child diagrams. In a sense, the whole requirements model—if applied correctly—is abstract throughout because it consists only of narrative statements (albeit in structured form) that do not necessarily correspond to real physical groupings of processes, entities, or control structures.

The abstraction/detailing relationship often has been erroneously named abstraction/decomposition. Although we, too, have been guilty of using this terminology, we now disagree with it. First, abstraction and decomposition are not opposites, and the essence of these relationship name pairs is that they should be opposites, reflecting the upward and downward viewpoints in a layered model. Second, decomposition *is* the opposite of aggregation, which is why we use it in the aggregation/decomposition relationship described above, where something is broken into the elements it contains. Consider this: An abstract requirement statement does not contain the more detailed requirements statements that describe it; however, a physical system element does contain the separable sub-elements of which it is an aggregate. If we take the elements of a physical system and assemble them, we get the physical system; if we assemble a set of detailed requirements, we merely have a collection of detailed requirements—the abstract and detailed requirements exist independently of each other, with an abstraction/detailing relationship between them.

Our categorizations of layered structures, then, have led us to an interesting paradox. The terms to which we objected earlier—functional decomposition and top-down functional decomposition—are frequently applied to Structured Analysis and its data flow diagrams, yet data flow diagrams, when used correctly to represent abstract requirements, do not involve decomposition at all: They involve detailing. When we use Structured Analysis to create essential models according to our own guidelines and those in [McMenamin 84] and [Robertson 98], we are not decomposing downward through the layers; we are adding detail. Going upward, we are not packaging or aggregating; we are abstracting.

Of course, if you are misusing SA to represent the aggregation and decomposition of physical structures, then anything goes, and we cannot take responsibility for the results (which are usually awful).

How do detailing of the required capabilities and decomposition of the physical structure relate to each other? As a system is developed, they proceed in parallel, with sufficient detail added to the required capabilities to satisfy the needs of a particular physical layer. This point is illustrated further in Part II.

### 3.6.3 Supertype/Subtype Relationship in Models

In the supertype/subtype relationship, an element in the higher layer—the supertype—includes all of the features that are common to its associated elements in the lower layer—its subtypes. These features—in the simplest case—are attributes (as they are called in information modeling) that are inherited by the elements on the lower layer. Starting from the lower level, supertypes are formed for sets of elements that share common attributes. Thus, we might have at the top level "vehicle," and at the level below "ship," "aircraft," and "land vehicle." Below "land vehicle," we might have "bicycle," "motorcycle," "ATV," and "automobile." This tells us, for example, that an automobile is a land vehicle and a land vehicle is a vehicle.

Supertype/subtype models are important in object orientation. This relationship is the foundation for inheritance—one of the essential and most powerful features of object orientation. Attributes of "vehicle," in the above example, are inherited by all the other elements, and attributes of "land vehicle" are inherited by all of the elements in its subtypes. Object orientation has taken this relationship and extended it to more complex forms of inheritance than just attribute inheritance: The lower layer may also inherit functions (or operations, or "methods," as they are sometimes called) and the behavior of the supertypes.

Supertype/subtype relationships are also referred to as generalization/specialization relationships, class hierarchies, inheritance structures, and "is-a" hierarchies. With the supertype/subtype relationship, it is important that the supertype contains all the commonalities of the subtypes. The main use of this relationship is to discover commonalities and to describe them only once, thus reducing redundancy. The structure then allows the lower layers to inherit whatever commonalities have been discovered.

Now that we have defined the supertype/subtype relationship, we can see that the relationship is, in fact, a subtype of the abstraction/detailing relationship. A supertype is an abstraction of its subtypes, and the subtypes are detailed instances of the supertype. So, all supertype/subtype relationships are also abstraction/detailing relationships, but the converse is not true: Not all abstraction/detailing relationships are supertype/subtype relationships, because not all abstraction/detailing relationships follow the "is-a" principle. For example, a process on a data flow diagram and its child diagram are an abstraction/detailing pair, but it is not true that a child diagram "is-a" parent process.

## 3.6.4 Controlling/Controlled Relationship in Models

This relationship distinguishes between up and down by having the upper layers control elements of the lower layers. Other terms used for this relationship are the control hierarchy, or the is-boss-of/is-supervised-by relationship. Sometimes, we simply say that the higher element uses the lower elements. The higher layer must have knowledge of the lower layer but the lower layer—that is, the one being used—does not necessarily have to know anything about the boss. In terms of client/server models, the client is the boss that delegates work to the server; the server provides certain services that are performed whenever a client asks for them.

In the requirements method, the control model controls processes in the process model, by activating or deactivating them. In the architecture method, we can model client/server behavior to avoid iterative cycles between architecture modules.

Structured Design, the software design method, provides another example of a controlling/controlled relationship. In its main graphical model, the structure chart, a given module invokes (that is, it uses, calls, or controls the execution of) modules in the layer below. Structured Design is one of several methods that can be used in conjunction with the requirements and architecture methods, as described in *Strategies for Real-Time System Specification,* Section 24.3, and in Chapter 4 of this book.

## 3.6.5 Layered Models Summary

We hope we have succeeded in dispelling the myth that all layered models are built top-down using decomposition, and have shown that this simplistic, one-size-fits-all view of these models is wrong. The four types of relationships in layered models, described above, are distinctly different from each other; they all serve distinct and important roles in system development; and they can be integrated smoothly, where appropriate, with other models, including object-oriented models. Figure 3.18 summarizes the key aspects of the four relationships in and between layers or their elements.

Even though the four relationships are different, it is convenient to have at least one terminology that can be used with all of them. For this purpose, the "family tree" relationship analogy—of parent/child, grandparent/grandchild, and ancestor/descendant—is commonly used. Although close inspection shows that the analogy does not really fit all four of the relationships (for example, children are not decompositions of their parents), these terms sufficiently describe above/below relationships.

We can now enlarge on the statements of Section 2.1.3 "Multiple Hierarchies." The four layered models we have described can be—and frequently are—used simultaneously to represent different aspects of one system. Using the requirements and architecture methods, the required functional capabilities of a system are captured by the process model—an abstraction/detailing model; the required behavioral capabilities are captured by the control model—a controlling/controlled model; information structures in the system might include supertype/subtype relationships, captured in an entity-relationship model; and the physical

|  | **Aggregation/ Decomposition** | **Abstraction/ Detailing** | **Supertype/ Subtype** | **Controlling/ Controlled** |
|---|---|---|---|---|
| **Aliases** | Whole/part; container/content; composed-of; consists-of; assembly/ subassembly/ component | (Erroneously: abstraction/ decomposition) | Generalization/ specialization; class hierarchy; inheritance structure; "is-a" hierarchy | Is-boss-of/ is-supervised-by; uses hierarchy; client/server |
| **Downward Usage** | Decompose; dismantle | Add detail; specialize | Inherit; specialize | Control |
| **Upward Usage** | Aggregate; assemble | Make abstract; generalize | Set membership; "is-a"; generalize; categorize | Controlled by |
| **Where Used, Roles** | Architecture model; object orientation (aggregate objects); requirements and architecture dictionaries | Requirements model; Structured Analysis; nesting in statecharts | Architecture model when used with object orientation; entity-relationship-attribute modeling | Control model (of requirements model); Structured Design; system control structures (occurs within a layer as well as between layers) |
| **Purpose of Usage** | Physical packaging; information-hiding; defining scope and visibility | Coping with complexity; reducing complexity | Similar to abstraction/ detailing; in addition: inheritance of attributes, functions, behavior | Separation of concerns; creating noncyclic client/server structures; simplifying cooperation |

*Figure 3.18: Summary of Relationships in Layered Models.*

structure is captured by the architecture model—an aggregation/decomposition model. Thus, to model a single system, not only can we use layered models of the same kind, as described in Section 2.1.3, we can also use layered models of different kinds. This allows us to represent different views of the system separately, but, when done as part of the requirements and architecture methods, the links between these views are carefully maintained.

This highlights the great flexibility of layered models. They are extraordinarily versatile, and allow us to represent just about any facet of systems and system development separately and at any desired level of detail, but with the links to the other facets also represented.

## 3.7 MODEL FRAMEWORK SUMMARY

Our modeling framework, shown in Figure 3.19—which is derived from Figure 3.7—now combines all the ideas described in this chapter. For most systems, especially larger ones, we exploit the idea that systems come in hierarchies. We have layers of specifications for the system, subsystems, sub-subsystem, and so on. But note that the flows between the layers go both ways—up and down. There is no sequence of development implied in this framework. We build groups of models as we discover subsystems in the hierarchy, and we do so in any order we want.

Forming subsystems is a difficult architectural or design decision, but exploitation of the information/material/energy classifications and of the generic subsystem categorization will guide us along the way. For software developers, we have many more guidelines in Chapter 6.

Each group of models separates the *what* from the *how:* We build separate requirements and architecture models. To help with the transition between *what* and *how* models, we build enhanced requirements models based on the architecture template. Thus, each group of models consists of three separate but related types: requirements, enhanced requirements, and architecture. Note that the arrows between the three models in the subsystems of Figure 3.19 go both ways— again, allowing these models to be developed in any sequence.

The information-hiding categories described in Section 3.6 are helpful for structuring all three models. They are generic enough to be applicable in many different application areas, yet precise enough to give a head start for partitioning. In many large applications, such subsystems have produced flexible, extendable, and maintainable systems. The case study in Part II demonstrates this idea with a specific example from a unique application domain.

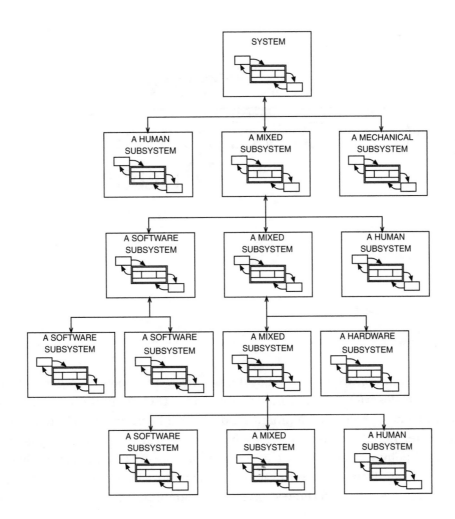

*Figure 3.19: The Modeling Framework.*

# Chapter 4
## System Development Models

### 4.1 OVERVIEW

In the last two chapters, we discussed systems and system models in general. In this chapter, we describe specific model notations, their definitions, and their rules and guidelines. Most development models have been extensively discussed in the literature; here, in this reference chapter, we want to assemble just the most important points. Whenever we add modeling aspects beyond the published literature, or deviate from common practice, we explain why we do so. Throughout this chapter, we cite references where more details and examples can be found.

Figure 4.1 shows an overview of the major models used in our framework. The vertical bar separates requirements models from architecture models, following the rationale discussed in Section 3.4. The horizontal bar separates the graphical representations, which simplify and clarify complex information, from the specifications, which include the precision and detail missing from the graphics. Single boxes represent elements that occur once per model; multiple boxes represent elements that may have multiple instances in one model.

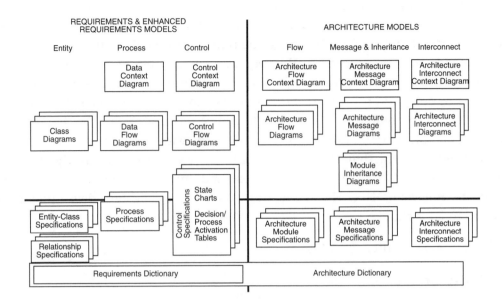

*Figure 4.1: A Summary of the Development Models.*

For simplicity, we have not shown in Figure 4.1 all the relationships between the elements: We have just bundled them into six vertical groups that have stronger connections within them than with other groups. For instance, the first vertical column, Entity, contains the entity modeling elements, including class diagrams, entity-class specifications, relationship specifications, and the subset of the requirements dictionary that defines the attributes of entity classes and relationships. The second column, Process, shows the classic SA elements, and the third column, Control, shows the extensions to SA for complex and real-time systems.

Moving to the architecture side of Figure 4.1, the architecture flow model elements are in the fourth column, followed in the fifth column by the message and inheritance model elements (mainly used for structured or object-oriented design in software), and finally, in the sixth column, the elements of the architecture interconnect model.

As illustrated above, all the models combine graphical elements with supporting specifications. In the following sections, we first discuss the basic graphical elements, then we present the diagrams built from those elements—which usually form the backbone of the model—and finally we discuss the specifications.

This sequence starts, in Section 4.2, with the details of the architecture models. You probably expected us to discuss requirements before architecture, but the architecture model represents the structure of both the entire final model and the final system, and is often the only thing that is observable in the real world.

In Section 4.3, we proceed to the requirements models, describing the notations used, independent of technological or organizational decisions, to document the process, data, and control structures. In Section 4.5, we discuss the relationships between the requirements and architecture models, and in Section 4.6, we comment on object orientation and its relationships with these methods.

Note, once again, that this chapter only discusses the models themselves: which models we have, how they are represented, and what rules and guidelines should be followed. How the models are used in real system development is deferred to later chapters.

## 4.2 ARCHITECTURE MODEL

### 4.2.1 Introduction

There is considerable debate among system engineers and others on the meaning of system architecture. Some contend that it is a superfluous notion that means nothing more than early system design. Others promote it as a discipline in its own right. There is certainly agreement that the boundary between system architecture and system design is fuzzy. In light of this debate, which is likely to continue indefinitely, the best we can do is to state our own definition and use it throughout this book:

> System architecture comprises the major physical properties, style, structure, interactions, and purpose of a system.

System architecting, which is carried out by system architects, is the activity of developing system architectures. Our architecture model captures the key elements of this definition, and we do not attempt to define precisely where in the model architecture ends and design begins. The reason is that it does not really matter: As long as you know how to develop a particular module and do it well, who cares whether you call it an architecture module or a design module.

The architecture model shows the physical reality of the system as it is, or will be, built. Everything in it conforms to reality: the components, their interfaces, their functionality, and so on. This real-world structure of the architecture model packages the requirements into building blocks, and it is the structure that is well known to those dealing with the system—they observe it every day.

The architecture model consists of several graphical components supported by specifications. One of these components, the requirements dictionary, is shared with the requirements and enhanced requirements models. The requirements dictionary is the foundation for the architecture dictionary, and it is shared by the system-level specifications and the hardware and software specifications.

The architecture mapping scheme is shown in Figure 4.2. Consider first its graphical components. Three different architecture context diagrams show the physical environment of the system: The architecture flow context diagram (AFCD) shows the physical flows that must pass to and from the environment; the architecture message context diagram (AMCD) shows messages received and sent by the system; and the architecture interconnect context diagram (AICD) shows the physical channels over which the flows and messages must travel.

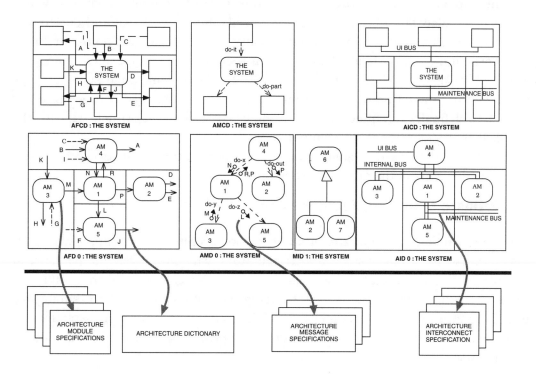

*Figure 4.2: Overview of the Architecture Model.*

The architecture models capture the structure of a system in terms of architecture modules, their specifications, and their relationships. The relationships are of three major types: communication (through information flow or messages), communication medium (the channels through which the communication flows), and inheritance (from more abstract architecture modules).

Figure 4.2 shows four different architecture diagram types that represent modules associated by the three different relationships: Architecture flow diagrams (AFDs) capture the system's architecture as a network of modules communicating through information, material, or energy flows; architecture message diagrams (AMDs) capture message communication between architecture modules; module inheritance diagrams (MIDs) depict the inheritance relationships between architecture modules; and architecture interconnect diagrams (AIDs) show the channels on which information, material, energy, and message communication flow between modules.

The supporting specifications are: architecture module specifications, which capture the allocation of requirements to specific building blocks and design and implementation details; architecture dictionary entries, which define the architecture flows and capture their allocation from the enhanced requirements model to architecture modules and interconnections; architecture message specifications, which capture the structure and content of messages exchanged between building blocks; and finally, architecture interconnect specifications, which capture the physical characteristics of the channels.

Before we discuss the diagrams and the specifications, we review the basic modeling elements of the architecture models.

## 4.2.2 Basic Modeling Elements

There are two basic architecture building blocks: architecture modules, which are inside the scope of our system; and terminators, which are systems, persons, or organizations outside that scope. As discussed above, there are three different types of relationship between these building blocks: communication, subdivided into flows and messages; channels; and inheritance. The following sections give definitions and symbols for these elements and provide some rules and guidelines for their use.

## 4.2.2.1 Architecture Module

**Definition**  An architecture module is the basic building block of our system, hardware, and software architectures.  There are dozens of terms for this concept used in other methods and in everyday life.  The level and scope of the model determine what architecture modules might apply.  Figure 4.3 shows some examples.

| Organizational | Technological Modules | |
|---|---|---|
| Modules | Hardware Modules | Software Modules |
| Company | Subsystem, Computer | Module, Package |
| Department | Processor (of any kind) | Component, Class |
| Subsidiary | Component | Subprogram, Procedure |
| Group | Assembly | Function, Macro |
| Team | Powertrain | Thread |
| Person | Engine | Library |

*Figure 4.3: Various Architecture Modules.*

The highest level of an organizational system could be a company, or perhaps a whole industry.  Companies can be structured by divisions, subsidiaries, or departments, and these can, in turn, be composed of groups, teams, and finally individual people.  Part of the architecture of an organizational system is the allocation of functions and tasks to these different units, just as it is in technological systems.

As shown in Figure 4.3, technological modules can, for example, be hardware elements like computers or mechanical devices, or software elements, all of which perform specified parts of the requirements.  Systems are often networks of such modules; the choice of modules, their configuration, and the requirements allocated to them constitute the system architecture.  We sometimes use the term "processor" for module.  "Processor" is equally neutral and can stand for anything that performs system processing: mechanical processors, electronic processors, and so on.  It can even apply to a person, though some might take offense at being considered a "human processor."

Within a computer, we can distribute work and allocate requirements to threads, for example, or we can create software modules or packages, further consisting of classes, subprograms, procedures, or whatever your favorite programming language calls the building blocks.

**Symbol**  A rounded rectangle (sometimes called a bubtangle) with a name and a number.  If we want to indicate the existence of multiple, identical copies of the architecture module, we use the multiple module symbol shown on the right in Figure 4.4.

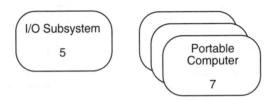

*Figure 4.4: Architecture Module Symbols.*

**Naming Rule**  One or more singular nouns, optionally with adjectives—the name(s) by which the building block is known in the real world.

**Additional Rules and Guidelines**  The names and numbers of modules should be unique throughout the model.  This avoids ambiguity.  If there are several similar modules, a single name can be used for all of them with a simple alphabetic or numeric modifier: PUMP_A, PUMP_B, and so on.

Modules can be nested.

### 4.2.2.2 Terminator

**Definition**  A terminator is something external to our system (for example, another system, a person, or an organization) with which our system receives, sends, or exchanges information, messages, material, or energy.  Terminators are also called externals, sources (if they only deliver input to our system), or sinks (if they only receive output from our system).

**Symbol**  A square or rectangle labeled with its name.  See Figure 4.5.

*Figure 4.5: Terminator Symbols.*

**Naming Rules** A terminator name should consist of a noun, or multiple nouns, optionally with adjectives. The name should not imply any actions, that is, it should contain no verbs.

### 4.2.2.3 Architecture Flow

**Definition** An architecture flow represents the information, material, or energy exchanged between architecture modules, or between architecture modules and the environment (that is, the terminators). These flows may either be single elements or groups of elements. When they represent information, it can be data, control, or both. (Contrary to *Strategies for Real-Time System Specification,* we no longer graphically distinguish between data and control in architecture flows. The dashed lines now represent messages, as described later.)

**Symbol** A vector with a name, as shown in Figure 4.6. The vector can have any number of horizontal and vertical (but not diagonal) segments. The bends may be sharp or rounded. The "rectangular" form of architecture flows distinguishes them from the "free-style" data and control flows that we shall see later, and it infers the more physical structure of the architecture.

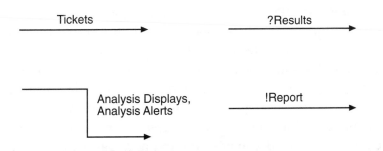

*Figure 4.6: Architecture Flow Symbols.*

**Naming Rules** An architecture flow name should consist of a noun or multiple nouns, optionally with adjectives. The name should not imply any actions, that is, it should contain no verbs.

Note that the direction of the vector says nothing about who triggers the flow. If that information is needed, the flow name can be preceded with a "?" or a "!" symbol. The question mark indicates that the flow is pulled or initiated by the receiver: "Would you give me a flow, please?" The exclamation point is used when the sender initiates the exchange and pushes the information to the receiver: "Take this flow!" In Section 4.2.2.5, we discuss these extensions to the notation in more detail.

**Additional Rules and Guidelines**

- An architecture flow may be a single element or a group of elements. A group should consist of related (cohesive) items, not just an arbitrary collection.
- Each element or group must have a unique, descriptive name. Many software languages support a data type as well as a name. This is a detailed software design issue that is best dealt with at that level, so typing of flows is not included with these methods.
- Every architecture flow name must appear in the architecture dictionary, and it must be defined down to its primitive elements.
- If a group of flows enters an architecture module, all of its members should preferably be used in that module. There are, however, cases where the most cost-effective design decision is to send a whole array or set of data to a module that does not need all of it. In this case, the reason for the design decision should be recorded in the module specification, and the information that is and is not used should be clearly identified. However, it is usually preferable to "Starve your architecture modules" and only feed them with flows they need.
- Architecture flows may split or merge when there is no decomposing or aggregating, that is, when the whole group goes to all the sinks or comes from all the sources. If the flow decomposes or aggregates at a split or merge point, the situation is less clear. In the requirements model, we allow this decomposition and aggregating, because, in that abstract model, we are not concerned with the physical mechanisms that make things happen. In the architecture model, we are concerned with those mechanisms, so the only time decomposing or

aggregating of architecture flows is allowed is when it involves no processing. This might be the case, for example, when the members of a group of electrical signals are each carried on a separate wire in a cable harness, and only the signals and their wires needed at each node are connected there.

- Different flows between the same modules may be sent via the same flow vector. They should not be grouped under a common name if they don't logically belong together. Their names are written next to the flow vector, separated by commas. Drawing one arrow instead of many is a simple way to unclutter the diagrams.
- Flows can be bidirectional to indicate that the architecture module receives and sends the same flow. Push and pull indicators do not make sense with bidirectional flows. If triggering must be represented, use separate flows or messages.

### 4.2.2.4 Message

**Definition**  A message is a request from one architecture module to another to do something. A typical message also conveys information between the modules, in either or both directions.

Architecture flows emphasize information, material, or energy exchange, and de-emphasize the triggering of the communication; messages do the opposite. A message shows the originator of the exchange. Optionally, it can show the information, material, or energy exchanged with that message.

**Symbol**  A dashed vector with a name, as shown in Figure 4.7. Like architecture flows, messages are represented by lines with any number of horizontal and vertical (but not diagonal) segments.

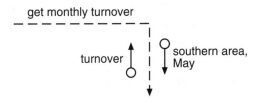

*Figure 4.7: Message Symbol.*

**Naming Rules**   Messages can have up to three label types, all of which are optional:

> message name
> input flow, input flow, . . .
> output flow, output flow, . . .

Message names usually contain verbs, suggesting the action required of the receiver. A message name can also include an object or entity to be acted upon. If the action name has no significance for the model, it may be omitted; in which case, only the input and/or output flows are named, and the message is identical in meaning to an architecture flow with push or pull indicators.

As well as being used alone, the input and output flows are used where the message name is not sufficient to convey the meaning of the communication, that is, where the information, material, or energy exchanged is also important. To indicate the flow parameters, we use the well-known symbol from Structured Design (known there as a data couple): a short vector pointing in the direction of the flow, with a hollow circle at the end. These message flows are labeled with their names, separated by commas, as seen in Figure 4.7.

The message may have input and output flows, input flows only, output flows only, or no flows at all.

If none of the three label types is shown, the message symbol simply indicates the presence of a message between sender and receiver without providing any details; in such a case, the details can be found in the message specification (see Section 4.2.5.5 for more information on message specifications).

**Rules and Guidelines**

- Use unnamed messages early in architecture model development as a reminder of the dependencies between modules. As soon as you know more about a dependency, name the message and/or any flows. Before you complete your model, make sure that you capture everything that needs to be known about the message either in the diagram or in a message specification.

Before we go on with the other two relationships between architecture modules—the inheritance and the interconnect relationships—let us compare flows and messages.

### *4.2.2.5 Flows and Messages*

An architecture flow shows what information, material, or energy is transferred between two or more architecture modules. The flow itself does not tell us which module initiates it; the emphasis is on the direction of the flow only. This is similar to the approach used in data flow diagrams, where the data flows themselves are more interesting than knowing which processes caused them. One can also compare flow-coupled modules with loosely coupled electrical circuits, where signals are exchanged, but otherwise the circuits have little influence on each other.

Messages, on the other hand, indicate the active and passive partners in a transaction: The active partner initiates the message; the passive partner receives and interprets the message. Information, material, or energy, if any, can flow in the same direction as the message ("Here are some important things for you! Tell me if you like them!") or in the opposite direction ("Could you please give me last month's data?"—resulting in information for the one who asked).

So, messages between two architecture modules have to answer these questions:

- Who initiates the communication (is the flow pulled or pushed)?
- A message vector clearly shows where the message begins (the initiator) and where it ends. A flow does not show this information unless we annotate it with a pull (?) or push (!) indicator.
- What information, material, or energy is exchanged?
- A message has the option of showing the items exchanged by including the parameters that travel with the message or are returned to the message sender. A flow always shows the exchange, but not necessarily the initiator.
- What is the name of the message?
- A message has the option of a name that describes the actions to be performed, or it may just show any parameters exchanged. A flow never indicates actions to be performed.

Figure 4.8 shows multiple possibilities for modeling flows and messages between architecture modules. The one you choose is partly an individual preference, and partly depends on the stage of the project (system modeling or software modeling, for example) and potentially on the implementation technology.

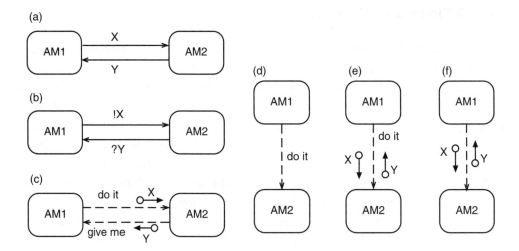

*Figure 4.8: Flows and Messages.*

Assume that all examples in Figure 4.8 portray the same excerpt of an architecture model. Variants *a* through *c* include two vectors each; variants *d* through *f* include one each. Even so, variants *e* and *f* include more information than variant *a*, since they show which architecture module is the active partner. Variants *b* and *f* show similar information, but variant *f* indicates that sending *X* and receiving *Y* are part of one message, while variant *b* leaves open whether the two are related. Variants *c, d,* and *e* have message names; the other variants do not.

Study these examples and decide which you would use in various circumstances. You will discover that variant *a* is most useful in early stages of requirements and architecture modeling, especially for higher levels of system and subsystem architectures. Variant *c* is appropriate for software design, especially with modular or object-oriented programming languages. Variant *d* might be useful for early client/server modeling, since it shows dependencies without further details, but those details, if they exist, should be added when the system architecture is established, resulting in variant *e*.

Both the push and pull indicators and the message notation are new to the architecture method since *Strategies for Real-Time System Specification* was written. They are added to the modeling tool kit largely to meet software needs, particularly when object-oriented techniques are used. As Figure 4.8 shows, there is some redundancy in these notations, which is deliberate: It serves the needs of the various stages of software development—simple architecture flows initially, flows with push or pull indicators early in software development, and messages when the design is nearing completion. The flows, whether simple architecture flows, or flows attached to messages, should balance with their originating requirements flows. The push or pull indicators and the messages are design artifacts with no counterpart in the requirements model.

### 4.2.2.6 Inheritance *Relationship*

Flows and messages represent basic relationships between architecture modules. Sometimes, we are also interested in another relationship. If an architecture module has some interesting features (for example, if it has certain attributes, can perform certain processes, or has a certain behavior), we might want to create architecture modules that inherit these interesting features, and maybe add more features to them. We have already discussed, in Section 3.6.3, the basics of this supertype/subtype relationship. This relationship is mostly used in software architecture models, where it naturally maps into inheritance structures in object-oriented programming languages.

At the system level, inheritance can be used to enforce similarity of abstract behavior or style. In other words, we can create system-level architecture modules that are very abstract and then adjust stylistic characteristics for use in the rest of the architecture. At the system level (and, to some extent, in software), inheritance is the subject of current research, and not yet fully developed. Inheritance is a very powerful and promising concept that has been used in large and successful industrial projects, so we mention it here, but we advise you to apply it carefully and only to the extent that it is clearly useful.

**Definition** An inheritance relationship links two architecture modules where the lower-level module (the sub-module) inherits (or takes on) features defined by the higher-level module (the super-module).

**Symbol** A solid arrow with a hollow triangular arrowhead pointing to the super-module. This is consistent with the Unified Modeling Language [Booch 98]. If multiple sub-modules inherit features from one super-module, we can draw either multiple arrows, or split a single arrow. See Figure 4.9.

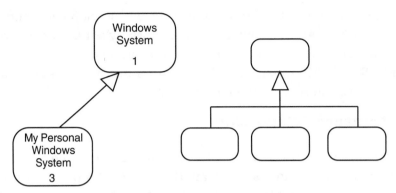

*Figure 4.9: Inheritance Symbols.*

**Naming Rules** Inheritance relationships are not named.

**Rules and Guidelines** Inheritance can extend through multiple layers, forming trees of inheritance. The recommendation is to keep them small: Two to three levels of inheritance are sufficient for most systems. In large systems (several years of development by dozens of people), there may be up to seven levels. Beyond that number, reconsider the overall structure.

Multiple inheritance is possible—arrows pointing to multiple super-modules—but be careful to follow the underlying concepts, especially ensuring that the inherited properties are not in conflict with each other.

Inheritance is a powerful but hazardous concept. From the point of view of coupling and cohesion that stem from Structured Design where we usually want to minimize coupling, inheritance is the tightest and strongest form of coupling possible between two modules. Tight coupling through inheritance is very helpful if you want changes from the root of the inheritance structure to ripple through large parts of the system, but those same changes can be disastrous if they contain errors.

A good discussion of inheritance's strengths and weaknesses can be found in [Page-Jones 95].

### 4.2.2.7 Architecture Interconnect

**Definition** An interconnect is the physical means or channel through which information, material, or energy is exchanged between architecture modules. It may consist of any medium: electrical, mechanical, optical, hydraulic, or many others.

**Symbols**   There are so many possible interconnect types that we make no attempt to assign specific symbols to each of them.  Figure 4.10 suggests possible symbols for an electrical bus, a mechanical linkage, and an optical link.  As shown on the right side of the figure, interconnects may split or merge in accordance with the real topology of the system.

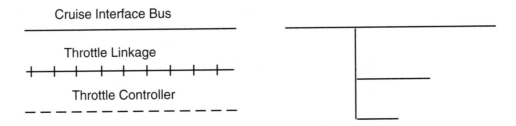

Cruise Interface Bus

Throttle Linkage

Throttle Controller

*Figure 4.10: Interconnect Symbols.*

### Rules and Guidelines

- Each user, company, industry, or discipline should decide on the interconnects that are important for its use, and should standardize their symbols.  Automated tools should provide a selection of symbols for different media, allowing the user to define what they represent.
- Notice the distinction between interconnects and interfaces.  An interface is a boundary between two system elements.  An interconnect has at least two interfaces: one with each module or terminator with which it is connected.

## 4.2.3 Context Diagram

We have now reviewed the individual symbols used in architecture models, and it is time to look at the diagrams in which these symbols are used, and specifications that support them.  We start at the top, with the context diagrams.  As we mentioned at the beginning of this chapter, there are three types of context diagram: the architecture flow context diagram (AFCD), the architecture message context diagram (AMCD), and the architecture interconnect context diagram (AICD).

**Definition**  Context diagrams show the system embedded in its environment of terminators. The architecture flow context diagram (Figure 4.11), the architecture message context diagram (Figure 4.12), and the architecture interconnect context diagram (Figure 4.13) show, respectively, the flows, messages, and interconnects linking the environment and the system.

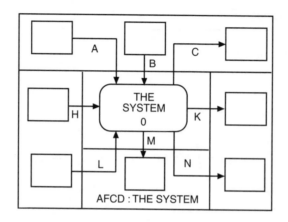

*Figure 4.11: Architecture Flow Context Diagram.*

## Elements of the Architecture Flow Context Diagram

- one architecture module (representing the system under development)
- terminators (one for each external item with which the system must communicate)
- architecture flows (into and out of the system)
- optionally, the architecture template to categorize sources and sinks (see Section 4.4.3)

## Rules and Guidelines for the AFCD

- The only absolute rules for the AFCD are that it must contain exactly one architecture module (representing the system), at least one terminator, and at least one flow.
- The context architecture module is assigned the number 0.
- There may be any number of terminators and flows.

For multidisciplinary systems, we normally use an AFCD. For software-only systems using architecture message diagrams, we can use an architecture message context diagram. Figure 4.12 is an example of this, with one boss terminator asking the system to "do it." Another terminator in the lower-right corner provides support without being part of the system under development. The third terminator may be a peer system, sometimes providing help, at other times receiving help.

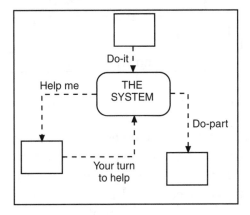

*Figure 4.12: Architecture Message Context Diagram.*

### Elements of the Architecture Message Context Diagram

- similar to the AFDC, with flows substituted by messages in any of the styles described in Section 4.2.2.4

### Elements of the Architecture Interconnect Context Diagram

- similar to AFDC, with interconnects instead of flows, and the optional architecture template

Figure 4.13 shows two interconnects between the system and its environment: a redundant BUS1 to the terminators in the user-interface part of the template, and EXT BUS to link all the other terminators with the system.

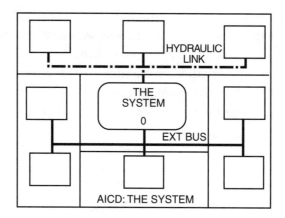

*Figure 4.13: Architecture Interconnect Context Diagram.*

With the AICD, the question arises: Who owns the interconnects between the system and the environment? Are they part of the system or part of the environment? The answer is that there is no fixed answer: Each case has its own circumstances. If the interconnect existed prior to the introduction of the system, then it probably belongs to another system; if it was introduced with the system, then it probably belongs to the system. In either case, establishing the interconnects with the environment and the flows that travel over them is a major part of system engineering, and must be resolved with all parties involved, regardless of ownership.

## 4.2.4 Networks and Hierarchies

Before we discuss the architecture diagrams into which the context module (that is, the system) is decomposed, let us study the different decomposition options.

Figure 4.14 is a class diagram illustrating the various types of architecture diagrams. For the purposes of this illustration, we show abstract classes (those that do not occur as actual diagrams) with dashed rectangles, and concrete classes (those that do occur as actual diagrams) with solid rectangles. There are five concrete diagram types, shown at the bottom of the figure, related through class relationships to the abstract classes above.

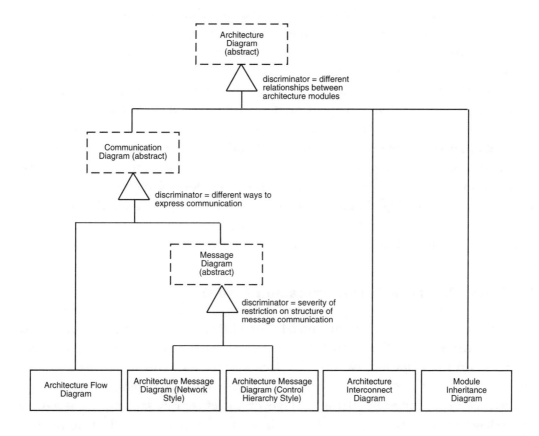

*Figure 4.14: A Class Diagram of Architecture Diagrams.*

Starting at the top, we have the abstract class, Architecture Diagram, attached to a class relationship expressing that everything below it belongs to the class: architecture diagram.

The first subclassification in Figure 4.14 divides architecture diagrams into three subclasses showing the communication between architecture modules, their interconnects, and their inheritance relationships. The last two of these sub-classes are represented by concrete diagrams. The other subclass is shown as an abstract class: the communication diagram. All communication diagrams show how architecture modules communicate with each other, but there are different types of communication; this calls for further subclassification: architecture flow diagrams (concrete) and architecture message diagrams (abstract). The architecture message diagram is further subclassified into the concrete network and hierarchical message styles. The five concrete diagram types at the bottom of Figure 4.14 correspond to the four diagram types we saw in Section 4.2.1 and in Figure 4.2, but with architecture message diagrams divided into two subclasses: the network and hierarchy styles.

Notice that Figure 4.14 is a class diagram of architecture diagrams and their relationships. It would also be possible to construct a class diagram of architecture modules and their relationships. Such a diagram would have aggregation/decomposition relationships instead of subclass/superclass relationships. It would also be possible to construct a class diagram of processes and their relationships in the Structured Analysis model (or the requirements model), and this, again, would be different, having abstraction/detailing relationships.

In the following sections, we discuss the different types of architecture diagram, and highlight the differences and similarities between the network and hierarchical models.

## 4.2.5 Architecture Communication Model

The architecture communication model summarizes all modeling elements that deal with the information, material, and energy exchange between architecture modules. In the following, we discuss network models, represented by architecture flow diagrams and network-style architecture message diagrams, and control hierarchies, represented by hierarchy-style architecture message diagrams. All of these diagrams are supported by three kinds of description: architecture module specifications, message specifications, and the architecture dictionary.

Figure 4.15 shows the two principal ways to split a system. The vertical cut through the cube shows the system split into components that share an aggregation/decomposition relationship as discussed in Section 3.6.1.

The horizontal cut through the cube results in architecture modules that are peers within the same level of system or subsystem. But there are different kinds of communication structures between these peers. Our starting point is that all architecture modules in an architecture communication diagram are equals that can communicate freely with each other. This results in a network structure with unrestricted flows or messages between any two or more architecture modules. Figure 4.15 shows this network view as an architecture flow diagram in the lower left, and an architecture message diagram (network style) in the lower center.

Sometimes, designers do not want this equality. Some architecture modules might operate more like generals and majors in the Army, or cardinals and bishops in the church. In such systems, the communication usually follows a hierarchical control structure. Messages are only sent down the control hierarchy, but the information, material, or energy can flow in any direction. As depicted in the lower-right corner of Figure 4.15, the downward flow of messages results in a controlling/controlled hierarchy, not in an aggregation/decomposition hierarchy. And remember, this hierarchy is still within one horizontal layer of the system.

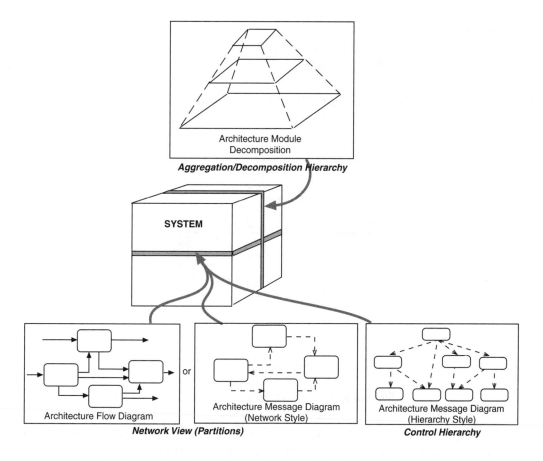

*Figure 4.15:  Communication Hierarchies, Networks, Layers, and Partitions.*

Should you get lost in the following discussions of the individual diagrams, come back to this overview. Make sure that you understand the differences between networks and hierarchies, and between aggregation/decomposition hierarchies and control hierarchies, as explained in Sections 3.6.1 and 3.6.4. In the architecture model, we use them all.

### 4.2.5.1 Architecture Flow Diagram

**Definition**  An architecture flow diagram (AFD) is a network representation of the architecture modules within a system or subsystem and of the flows between them.

**Elements**

- architecture modules
- architecture flows (with or without push or pull indicators)
- optional: architecture template

Figure 4.16 shows a generic architecture flow diagram with four architecture modules. One is in the central processing region of the template, one in the user-interface region, and one each in the input and output processing regions.

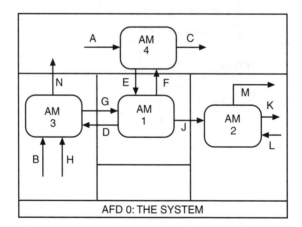

Figure 4.16: Architecture Flow Diagram.

Figure 4.17 shows the same diagram, but the flows there are annotated with push and pull indicators. AM 4 is pulling Input A from the environment, pushing E to AM 1, pulling F from it. The environment pulls Output C from AM 4. AM 3 is rather passive: D is pushed in from AM 1, and G is pulled out by AM 1, so AM 3 could be considered a server for its client, AM 1. The server communicates with other systems in its environment (by pulling Inputs B and H and pushing out N).

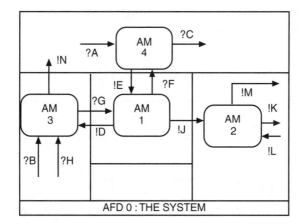

*Figure 4.17: Architecture Flow Diagram with Push and Pull Indicators.*

## Rules and Guidelines

- An AFD can be drawn with any number of architecture modules and architecture flows. There should be as many modules as one finds in the real system (for example, departments, computers, components, and so on). The guideline of limiting the number of modules per diagram to 7±2 does not apply.
- Although there is no limit on the number of architecture modules in one AFD, we can sometimes reduce complexity by layering architecture flow diagrams. The diagram then shows the aggregate architecture module and a further AFD in the layer below shows the decomposition of this aggregate. This should only be done if an aggregate makes sense in the real-world system.
- If flows alone are sufficient to support the architecture definition of the system, then push or pull indicators should not be used. If the instigator of a flow is important to understanding the architecture, then the notation should be used.
- Experience shows that this added control information becomes more important at the lower design levels, especially in software design.
- An alternative to push and pull indicators is a description of this information in the architecture module specifications, or in the dictionary definitions.

- If control aspects really become important, flow diagrams can be replaced with message diagrams, as described below.

Figure 4.18 shows a decomposition of AM 1 of Figure 4.16.

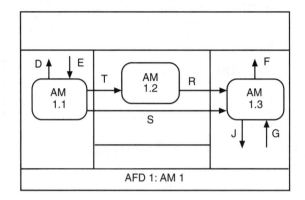

*Figure 4.18: Child Architecture Flow Diagram.*

**Rules and Guidelines for Decomposition**   These rules are similar to those in Structured Analysis.  Here is a short summary:

- An architecture flow diagram must be named and numbered the same as its parent architecture module.  Architecture module numbers must comprise the diagram number appended by one additional number.
- The architecture modules on AFD 0 (that is, the decomposition of the one architecture module in the context diagram) are numbered consecutively from 1.
- Flows in and out of a parent architecture module must balance with corresponding flows in and out of its child diagram.  This can be achieved by using identical names or by decomposing flows between parent and child.
- When, through aggregation or decomposition, flows are grouped between layers, all components of the group must be used in the child diagram.

## 4.2.5.2 Architecture Message Diagram—Network Style

With the architecture message diagram, we can downplay the role of flows and use messages to make the controlling/controlled structure dominant. The origins and destinations of the messages are clearly shown, while the flows are optional. In order to make it clear that AFDs and AMDs are alternatives to each other, we use the same example as shown in Figure 4.17: A given set of modules can be the basis for either an AFD or an AMD.

**Definition** An architecture message diagram is a representation of the architecture modules within a system or subsystem, and of the messages between them.

### Elements

- architecture modules
- messages (with or without flows)
- optional: architecture template

Figure 4.19 shows the same system as Figures 4.16 and 4.17, but it uses the message format. Message m1 entering AM 4 requests C as a response. This corresponds to the output flow C in Figure 4.16, or the pull indicator on C in Figure 4.17.

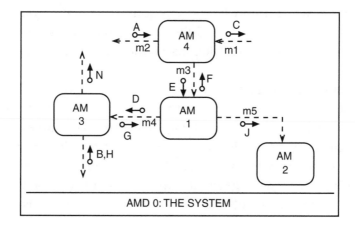

*Figure 4.19: Architecture Message Diagram.*

Compare the messages of AM 3 with Figures 4.16 and 4.17. There is a message sending N and another message requesting B and H. Consider what circumstances would prompt you to use the form from each of the three diagrams.

Another possibility has been chosen for AM 2. Only the triggering and flow J from AM 1 through message m5 are shown. The other flows that the module uses as inputs and outputs (M, K, and L, as shown in Figure 4.16) are not yet included. They can be added later, described in the module specification, or shown in the child diagram of AM 2.

## General Rules and Guidelines

- AFDs and AMDs are almost equivalent, except that AMDs require a message for any communication to occur. In some cases, no message is needed, and then only an AFD can represent the system. For example, a radio station sends data and a radio receiver receives data; no commands or messages are transferred between them.
- Where messages are needed, you may use the annotated AFD or the AMD—both diagrams can represent the same information. In the annotated AFD, the flow structure is more visible; in the AMD, the message/call structure is more visible (you can see who the boss is more clearly).
- There are no restrictions on sources and destinations of messages. They can start and end in the environment or at any architecture module. In general, every module can exchange messages with any of its peers (but note the restrictions in the hierarchical form described in Section 4.2.5.3).
- Avoid uninterpretable situations: Do not draw two unnamed messages between the same two modules. Do not use identical message names or identical parameter names between two modules.
- Follow the KISS principle (Keep It Simple, Stupid!). Focus first on messages without names to indicate dependencies between modules. Try adding either message names only, or parameters only, to emphasize the more important feature. Name everything only in detailed design.
- Each module of an AMD can be decomposed into a separate AMD, in which case, the balancing rules and guidelines in Section 4.2.9 apply.

### *4.2.5.3 Architecture Message Diagram—Hierarchy Style*

Sometimes, we want to restrict the message configuration in our systems. A popular restriction is to forbid message cycles, such as Module A sending a message to Module B, B sending a message to C, and C sending a message back to A. Over the years, we have learned that hierarchies are easier to manage than networks. To exclude cyclic messages in architecture message diagrams, we simply arrange the modules in a top-down fashion so that the sender of a message is always above the receiver. Many design methods—especially for software—use this kind of hierarchical structure.

Note that although we draw the control hierarchy top-down, all the architecture modules in this control hierarchy are, in the large, still peers on the same layer of the aggregation/decomposition hierarchy.

Assume that AM 1 in Figure 4.19 is internally organized in a hierarchy, as shown in Figure 4.20. Within this diagram, AM 1.2 is the boss, sending messages to AM 1.1 and AM 1.3. AM 1.1 uses the services of AM 1.3 by sending a message, m12, and it therefore controls AM 1.3. This constitutes a hierarchical layering, with AM 1.2 above AM 1.1, and both above AM 1.3.

As an exercise, add push or pull indicators to the flows of Figure 4.18, using the information from Figure 4.20.

**Definition** An architecture message diagram (hierarchy style) does not contain any cyclic messages. It can therefore be arranged in a control hierarchy with messages only traveling downward.

### Elements

- architecture modules and messages, similar to network style AMDs described above
- the architecture template should not be used, since it is incompatible with the top-down control structure

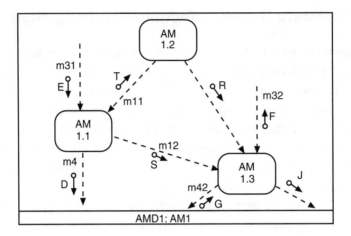

*Figure 4.20: Architecture Message Diagram—Hierarchy Style.*

### Rules and Guidelines

- When using AMDs, to avoid cyclic messages, arrange the architecture modules in a control hierarchy.
- Avoid just passing messages through a module: Instead, pass them directly to the receiver, bypassing any intermediate modules.
- You can start with unnamed messages, just indicating that a module is the boss of other modules. Add flow names as needed, for information sent with the message or information returned.
- Add message names when the receiving module can perform multiple tasks. If the message corresponds to the one and only function that is indicated by the module name, do not label the message.
- Obey the balancing guidelines described for the network-style AMD, above. In comparing Figure 4.20 with Figure 4.19, note the decomposition of message m3 into m31 and m32, as well as the decomposition of message m4. These decompositions must be explained in the message specification.

## *4.2.5.4 Architecture Module Specification*

**Definition**  An architecture module specification (AMS) contains the physical definition of a module, with cross-references to the enhanced requirements model components that are allocated to it.  These specifications typically include numerous references to outside sources of information; in fact, they *should* make such references rather than duplicate information that exists elsewhere.

**Rules and Guidelines**  Every module must have an AMS.  The form of an AMS is unique to each company or even each project.  AMSs can, for example, be embedded in the system specification adjacent to the modules they describe, collected together in an appendix to the model, or made into a separate document in which each AMS is a separate section.  Regardless of the form chosen, their content should be consistent throughout the organization, and clearly established before each project is started.

Below is a summary of the typical contents of an AMS:

- **description**—a brief overview of the module: what it is, what it does, how it does it, and its main role in the system.
- **cross reference**—a listing of the enhanced requirements model's processes, CSPECs, and stores that are allocated to the module and its sub-modules (if any), possibly as a traceability matrix.
- **design rationale**—a statement of how and why the particular design was chosen, with reference to other designs that were considered and trade-off studies that were made (referencing other documents and sources as needed).
- **design justification**—a statement of why you think the module will do what you say it will, its capabilities and capacities, and how it will meet the requirements allocated to it.
- **required constraints**—as defined in Section 2.3.2, listed together with their sources (including industry standards and regulations). For example,

  - Reliability (MTBF, . . . )
  - Maintainability (MTTR, serviceability, testability, field replacement vs. shop repair, . . . )
  - Safety (hazards to operators, others, . . . )

- Physical (size, shape, weight, electrical power, environmental, . . . )
- Design (required use of existing modules, techniques, components, . . . )
- Manufacturability (standardized components, ease of assembly, . . . )
- Cost
- Schedule
- . . . and so on.

- **interfaces**—a statement of what the module offers to others (outputs) and what it expects from others (inputs), in user-defined formats. For software design, the format might contain lists of functions with their parameters and types. For system specifications, this paragraph might be omitted when the diagrams are precise enough about flows between modules.

### 4.2.5.5 Message Specification

**Definition**  A message specification defines the details of a message. Its form depends very much on where and how the message is used in the architecture model. Instead of putting every annotation of a message in the diagram, you can just use the name and put all the other details into the message specification. This keeps the diagrams simpler and more readable. The following template suggests items that might be specified:

- **name of the message:**
  - must be compatible with the services offered by the receiving architecture module.
  - may be identical to the name of the receiving architecture module when the module performs just one function. In this case, the name may be omitted. This is identical to the form used in Structured Design, where the call arcs are unnamed, since they point to exactly one function.
- **parameter specifications:** (for input and output parameters)
  - parameter names (as used by the sender of the message) and their types.
- **message composition:** if the message is an aggregate of several submessages.

- **characteristics of the message:** synchronous, asynchronous, time-out, and so on. (This has to be cross-checked with the behavior description of the architecture module specification. For example, is it capable of receiving asynchronous messages?)

### Rules and Guidelines

- A message specification can be developed before we know the internal details of an architecture module. It represents a request that eventually must be handled by the architecture module. The more we know about the request from the outside, the easier it is to construct the inside of an architecture module.
- Eventually, the message, with its parameters, must be fully compatible with the interface description of the architecture module.
- Names distinguish between messages, so, to avoid ambiguity, limit yourself to one unnamed message between two architecture modules.
- As noted in Section 4.2.5.3, unnamed messages can be used early in the architecture development, just to establish that there is a message, before knowing any details. They can also be used in detailed software design, where architecture modules are functions and messages are function calls.

## 4.2.6 Architecture Interconnect Model

In Section 4.2.5, on the architecture communication model, we discussed the principles and different forms of hierarchies and networks. These principles also apply to the architecture interconnect model. Comparing Figure 4.21 and Figure 4.15, you see that the aggregation/decomposition structure we use for AFDs and AMDs also applies to AIDs, because flows and messages both travel on channels. A given layer of the architecture interconnect model is simpler than its communication model counterpart in that we require only the architecture interconnect diagram—a network of physical channels linking architecture modules.

In this section, we discuss architecture interconnect diagrams and their supporting specification, the interconnect specification.

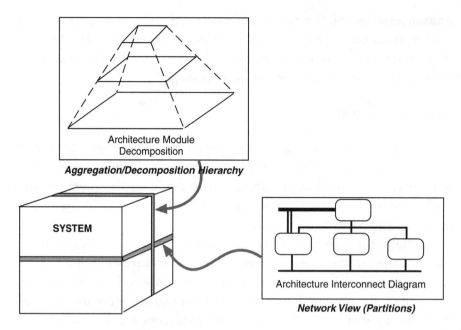

*Figure 4.21:* Interconnect Hierarchies, Networks, Layers,
and Partitions.

### 4.2.6.1 Architecture Interconnect Diagram

**Definition** An architecture interconnect diagram (AID), as shown in Figure 4.22, is a graphical representation of the architecture modules of a system or subsystem, and of the physical channels that the modules use for exchanging information, material, energy, or messages.

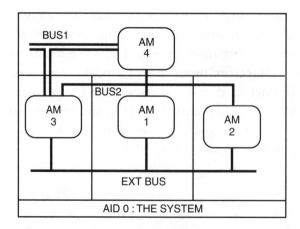

*Figure 4.22: Architecture Interconnect Diagram.*

## Elements

- architecture modules
- interconnects

## Rules and Guidelines

- The architecture modules on an AID must also be on the corresponding AFD or AMD.
- An AID represents part of a system or subsystem architecture. For software allocated to only one processor, we do not need AIDs, since the internal channels are handled by the compiler or run-time system and are of no significance in our models.
- As with AFDs and AMDs, we can decompose AIDs into child AIDs for individual architecture modules. Figure 4.23 shows an example for AM 1. To achieve balance between layers, those interconnects linking architecture modules in the higher-layer diagram must be repeated in the lower layer. There, the interconnects come from the outside (as an open-ended arc) and show the exact linking points with decomposed modules. BUS2 and EXT BUS provide examples of balancing between Figures 4.22 and 4.23. Figure 4.22 and the AICD in Figure 4.13 provide another example.

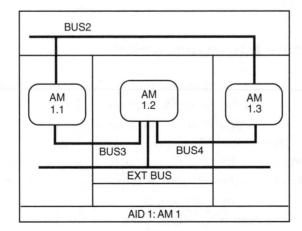

*Figure 4.23: Child Interconnect Diagram.*

- Architecture interconnects can be used without flows allocated to them. This is useful, for example, in modeling electrical systems where the power and ground bus configurations are critical and need detailed specifications. In such cases, these buses can be shown as interconnects (which they are) and defined in detail in the interconnect specifications. Although there are flows (electrical currents) traveling over these buses, they are not a direct part of the system functionality and are usually not shown on the flow diagrams.

### 4.2.6.2 Architecture Interconnect Specification

**Definition**   Architecture interconnect specifications (AIS) contain the physical definitions of interconnects or channels. They describe the characteristics of the transmission media on which information, material, energy, or messages travel.

### Rules and Guidelines

- AISs are similar in most respects to AMSs, except that they more often reference standard industry specifications, and the requirements elements that are allocated to them are data and control flows. This mapping of flows to interconnects is recorded in the architecture dictionary, not in the AIS. Otherwise, the description, design rationale, design justification, and required constraints follow the same guidelines as for AMSs.

## 4.2.7 Architecture Inheritance Model

A new feature added to the architecture model since *Strategies for Real-Time System Specification* was published is the inheritance relationship. Since inheritance is totally different from communication and interconnects, we have devoted a separate diagram to it, the module inheritance diagram (MID).

Analogous to Figures 4.15 and 4.21, Figure 4.24 shows that on any layer of the aggregation/decomposition structure of a system, modules can inherit features from other modules. In other words, supertypes and subtypes can appear anywhere in the system hierarchy. In practice, we rarely use the inheritance relationship in conjunction with module decomposition, so we show this supertype/subtype hierarchy separately, wherever we find a need to factor out commonalities through inheritance.

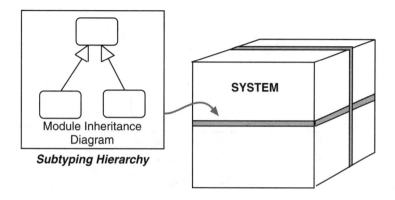

Figure 4.24: Inheritance Model.

## 4.2.7.1 Module Inheritance Diagram

The module inheritance diagram (MID) follows the inheritance relationship discussed in Section 4.2.2.6. Illustrated in Figure 4.25, the MID is the only addition to the model dealing with inheritance. Supertype modules on an MID rarely appear on any other architecture diagram. However, they do have module specifications, just like any other module.

Assume AM 2 in Figure 4.25 is the same AM 2 shown in Figure 4.16. Figure 4.25 shows, through the inheritance vector with the open arrowhead, that AM 2 inherits features from AM 6. Figure 4.16 shows that AM 2 is in the output processing region of the architecture template. The inheritance relationship might, therefore, mean that AM 6 defines generic functions and protocols for a certain output device. AM 2 inherits, or conforms to, all these features, and specializes them by adding more features. Figure 4.25 shows that AM 7 also inherits features from AM 6, but AM 7 has multiple inheritance, since it also has an inheritance relationship with AM 8.

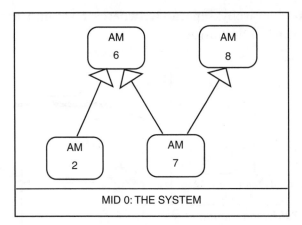

*Figure 4.25: Module Inheritance Diagram.*

**Definition**  A module inheritance diagram is a graphical representation of inheritance relationships between architecture modules.  It can show single or multiple inheritance over any number of levels.

**Elements**

- architecture modules
- inheritance relationships

**Rules and Guidelines**

- Same as those for the inheritance relationship, discussed in Section 4.2.2.6.
- In addition, modules at the lowest levels in an inheritance structure must also appear on architecture flow diagrams.  The modules above those levels can be abstract, simply collecting places for the common features of the concrete modules below.

## 4.2.8 Architecture Dictionary

**Definition**  The architecture dictionary is the repository of definitions of all flows in the architecture model.

**Elements**   The dictionary contains at least the following information for each flow:

- its name
- its structure—the components that make up the flow
- its physical description—electrical waveform, type of energy transfer, word length, for example
- its type—data or control flow
- its source(s)—the architecture module or terminator from which the flow originates.  Note that if a flow is entirely contained in a single module, that module is indicated as the source, and the destination and channel are left blank.
- its destination(s)—the architecture module or terminator to which the flow goes
- its channel(s)—the means by which the flow travels from its source(s) to its destination(s)

The architecture dictionary can be augmented with other company- or project-specific information.  Figure 4.26 shows an excerpt of the architecture dictionary based on the generic diagrams we have used throughout this chapter.

| Name | Composed of | Physical Description | Type | Origin | Destination | Channel |
|------|-------------|---------------------|------|--------|-------------|---------|
| A | A1 + A2 | | D | Term 1 | AM 4 | BUS 1 |
| E | * comment * | See electrical waveform spec XXX. | D | AM 4 | AM 1 | BUS 2 |
| D | {zzz} | | D | AM 1 | AM 3 | BUS 2 or EXT BUS |
| S | S1 + [ S2 \| S3] | | D | AM 11 | AM 13 | BUS 2 |
| T | *Primitive description* | Boolean | C | AM 11 | AM 12 | BUS 3 |

*Figure 4.26: Architecture Dictionary.*

### Rules and Guidelines

- By far, the most common case is that a flow has only one channel available for its needs. The main purpose of the last three columns of the dictionary is to resolve ambiguity when more than one channel is available for a flow.
- When a flow is assigned to multiple channels, the architecture module specification of the originating module should explain the circumstances in which each channel is used. This is especially useful in distributed software design, in which flows are sometimes dynamically allocated to different channels.
- For split or merged flows, a channel must be assigned for each origin/destination pair. Again, the module specification should clarify the use of the different channels.

## 4.2.9 Architecture Model Balancing

The principles of leveling and balancing are fundamental to Structured Analysis and to all of its derivative methods. The idea is simply that what goes in and out of the parent must also go in and out of the child, and these ins and outs are graphically displayed on the diagrams. Here is a summary of all the different kinds of balancing in the architecture model:

- architecture flow diagrams—balancing between AFDs follows exactly the same principles as balancing between DFDs.
- architecture message diagrams—balancing applies to AMDs, but they require some special considerations that are described in Section 4.2.9.1 below.
- module inheritance diagrams—since these do not contain flows or messages, balancing in the usual sense does not apply. Their link to the rest of the architecture model is through the modules they share with AFDs, as described in Section 4.2.7.1.
- architecture interconnect diagrams—interconnects into and out of an AID and its parent module must balance.
- architecture module specifications—architecture module balancing is captured in the AFDs and AIDs. AMSs may optionally list module inputs and outputs if further clarification is needed. At the lowest level of decomposition, whatever representation is chosen for the

detailed design must balance with the inputs and outputs of the parent module. These representations include, for example, circuit diagrams for electrical modules, object diagrams for software, and so on.

- architecture interconnect specifications—every interconnect must have a specification and vice versa, but there are no links between them, so balancing does not apply.

- architecture dictionary—every architecture flow on the AFDs must be listed and defined in the architecture dictionary. Elements of a group flow must also be listed and defined, including any that do not appear explicitly on the diagrams. Every architecture flow between modules must be allocated in the architecture dictionary to one or more interconnects between those modules. In cases where no explicit interconnect is shown on the AID—as is often the case with software subsystems—no allocation is made in the dictionary: The allocation is implicit. Architecture flows that are entirely contained within a module may optionally have their allocation to that module represented in the architecture dictionary, in which case they are included in the "origin" field.

### 4.2.9.1 Architecture Message Diagram Balancing

- The balancing rules and guidelines for AMDs below may seem to deviate from balancing principles, but they do conform with the underlying philosophy. Due to the large amount of information that is often involved, however, balancing is not always shown graphically in its entirety.

- An AMD may be the child of an AFD. In fact, with AFDs used at the system levels and AMDs at the software levels, this interface must occur at the system/software boundary. The flows in and out of the AMD, whether or not they are shown explicitly, must balance with the flows in and out of the parent module in the AFD.

- For AMDs, a child diagram must have the same interface as its parent module, but not all details need to be shown everywhere. Including additional details in the child is acceptable; including fewer details in the child is bad style. Not showing everything in the graphics is acceptable: Details can be deferred to the architecture module specification, the message specification, or the architecture dictionary. But whatever is shown on a diagram must be correct, even if it does not tell the full story.

- The easiest way to achieve balance is to use identical names and parameters in the parent and child. Alternatively, for example, a message arrow might only appear at the parent level, with either a name or parameters added in the child; or, the parent might have a message name, with parameters added in the child; or, the parent might show parameters, with the message name added in the child. In summary, the parent level should show the most important parameters, with the child level adding more detail.
- Parameter groups in a higher layer can be decomposed and used to annotate messages in a lower layer. The composition must, of course, be defined in the dictionary.
- Message groups can be decomposed and used to name messages in lower levels. The message groups must be defined in the message specifications.
- All of the components of group parameters or messages must be used in lower-level diagrams.

Messages between architecture modules must be consistent with the interface specifications in the architecture module specifications.

## 4.3 REQUIREMENTS MODEL

### 4.3.1 Introduction

The requirements model captures all of the system's required capabilities and performance discussed in Chapter 2. It establishes the core set of technology-independent requirements—the essence of the system's purpose. The concept of essential requirements was originated by McMenamin and Palmer, and their classic text [McMenamin 84] is highly recommended for further insight. The requirements model comprises three major sub-models and their supporting specifications, as shown in Figure 4.27. Each of the three sub-models has its own very specific role. In the following, we discuss the components of these sub-models.

**Entity Model:** Captures the required memory or storage capabilities of the system and defines potential access paths to stored information, material, or energy. This model is discussed in Section 4.3.2.

**Process Model:** Captures the required processing capabilities of the system in terms of functions and the flows exchanged between them. This model is discussed in Section 4.3.3.

**Control Model:** Captures the required behavioral capabilities of the system, representing its various major operating modes. It does so by determining which processing capabilities are active in which system states. This model is discussed in Section 4.3.4.

These models are supplemented by the requirements dictionary, which is the single repository of definitions for all elements used in the three models.

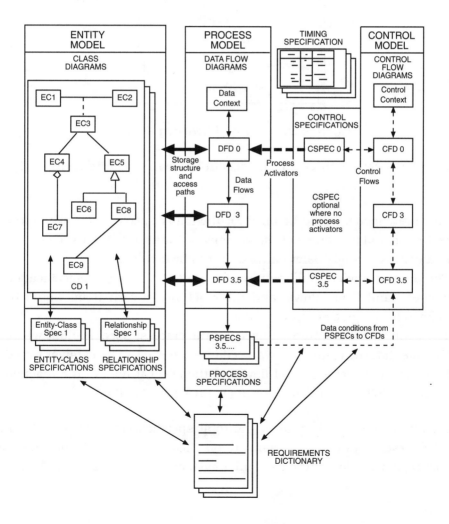

*Figure 4.27: Requirements Model Overview.*

The process and control models interact with each other: The control model establishes the conditions under which the process model may or may not perform its transformations. Consider the way these sub-models would specify the chemical reaction shown in Figure 4.28. Two chemicals, A and B, may or may not react depending on the presence or absence of a catalyst.

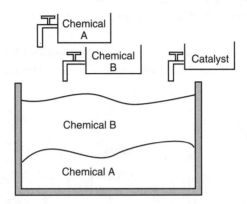

*Figure 4.28: Chemical Reaction Analogy.*

The roles played by the three sub-models in specifying requirements of this reaction are as follows:

- The entity model would be used for the entity specification, where the definition and attributes of the chemicals A and B, of the catalyst, and of any relationships between them would be defined.
- The process model would be used for the transformation specification where A and B are flows, and the reaction between them would be defined in the process specifications.
- The control model would be used for the catalyst specification, where the role that the catalyst plays would be specified. The catalyst would be represented by a control flow and the effect it has on the reaction would be defined in the supporting control specifications.

All three sub-models contribute to the total specification, but not all three are required for every system. Concentrate on those that provide the most understandable representation of the particular system. Which to start with and which to exclude should be based on the needs of the system and the availability of people with knowledge of the three domains.

## 4.3.2 Entity Model

The entity model captures the entity structure of a system. It is a model of the information, material, and energy that the system must record: items of sufficient interest that the organization or system must keep them in retrievable form.

We can divide these entities into two categories: those that come from the environment and those that must be available within the system when needed. This second category often results from system actions that are stored for later use. It is these stored entities that are captured in the entity model.

Like all our models, the entity model includes diagrams and supporting text. Figure 4.29 shows the graphical model—the class diagrams—and the specifications of entity classes, relationships, and attributes. The following sections define the basic elements, the class diagrams, and the three types of specifications.

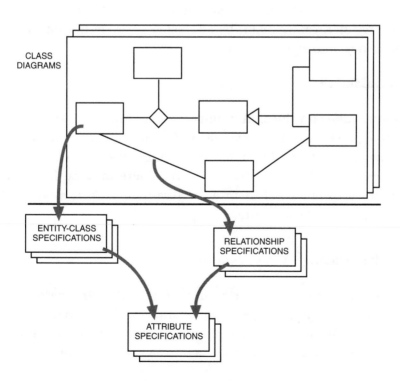

*Figure 4.29: Entity Model Overview.*

### 4.3.2.1 Basic Modeling Elements

We use three major elements to build class models:

- entity classes: the physical or abstract items that we need to record
- relationships: the relevant associations between the entity classes
- attributes: the facts and features of the entity classes and their relationships

Let us take a closer look at each of these, starting with attributes.

### 4.3.2.2 Attribute

**Definition** An attribute is a named property of an item that is of interest in our system.

For information systems, any data element that is stored in the system can be an attribute. For physical (material) items, properties like weight or color can be attributes, as can more abstract properties like durability or maintenance intervals. For energy storage, we might be interested in properties like form of energy, amount, efficiency, and so on.

**Rules and Guidelines**

- Attributes take on values. Anything that can take on a value, such as a number, a string, a binary value, and so on, can be an attribute.
- Test the relevance of the attribute, asking, even if it can take on a value, is it of interest to the system? There may be hundreds of attributes, but not all of them are relevant to a given system. Only model those that really matter.

### 4.3.2.3 Entity Class

It is tough to define this term, since nearly everything in the world can be considered an entity class. It only needs to be interesting enough for somebody to remember facts about it. Examples of entity classes are: for a bank, things like clients or accounts; for a travel agency, a journey or a city; for a lawyer, abstract things like contracts or cases; for a car, physical parts like the chassis or motor; and so on.

**Definition**   An entity class is an item or a class of items that we want to track or whose information we want to record.  Three tests can help determine whether something is an entity class:

- Is this item identifiable?  If we see two of them, can we tell which is which?
- Are we interested in any facts or features of the item, that is, its attributes?
- Are there more than one of these items?

The more affirmative responses you have for these three questions, the greater the likelihood that you have an entity class.  A single no does not mean that the item is not an entity class.  If the entity class is not easily identifiable, perhaps we could make it identifiable; if it has no attributes, maybe it is just a very simple entity class; if there is only one instance of it, maybe that is all our system needs.  But two or three negative responses should make us question whether we really need this item.

We use the term "entity class" in this book for a set of similar items described by one name.  Some authors call this an entity set or an entity type, and then call an individual member of the set an entity, or an "instance" of the entity set.  In object orientation, the entity set is called an "entity class" (or just "class" for short), and the individual member, an "object."  Since both terminologies are useful and refer to the same concepts, we use them interchangeably.

Entity modeling only captures the static properties of the entities, while most object-oriented approaches also include behavior and functionality.  We deliberately keep these properties separate in the requirements models (that is, static properties in the entity model, behavior properties in the control model, functional properties in the process model), and defer the packaging to the architecture models.  Keeping the viewpoints separate for requirements analysis and definition is, in our experience, more successful in large-system development projects than packaging into classes and objects too early.  By assigning stores to modules, the architecture models discussed earlier assign each element of the entity model to an architecture component, thus achieving the same benefits as object-oriented methods.

**Symbol**  A rectangle with the name of the entity class and, optionally, a list of attributes.  See Figure 4.30.

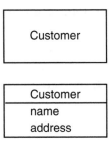

*Figure 4.30: Entity-Class Symbols.*

### Rules and Guidelines

- Name entity classes with nouns or noun phrases in singular form.
- The name of the entity class must be unique within the scope of the system.
- Include attributes that are helpful in understanding the entity class or its role in the system.

### 4.3.2.4 Relationship

**Definition**  A relationship is an association between two or more entity classes at certain times, that the system must record.  An association of two entities is called a binary relationship; of three or more is called an *n*-ary relationship (for example, ternary, for three entity-classes).  Relationships do not have a direction (note the absence of arrowheads in Figures 4.31 and 4.32).

Like entity classes, relationships are sets:  The relationship, Buying, in Figure 4.31 is the union of all links between customers and tickets.  The particular link between customer Joe Miller and Ticket No. 25342 is an instance of the relationship.

A relationship that links two instances of the same entity class is a recursive relationship:  Nesting, in Figure 4.32, is an example.

**Symbols**  The diamond symbol introduced by Peter Chen [Chen 76] to denote relationships is the best known notation, and we retain it for *n*-ary relationships where n>2, but in deference to the current popularity of the UML in the software world [Booch 98], we use a straight line with a label for binary relationships. These notations are illustrated in Figures 4.31 and 4.32.

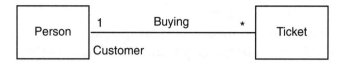

*Figure 4.31: A Binary Relationship.*

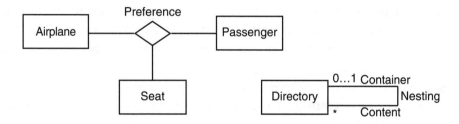

*Figure 4.32: A Ternary Relationship and a Recursive Relationship.*

Relationships can be annotated with up to three pieces of information:

- relationship name
- multiplicity (also called cardinality)
- role names

Multiplicity specifies how many instances of an entity class participate in an instance of the relationship. We show multiplicity with a special notation on the links between the entity class and the relationship. We use

1      if exactly one instance of the entity class is involved with each instance of the relationship. A "1" is often the default when no explicit multiplicity is given.

*      if zero or more instances of an entity class can potentially be involved with an instance of the relationship.

m...n  for minimum and maximum indicators: For example, 3...15 means that at least 3 instances of the entity class, but no more than 15, are involved in the relationship.

?      if the multiplicity has not yet been determined.

In Figure 4.31, you can read the multiplicities in the following way: Each customer can buy many (*) tickets; each ticket can be bought by exactly one customer. Alternatively, an instance of the Buying relationship involves exactly one customer and any number of tickets.

Zero plays a special role in multiplicity: It indicates optional participation of the entity class in the relationship. Any value other than zero represents mandatory participation.

Even though participation is fully determined by the multiplicity notation, it is a very useful concept that merits further discussion. It indicates whether each instance of an entity class can or must participate in the relationship. If the entity class participates, then the multiplicity notation tells us in how many instances of the relationship it potentially participates. Note that the asterisk (*) is shorthand for 0...n, meaning that the instances of the entity class can participate potentially many times.

Rereading the example in Figure 4.31, we see that customers can buy tickets but doing so is not mandatory. Each ticket must be purchased by a customer. Although they exist, tickets that have not yet been purchased by a customer are not of interest to us, so they are not included in the model.

The following multiplicities—described here in terms of participation—are most common:

| | |
|---|---|
| 1 | must participate exactly once |
| 1...n | must participate, potentially many times |
| 0...1 | can participate, but only once |
| * | short for 0...n: can participate, potentially many times |

Role names can be added to the links between entity classes and relationships to indicate the role the entity class plays. This should always be done for recursive relationships, as in Figure 4.32, where a directory is the container for many other directories, but role names can be used with other relationships, too.

## Rules and Guidelines

- Use verbs to discover relationships but nouns to name them, because nouns and noun phrases do not indicate direction. Verb phrases are directional and therefore carry the risk of ignoring the other direction.
- Recursive relationships should have role names.

- Do not worry too early about multiplicities and participation. Add them where they are obvious, but use question marks as a reminder to ask more questions later.

### 4.3.2.5 Special Relationships

Some relationships occur so often in entity modeling that it is worth giving them special names and symbols. The most common ones are described in the following, but whenever a particular relationship occurs very frequently in a particular project or organization, it is a candidate for similar treatment.

#### SUPERCLASS/SUBCLASS RELATIONSHIP

**Definition**  The superclass/subclass relationship is the UML term for the supertype/subtype relationship, described in Section 3.6.3. It classifies entity classes in hierarchies, where a higher-level entity class contains common facts and features that are relevant for all entity classes to which it is linked on the lower levels. The higher-level entity class is called the superclass or supertype, and the lower-level entity classes are called the subclasses or subtypes. Often, as we have mentioned, this is called an "is-a" relationship, because a subclass *is a* kind of superclass.

**Symbol**  An open arrowhead. The link to the superclass is identified by the direction of the arrowhead, as in Figure 4.33.

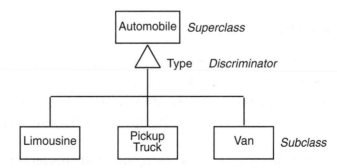

*Figure 4.33: Superclass/Subclass Relationship.*

Subclasses can be exclusive or overlapping. A given entity class can only belong to one exclusive subclass, but it can belong to several overlapping subclasses. An example of an exclusive subclass is that an adult person is either a man or a woman. Examples of potentially overlapping subclasses of person are doctor, vegetarian, and athlete.

Superclasses can have mandatory or optional participation. In some cases, every instance of the superclass must be classified as one of the subclasses; in other cases, there can be instances of the superclass that do not belong to any subclass. This leads to four variations of the subtyping relationships, as shown in Figure 4.34.

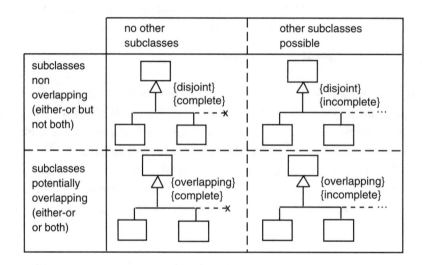

*Figure 4.34: Different Kinds of Subclasses.*

## Rules and Guidelines

- Always check that an "is-a" relationship makes sense by reading it as a sentence: "A first-class ticket *is a* ticket."
- Allocate to a superclass the attributes that are common to all subclasses; allocate to a subclass the attributes that are applicable to it alone.
- Subtyping/supertyping requires a thorough understanding of the subject matter. Do not try to classify too early, and do not create too many layers of subclasses. Two to three layers are fine for medium-size projects; six to seven layers can occur in very large projects.

- Only use the superclass/subclass relationship when the common features of the subclasses are recognized in the application domain. Do not invent similarities that the customer does not accept, even if they may simplify the implementation.

## AGGREGATION/DECOMPOSITION RELATIONSHIP

**Definition**   The aggregation/decomposition relationship, described in Section 3.6.1, represents the decomposition of an aggregate, or whole, into its components or parts.  From the perspective of the whole, we can express this relationship as, "The whole consists of, or is composed of, these parts."  Seen from the parts, we would say, "This item belongs to, or is part of, the whole."

**Symbol**   A straight line linking the aggregate and a part with a diamond symbol at the aggregate end, as in Figure 4.35.

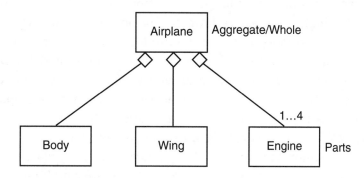

*Figure 4.35: Aggregation Relationship.*

## Rules and Guidelines

- See whether sentences with "consists of," "is composed of," "belongs to," or "is part of" make sense when using this relationship.

## ATTRIBUTES AND ASSOCIATIVE ENTITY CLASSES

Both entity classes and relationships can have attributes.  To accommodate this, the entity-class box symbol can be divided into two compartments, with the name in the upper compartment and the attributes in the lower one. In Figure 4.36, the entity class Customer has the following attributes: Name, Address, and Phone no. When relationships have attributes, an additional notation is needed. For example, the Ordering relationship in Figure 4.36 has attributes Order number and Order date. Since it is graphically difficult to attach attributes to the relationship line symbol, we add a box similar to the entity class symbol, link it with a dashed line to the relationship line, and enter the relationship's attribute names in the lower compartment. The name compartment may be temporarily left empty (for now).

It is a fact in entity modeling that simple concepts over time grow more complex. Each attribute and each relationship can evolve into an entity class of its own.

Many data modelers convert relationships into entity classes as soon as they discover an m...n multiplicity, or as soon as they find an attribute for a relationship. In both cases, they are influenced by the fact that in a relational database, they must use a separate table for such relationships.

Such technological considerations violate one of the underlying principles of the requirements model—that it is technology-independent. In this case, an immediate penalty is that the modifications blow up the model's size. After all, a model with two entity classes and one relationship is much simpler to read and understand than one with three entity classes and two relationships.

The only good reason to transform a relationship's attribute box into a full-blown entity class—an associative entity class—is when the relationship itself must participate in another relationship. Since only entity classes can participate in relationships, we add a name to the attribute box, making it an associative entity class.

**Definition** An associative entity class originates from a relationship, and therefore only exists in association with that relationship. If the relationship were removed, the associative entity class would also be removed.

**Symbol** An associative entity class and the relationship that originated it are linked by a dashed line, as shown in Figure 4.36, where Order is an associative entity class spawned by the Ordering relationship. As shown in the lower half of Figure 4.36, the associative entity class may have a relationship with another entity class. This entity class may be of any type—associative or not—and may be within or outside the scope of the current model.

One of the UML rules is that the names of a relationship and its associative entity class must be identical, and we endorse this rule. We want the names of our entity classes to be nouns, and this gives us a good reason to use nouns for relationship names: That way, the relationship names can then "grow" into associative entity classes without any name changes.

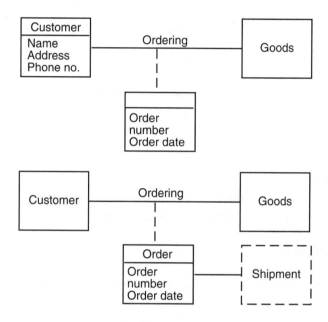

*Figure 4.36: Associative Entity Classes.*

## Rules and Guidelines

- Do not convert the relationships with attributes into associative entity classes too early. Only when a relationship needs to enter into other relationships should you use this concept.

### 4.3.2.6 Class Diagram

**Definition** A class diagram is the graphical representation of the information, material, and energy the system is required to retain or store—the static aspects of the system. Figure 4.37 shows an example.

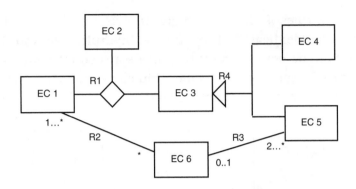

*Figure 4.37: A Class Diagram.*

## Elements

- entity classes
- relationships or associations, including all annotations and special relationships mentioned in the previous section

## Rules and Guidelines

- Logically, there is only one, possibly very large, class diagram in a system model, but it is usually split into readable portions showing the entity classes and relationships for separate parts of the system. Each entity class and relationship exists only once, even though it may be drawn in several diagrams.
- There can only be one specification for each entity class and each relationship, even if they are drawn on multiple diagrams.
- There are no restrictions for the number of entity classes and relationships per diagram.

### 4.3.2.7 Entity Class Specification

We provide an entity class specification template with predefined categories to guide the modeler, just as we do for architecture module specifications. This does not necessarily mean that you must use this form to specify entity classes, but you should consider everything that is required here and capture it somewhere in your entity model.

- **name**—the name by which the entity class is known in the business or system (identical to the name used in the class diagrams).
- **alias(es)**—any other names used for the same entity class.
- **purpose (what/why)**—defines the meaning of the entity class to the system. What is it? What is it used for? Why does it exist?
- **properties**—useful information learned from the customer, or elsewhere, about this entity class. Usually written in plain English.
- **create/delete rules**—the conditions under which new instances of the entity class are created or existing instances are deleted.
- **attributes**—the names and descriptions of the attributes of this entity class.
- **others**—comments and additional remarks.

## Rules and Guidelines

- Use the alias field only if the customers cannot agree on one term. Don't try to find synonyms if nobody asks for them.
- When defining the purpose of an entity class, it is sometimes helpful to ask: "What would the business do without this thing?"
- The properties field is a useful collection of thoughts for further modeling: more relationships, additional attributes of the entity classes, multiplicity information, and so on.
- The create/delete section links the entity model to the process model. The process model should include processes responsible for the create/delete actions.
- The others field is often used to record unanswered questions.

## *4.3.2.8 Relationship Specification*

The graphical representation of a relationship already contains a lot of information if the annotations discussed in Section 4.3.2.4 are used. The relationship specification goes beyond this to capture everything we want to know about the relationship, including the following:

- **name**—the name by which the relationship is known in the business or the system (identical to the name used in the class diagrams).

- **alias(es)**—any other names used for the same relationship.
- **purpose (what/why)**—define what real-world situation is represented by the relationship and specify who is interested in it and for what purposes it will be used.
- **multiplicity and participation**—For each instance of a participating entity class, is it optional or mandatory that the entity class participates? How many instances are involved in a single instance of the relationship? In addition, for *n*-ary relationships, the associations between participating entity classes can be defined here—this information is not shown on the class diagram.
- **rules of association**—enumerates the conditions under which the relationship is created, changed, or deleted.
- **attributes**—the names and descriptions of the attributes of this relationship if there are any.
- **others**—comments and additional remarks.

## Rules and Guidelines

- If you found a noun for the relationship name, you can use the alias field to capture verb phrases that explain the relationship.
- The purpose field for relationships is more important than it is for entity classes. Try separating the *what* from the *why:* "The relationship captures . . ." (the *what)* "so that (a) . . . (b) . . . (c) . . ." (the *why).*
- There should be at least one *what* sentence, with at least one, and preferably multiple, reasons *(why)* for the relationship.
- Participation and multiplicity are shown on the class diagram, but for ternary or higher relationships, multiple combinations are possible. The field can capture any interesting facts about participation and multiplicity.
- The rules of association are also known as the create and delete rules. No relationship is really well understood unless the prerequisites and events for its creation and deletion are known. The definition of a relationship says it is an association that is valid at certain times: These times are defined by the create and delete conditions. Furthermore, these conditions correlate the entity model with the process model. The latter must have processes responsible for creating, using (that is, traversing, searching, and so on), and deleting relationships.

## *4.3.2.9 Attribute Specification*

To complete the entity model, the attributes of entity classes and relationships must be specified. Attributes are the atoms of our modeling universe, and we normally capture them in the requirements dictionary (see Section 4.4) together with all the other primitive elements of data flows, control flows, and so on. However, if we want to capture more than the requirements dictionary allows, we can use the following template.

- **name**—the name of the attribute (of an entity class or relationship).
- **alias**—any other names used for the same attribute.
- **characteristics**—the meaning of this attribute within the system. The attribute name does not always convey everything: Customer name is pretty self-defining, but what about Person-month-percent-age?
- **purpose**—how is the attribute used? If you cannot find a good reason for the attribute, you should consider removing it.
- **structure**—for complex attributes (repeated attributes, multi-valued attributes, attribute groups, and so on), define the structure using the syntax of the requirements dictionary (see Section 4.4).
- **derived value**—indicate whether the value of this attribute is derived (or derivable) from other parts of the model.
- **derivation**—if an attribute value is derived, provide the derivation algorithm, rule, or formula.
- **value range**—indicate lower and upper bounds for the attribute value.
- **domain**—many companies use lists of predefined domains to ensure that the format for certain attributes is defined in only one place. Examples of domain names are integer, real, string, and boolean. Others are date, long name, short name, year, zip code, and so on. Domains can be made specific to special application areas. If a standard domain library is available, reference it here. Otherwise, define the domain locally.
- **units/precision**—define the unit of measurement and the precision, if needed, for this attribute (for example, meters; or centimeters, two decimals).
- **others**—Comments and additional remarks.

### 4.3.3 Process Model

The process model, based on Structured Analysis [DeMarco 78], captures the required processing capabilities of the system in terms of functions and the flows exchanged between them. The process model consists of a leveled set of diagrams and process specifications that support the diagrams, as shown in Figure 4.38.

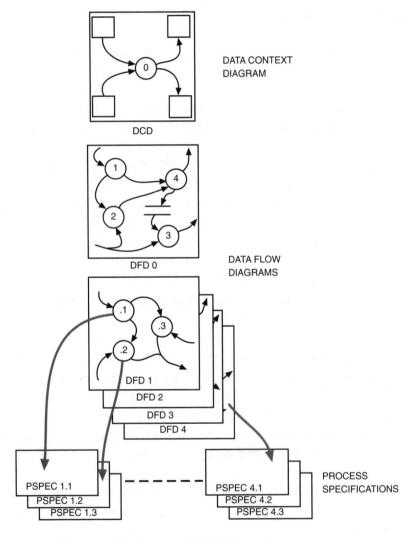

*Figure 4.38: Process Model Overview.*

At the highest level is the data context diagram (DCD), showing the system as one process embedded in its environment. The lower-level data flow diagrams show more details of this process in terms of subprocesses and their communication.

The most detailed processes are described in process specifications (but see Section 4.3.3.8, "Detailing Diagrams," for an elaboration of this statement). All the flows and stores in the layered set of diagrams are defined in the requirements dictionary, as shown in Figure 4.27, the requirements model overview.

A great deal has been published about Structured Analysis, which is the basis for the process model. We will only cover the basic ideas, some practical hints, and some deviations from published literature. For more information, refer to the books discussed in Section 4.7, and to the Bibliography.

In classical Structured Analysis, the terms "data store" and "data flow" are used. We include material and energy in the stores and flows, and therefore abbreviate data store to just "store." However, we apply our wider meaning to the terms "data flow" and "data flow diagram" to distinguish them from control flow and control flow diagram. When we just use "flow," we include information, control information, material, and energy.

### 4.3.3.1 Basic Modeling Elements

Four modeling elements are used in the diagrams of the process model:

- data flow
- process
- store
- terminator

### 4.3.3.2 Data Flow

**Definition** A data flow is a pipeline through which information, material, or energy of known composition flows.

**Symbol** A vector with a name, as shown in Figure 4.39.

CUSTOMER ORDER

*Figure 4.39: Data Flow Symbol.*

**Naming Rule**  The name of a flow must not imply any processing, that is, there must be no verbs in flow names, only nouns and adjectives.

### Additional Rules and Guidelines

- A data flow may be a single element or a group of elements.
- Each element or group must have a unique, descriptive name. The name of the flow must be indicative of its content. If you can't find a good name for a group flow, you are probably grouping unrelated elements together.
- Every flow *must* be defined in the requirements dictionary, down to its primitive elements (that is, its attributes).
- If a group flow enters a process, all of its elements must be used in that process.
- If a group flow enters a process that does not use all of the group's elements, form new groups, as shown in Figure 4.40, containing only those elements that are used. In other words, follow the maxim: "Starve your processes."

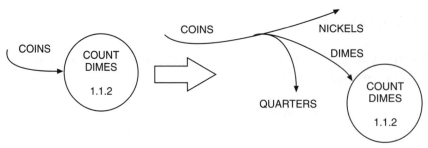

*Figure 4.40: Splitting a Flow.*

- Flows may split or combine—also shown in Figure 4.40. This is a mechanism for decluttering the flow diagram, and for getting the right data to a process.
- Different data between the same two processes may travel via the same flow vector—they should not be grouped if they do not logically belong together. Simply list the names separated by commas.

### 4.3.3.3 Process

**Definition** A process indicates the transformation of incoming flows into outgoing flows.

**Symbol** A circle or bubble, with a name and a number. See Figure 4.41.

*Figure 4.41: Process Symbol.*

**Naming Rule** The process name should include a verb acting on a specific object or group of objects. Use strong, active verbs to name processes.

### Additional Rules and Guidelines

- The name of a process should summarize all of the processing it performs. Processes must group related functions.
- A process represents the system's actions. Flows may only be transformed in processes.
- Conservation of data: A process must not create data from nothing, and it must use all the data it receives. In other words, the output of a process must be a function of its input, nothing more and nothing less.

### 4.3.3.4 Store

**Definition**  A store is simply data, material, or energy flow(s), retained for later use, possibly in a sequence that is different from their order of arrival.

**Symbol**  Parallel lines with the name of the stored data, material, or energy:  See Figure 4.42.

*Figure 4.42: Store Symbols.*

**Naming Rule**  Identical to the flow-naming rule.

**Additional Rules and Guidelines**

- The rules and guidelines for flows also apply to stores, with the following additions.
- A store may be read-only, read/write, or both.  Write-only stores only make sense at the system boundary: that is, on the context diagram, where it is preferred to show a store as a terminator with a name that signifies what it is.  But even here, some other system presumably reads the store.  Eventually, usually in the architecture model, the means by which read-only stores are loaded must be specified.
- Flows from a store must include the net content of the store.  Flows into a store must include the net content of the read/write parts of the store.
- Information stores are nondepletable by default.  Their contents remain when read; they only change when overwritten.  If an information store is to be depletable, this property must be stated in the dictionary definition.  Energy and material stores are, by the nature of their contents, depletable.
- If a flow to or from a store contains the whole content of the store, then the flow inherits the name of the store and may be left unnamed on the diagram.

- A store should be shown on the highest-level diagram in which it is accessed by two or more processes. On lower layers, it is sufficient to only show the flows to and from the store. It is a question of style whether or not the store symbol is repeated on other levels. Different authors suggest different rules. Not repeating stores simplifies the diagrams; repeating them makes the links between the levels more obvious, but it goes against the nonredundancy principle of Structured Analysis and its derivatives. (See Part II for more on style differences.)
- A store may be drawn multiple times on one diagram for convenience of layout and to prevent spaghetti flows. It is good practice to mark repeated stores with an asterisk to alert the reader.

### 4.3.3.5 Terminator

The definition, symbol, and naming rule for requirements model terminators are identical to those for architecture model terminators, as stated in Section 4.2.2.2. In fact, the terminators in a specific requirements model always appear in the corresponding architecture model. There can be additional terminators in the architecture model due to physical needs not considered in the requirements model. See Part II for illustrations.

### 4.3.3.6 Data Context Diagram

**Definition** The data context diagram (DCD), Figure 4.43, establishes the data boundary between the system and its environment. It shows the terminators, the system function, and the flows between them. It is the highest-level data flow diagram for the system.

- one process (representing the system)
- terminators
- data flows
- stores (optional)

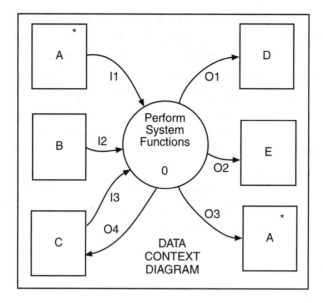

*Figure 4.43: Data Context Diagram.*

## Rules and Guidelines

- The only absolute rules for the data context diagram are that it must contain only one process (representing the system function), at least one terminator, and at least one output flow.

    Some practitioners of basic SA label the context process with the name of the system rather than with the function that it performs. This is a questionable practice at best, violating the active naming principle of processes. In fact, with the Hatley/Hruschka/Pirbhai methods, the practice is fundamentally wrong, because it is the role of the architecture model, not the requirements model, to name the system and its physical elements.

- By convention, the context process is always numbered 0. Any number of terminators and flows are allowed. For better readability, terminators may be repeated. As mentioned in connection with architecture context diagrams and with stores, it is good practice to mark repeated terminators with an asterisk to alert the reader.

- Sometimes, it helps to distinguish active terminators (persons, organizations, machines, systems, and so on) from passive terminators (files, reports, and so on). In such cases, the passive terminators may be shown as stores, but the name should make it clear that the store is external to the system.

### 4.3.3.7 Data Flow Diagram

**Definition** A data flow diagram (DFD), as shown in Figure 4.44, is a network representation of a system's required processing capabilities. The system could be automated, manual, or mixed. The DFD portrays the requirements in terms of functional processes, the flows exchanged between them, and the stores they share.

**Elements**

- process
- data flow
- store

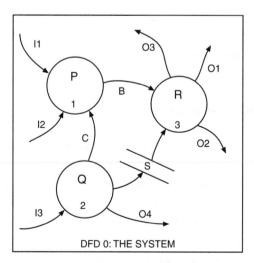

*Figure 4.44: Data Flow Diagram.*

Figure 4.44 shows the child data flow diagram of the context process in Figure 4.43: It has three processes, one store, and several data flows. The three processes describe the context process in more detail, and the input and output flows (I1–I3 and O1–O4) correspond to those in the context diagram. New local flows (B, C, and the input and output of store S) are added. Remember, processes show required processing capabilities, independent of which architecture modules will eventually perform them.

**Drawing Guidelines**   A DFD can have any number of processes, data flows, and stores, but the guideline is to limit the number of processes to 7±2. The upper limit ensures that our capacity for understanding is not exceeded; the lower limit minimizes the number of diagrams and ensures there is sufficient information on each one. There are legitimate exceptions to both limits: There would be no harm in allowing a large number of similar, parallel subprocesses to exceed the upper limit; the details in the lowest-level diagrams might require fewer than five subprocesses.

**Naming and Numbering Rules**   A data flow diagram takes on the name and number of its parent process. The context process is numbered 0; its child diagram is DFD0, with positive integer process numbers. The process numbers on diagrams below DFD0 are (explicitly or implicitly) prefixed with the number of the parent process. We usually include the number of the parent process in the title, and just number the child processes with .1, .2, .3, and so on, to declutter the bubbles.

**Additional Rules and Guidelines**

- DFDs are non-procedural, and the processes within them are concurrent (no sequencing implied, although the flows show causality). The numbering sequence has no formal significance, but if it can be used to clarify the meaning of the diagram, there is no harm in doing so.
- DFDs are models of the system's functional requirements; they do not represent the system's implementation.
- In this idealized model, the processes are assumed to operate instantaneously: Their outputs appear the instant their inputs are available, and it is never necessary for one process to wait for another to complete its task.

- In the absence of a control model, processes are assumed to be input-triggered: Whenever there are sufficient inputs for a process to perform its transformation, it will do so. This applies to every primitive process, and since higher-level processes simply represent the collective actions of primitives, it applies to all processes.
- The purpose of the DFD hierarchy is to provide a visual guide to the system's functions and the flows between them. If the model is difficult to understand, then we have failed in this goal.
- After a DFD is completed, spend some time improving its layout. Eliminate (or at least minimize) crossed flows. Try to follow the natural reading directions for flows (in the western world: from top left to bottom right), or emphasize natural symmetries or asymmetries.
- Beware of unnameable flows or processes—they probably need repartitioning. If all the elements of a flow or process share some significant common feature, then that feature can be used in the name. Conversely, if no good descriptive name is evident, then the elements probably do not share a significant common feature—they are not cohesive.
- "Starve your bubbles." A process with many data flows needs repartitioning, or perhaps the data flows could be grouped.
- Don't sit around thinking about it—get started on your diagrams and then improve them. The mind is better at improving things than creating them.

### *4.3.3.8 Detailing Diagrams*

As illustrated in Figure 4.45, a process has two options for a more detailed description: a child DFD or a process specification (PSPEC). A process described in a PSPEC is called a functional primitive; the PSPEC itself is not detailed any further.

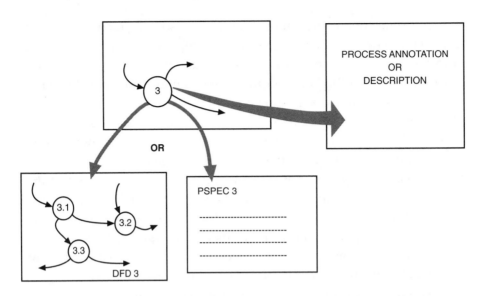

*Figure 4.45: Process Detailing and Description.*

As shown in Figure 4.45, a process, like every other element of the models, may also have descriptions or annotations. There is one mandatory purpose for these relating to derived requirements, which we discussed in Chapter 2, and some optional purposes.

A major part of the development process is to make design decisions based on requirements at a certain architectural level, and from those design decisions, to create new, derived requirements that are imposed on lower levels. In this situation, both a PSPEC and a child data flow diagram may be needed for one process— the PSPEC to describe the original requirement, and the DFD to describe the derived requirements. It is essential that both the original and the derived requirements are retained in the model. There are two ways to do this: one is to retain both the PSPEC and the DFD as children of the parent process; the other is to move the PSPEC to the annotation and description field. From the methods point of view, either choice is acceptable, but since most automated tools do not allow both a child DFD and a child PSPEC for one process, the practical preference is to put the PSPEC in the annotation and description field. When this is done, it must be clearly stated that this was originally a PSPEC and that it remains a necessary requirement of the system.

Derived requirements are a major part of the modeling process. In typical systems, we end up with many more derived requirements than original requirements. Also, the identification and management of derived requirements is per-haps the most profound difference between these methods and classical Structured Analysis. Derived requirements have always existed, but in classical SA, all the requirements were lumped into one massive model that often became quite unmanageable. With the methods in this book, requirements derivation goes hand in hand with the structure of the architecture model, and although the overall size of the requirements model is no less massive, it is divided into manageable chunks that correspond to their respective architecture modules.

The other purposes for the annotation and description field are optional as mentioned above, but they have great value in the modeling process and should be used extensively. Some of the purposes are

- to record the known facts about an incompletely specified process for later use when completing the model
- to provide a summary of the purpose of a non-primitive process for those who do not need more detail
- to record the rationale for detailing a process in a certain way—there are generally numerous options for detailing, and the reasons for the particular choice are useful for later work on, and updates to, the model

It is good practice to write something descriptive for every process and every DFD as you develop the model.

The balancing rules tie together the different levels of the model, and they must hold for every process from the context diagram down to the PSPECs. At every level, the inputs and outputs of a child must exactly match those of its parent, including PSPECs that have been moved to the annotation and description field. See Section 4.4.2 for more on requirements model balancing.

### 4.3.3.9 Process Specification

**Definition**  A process specification (PSPEC) describes how the outputs of a process are generated from the inputs—nothing more and nothing less. Every input must be used, and every output must be generated from one or more of the inputs.

**Elements**  Process specifications can use any textual or graphical form that satisfactorily and unambiguously describes what that process has to do. Figure 4.46

shows the elements that every PSPEC should contain: process name and number, inputs, outputs, and transformation.

```
PSPEC 4: GET SELECTED PRODUCT

INPUTS:

OUTPUTS:

TRANSFORMATION:
------------------------------------------------
------------------------------------------------
------------------------------------------------
```

*Figure 4.46: Generic PSPEC Format.*

The transformation may be described using Structured English, or any kind of graphics, charts, mathematical equations, block diagrams, decision tables, or any other means of specifying the required processing. Structured English is the most common form for PSPECs, but all the styles shown in Figure 4.47, and others, can be used. The guideline is: If you would have used a figure, diagram, table, or other illustration in a traditional narrative specification, then you should almost certainly use it in a structured specification, and its place is in a PSPEC. The fact that no current automated tool supports this should not deter you from doing it: Create the illustration independently of the tool, and reference it.

## Rules and Guidelines

- The process specification name and number should be the same as the functional primitive process it describes.
- A process specification must be written for every functional primitive process. (Remember: A functional primitive process is not further detailed into a child DFD unless new requirements are derived from it, whereupon it remains a primitive in the original requirements model, but becomes non-primitive in the model allocated to the module in which the derivation occurred.)
- The process specification must state *what* happens to the inputs to create the outputs. It should leave the details of *how* to the architecture model.

- If the process requires a large table of data, a set of equations, or some other large block of information, put it in an appendix and reference it in the PSPEC.
- PSPECs may contain computational constraints, such as accuracy of computations, timing constraints on algorithms, and frequency of performance.

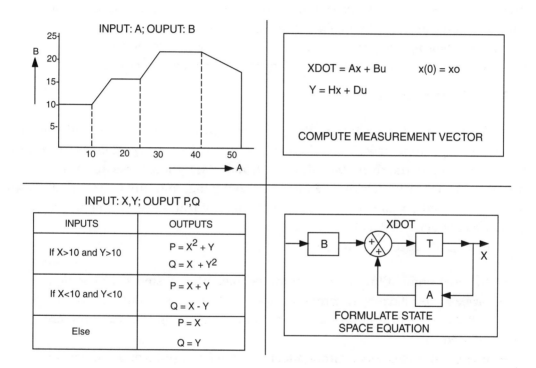

*Figure 4.47: Different Styles for PSPECs.*

## 4.3.4 Control Model

The control model captures the required behavioral capabilities of the system, that is, its major operating modes. It does so by determining which processing capabilities are active under which external or internal conditions or system states.

The control model consists of control specifications and control flow diagrams. Control specifications activate and deactivate processes in the process model under the appropriate conditions. Figure 4.48 is an overview of most of the requirements model, with the control model highlighted. It shows the process model on the left, control specifications in the center, and control flow diagrams on the right. The thick black arrows from control specifications to processes represent process activators, the major responsibility of the control model.

Control flow diagrams route control flows to and from control specifications, just as data flow diagrams route information, material, and energy to and from process specifications. Control flows from control specifications travel to other control specifications or to the environment.

In the following sections, we discuss control flows, control specifications, control flow diagrams, and how they work together to control processes.

### 4.3.4.1 Control Flow

Systems receive input flows from the environment, transform them, and transmit the resulting output flows. We choose to classify flows as data flows or control flows according to the roles they play in our models: Where flows are transformed directly from input to output, the incoming, outgoing, and any intermediate flows are all classified as data flows; flows that are used in activating or deactivating processes are classified as control flows.

There are three sources for control flows:

- the environment (from terminators: people, other systems, and so on).
- process specifications, through tests on the values of data flows. We call these control flows "data conditions," reflecting the way they are created.
- control specifications, through logical transformations of input control flows.

Independent of a control flow's origin, its purpose is to influence the activation and deactivation of processes, or to convey control information to the environment. In *Strategies for Real-Time System Specification*, there is a detailed discussion of the distinction between data and control flows.

We discuss the graphical representation of control flows when we describe control flow diagrams in Section 4.3.7.

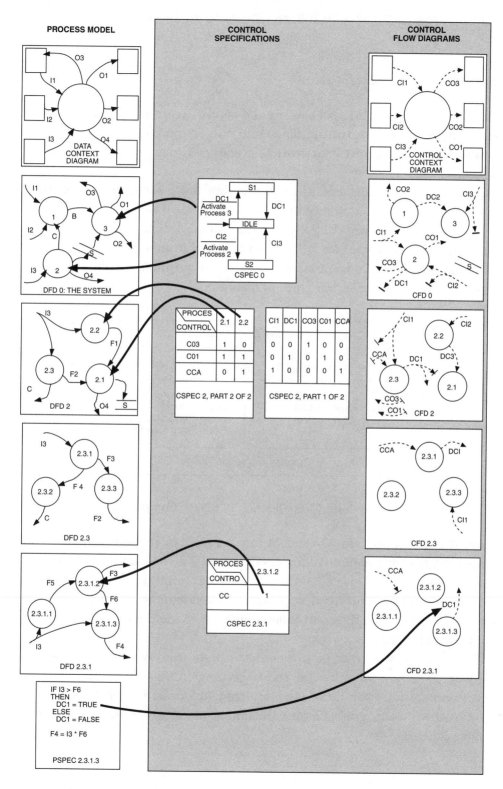

*Figure 4.48: Requirements Model with Control Model Highlighted.*

### 4.3.4.2 Control Specification

Control specifications (CSPECs) capture the control processing requirements of the system. They transform control flows into one or more of the following: process activators (activating and deactivating processes), new control signals, or new data flows.

Control specifications contain two types of finite state machines: combinational and sequential. Combinational machines have no memory: They transform current control inputs directly into current control or data outputs. Sequential machines do have memory: Based on previous inputs, they transform current control inputs and the current state, into current outputs. Figure 4.49 shows the components used for these two types of machine.

| Control Specifications | |
|---|---|
| Combinational Machines | Sequential Machines |
| Decision Tables<br>Boolean Expressions | State Transition Diagrams<br>State Charts<br>State Transition Tables<br>State Transition Matrices |
| Process Activation Tables | |

*Figure 4.49: Classification of CSPEC Components.*

A control specification can consist of any number of the components shown in Figure 4.49, allowing combinations of components to specify the control transformations. Figures 4.50 and 4.51 show two typical, multipart CSPECs: for a combinational subsystem, and for a sequential subsystem, respectively. For consistency with Figure 4.48, the control flows enter from the right and the process activators exit to the left.

If a CSPEC is large, that is, if it contains more than two or three components, then we add a "CSPEC guide" at the beginning to show its internal structure. There is no set form for these guides: They are described in *Strategies* (where they are called "users' guides"), and are similar to Figures 4.50 and 4.51, but with the flows labeled.

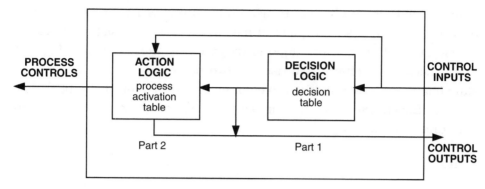

*Figure 4.50: Typical Combinational* CSPEC.

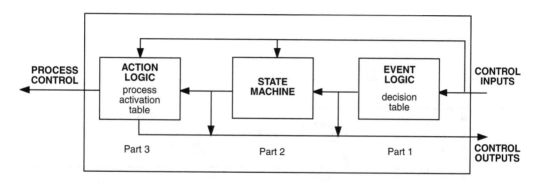

*Figure 4.51: Typical Sequential* CSPEC.

**Naming and Numbering Rules**   A CSPEC has the same name and number as the corresponding DFD and CFD. If the CSPEC has multiple components, each one is given a part number, as in "Part M of N."

Let us take a closer look at the various components used in a control specification.

### 4.3.4.3 Sequential Machines—State Transition Diagrams and State Charts

**Definition**   In *Strategies*, we used conventional state transition diagrams to represent sequential machines. These diagrams are enhanced with some nice features in [Harel 87], and are renamed there as state charts. The enhancements, which can readily be incorporated into CSPECs, include nested states, guards, and the history construct. Both state transition diagrams (STDs) and state charts are graphical representations of sequential machines. They consist of states, events that cause state changes, and actions triggered by these events. Figure 4.52 shows a generic state chart. We use the two names—state transition diagrams and state charts—interchangeably. We do not encourage use of all the extensions proposed in [Booch 98], since they make the diagrams unnecessarily difficult to read and understand.

### Elements

- states (potentially nested)
- transitions (labeled with events and, optionally, actions)

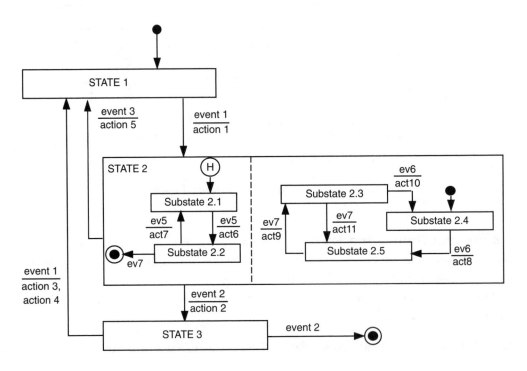

*Figure 4.52: A Generic State Chart.*

**State**  A state is a condition in which the system is performing certain processes, and in which the system is waiting for an event to occur, due to

- external stimuli (control flows from the environment)

and/or

- internal processing (data conditions created in the process model or internal control flows created in a control specification)

When the event occurs, the STD moves from one state to another. A state can therefore be considered as the period between the event that brings the system into the state and the event that causes the system to leave the state. A state can also be considered a decision point, where the system is waiting to make a choice between different transition paths.

A state may be associated with a set of processes that are active during that state. An STD can only be in one state at a time (although there may be parallel substates, as described below).

A state can be divided into parallel regions of separate behavior, each region containing a nested state chart, as illustrated by State 2 in Figure 4.52. The concurrent regions are separated by dashed lines, and there may be any number of such regions.

A flight management system for an aircraft provides a real-world example of concurrent states. This system might have two major states: On Ground and In Air. The In Air state might have two parallel regions, one representing vertical navigation, the other lateral navigation. The vertical navigation region might have the states Take Off, Climb, Cruise, Descent, and Landing. The lateral navigation region might have the states Heading Path, Turn Path, and several others. In each of the two regions, only one state is in effect at any given time, but the two regions are concurrently active, so two states are in effect simultaneously.

Two special states have their own graphical symbols: The start state is identified with a black bullet; the end state with a bull's-eye. In the above example, On Ground would be both the start and end state, entered at system start-up and left at system shut-down.

Sometimes, an STD does not have a fixed start state. Instead, it returns to the final state it was in when last active. This is indicated by the history marker: a circle with an "H" inside. In the above example, suppose the In Air state only applied to automatic flight, and there were a third major state for manual flight.

In this scenario, after switching from In Air Auto to In Air Manual and back to In Air Auto, the system might return to the vertical and lateral flight phases it was last in, and then check to see if they still applied.

**Transition**   A transition is a path along which the STD moves from one state to another in response to the occurrence of an event. The event might also trigger actions in addition to the transition. The transitions in an STD represent the allowed transitions: If there is no transition between two states, the system cannot move between those states.

A transition is drawn as a vector (usually made up of horizontal and vertical segments) and is labeled with one or more events; optionally, it may also be labeled with one or more actions.

The start transition is sometimes not labeled at all (which indicates: Go to this state at start-up); sometimes it only has an action (which means: Do this action at start-up); or it can be fully labeled with events and actions. All other transitions, including those to end states, must have at least one event, and may also have actions.

A transition that ends at the border of a state activates any nested state charts at their specified starting points. A transition starting at the border of a state deactivates any nested state charts, and takes the system to the next state. In Figure 4.52, this means that when Event 2 occurs, whatever went on inside State 2 is terminated, Action 2 is executed, and the system goes to State 3.

**Event**   A system moves from one state to another only when a transition event occurs. Transition events are derived from control flows, usually when control flows change state. As we discussed earlier, control flows may originate from outside the system, from CSPECs inside the system, or from PSPECs through threshold tests on data flows.

Events can be specified in the following ways:

- by a single control flow: by stating the name of the control flow, meaning "whenever this signal occurs," or by stating certain values of the control flow (for example: ALARM = TRUE; SWITCH = POWER_OFF; INDICATOR = HIGH)
- by time event (for example: 30 seconds elapsed; 5 minutes elapsed)
- by any combination of the first two, using operators like AND, OR, NOT, =, >, <, and ≠ (for example: Alarm AND > 5 p.m.)

Events can be "guarded" with conditions, so that the transition takes place only if the event occurs while the guard condition is true. Guards can be formulated in one of two ways (or occasionally as combinations of the two):

- as expressions comparing values of data flows or stores within the scope of the state chart (that is, in the DFD to which the CSPEC belongs). These expressions must evaluate to true or false (for example [ORDER_VALUE > $5000]).
- for state charts with substates, the guard can refer to a concurrent substate: The transition takes place if the other subsystem is currently in the indicated substate (for example, [IN Cruising] or [NOT IN Warm_Up]).

Note that we only use guards in combination with data flows or substates. Boolean functions of data flows and stores can always be included in the process model to create control flows that can be used as events. This approach sometimes gets complicated, and guards may be helpful. Use guards with caution, though: Having too many may indicate thinking in low-level programming terms instead of major system state changes.

**Action** Actions define the processing the system does as a result of a transition. Actions always result in the system doing something—creating new control signals and/or activating processes. In *Strategies*, we adopted the special convention that an action remains in effect until the next transition occurs. This is largely to simplify the activation of processes; when an action activates a process, the process remains active until the next transition occurs (when it goes inactive, unless the next transition also turns it on).

Activating a process directly from a state chart is indicated by including the process name (or its number) as the action label of a transition. To create a new control flow, we simply use the name of the control flow as the action label.

Multiple actions are separated by commas. For example, "PAPER_LOW; ACTIVATE 2.3, 2.1," means that the transition generates a control flow: "PAPER LOW," and activates the processes numbered 2.3 and 2.1.

#### 4.3.4.4 Other Representations of Sequential Machines

There are a number of alternative ways to represent sequential machines. The STD/state chart form is the best known, and it has the benefit of graphical representation. If the state machine is very complex—many states and/or many transitions—then the benefits of the graphics are lost. In such cases, a matrix or tabular form may be preferred, as shown in Figure 4.53. The format for the representation may be freely chosen provided that the following four pieces of information are contained:

- the source state for each transition
- the destination state for each transition
- the event(s)
- the action(s)

The number and ratio of states and transitions influences the choice between diagrams, tables, and matrices. If there are few states with few transitions, diagrams are the obvious choice. Even with many states but few transitions, diagrams can work with careful layout; a matrix, on the other hand, would be quite sparse in this situation. With many transitions between few states, the state/state matrix works best. With few events used many times with different states, the state/event matrix might be best. Finally, with many states and transitions, the state transition table is a good choice.

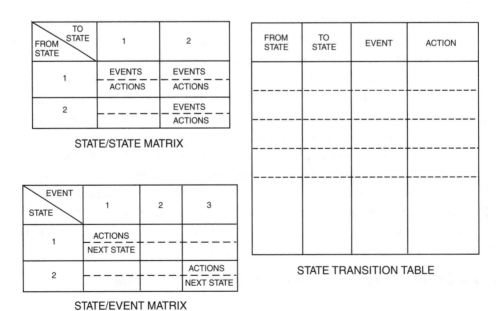

*Figure 4.53: Alternative Representation for State Models.*

Since all the combinations of rows and columns are present in matrices, checking them for completeness and consistency is easier and more systematic than it is for diagrams or tables.

Notice that to represent nested states, a matrix or table is needed for the top-level state machine, and a separate one for each nested machine. The nesting hierarchy must be described with narrative or with a numbering scheme. Notice also that start and end transitions (the bullets and bull's-eyes) must be represented in the matrices and tables as start and end states.

### 4.3.4.5 Combinational Machines—Decision Tables and Process Activation Tables

If a system or subsystem does not involve sequential states, then decision tables may be used to show control processing. Decision tables simply map input control flows to output control flows, as shown in Figure 4.54, with inputs on the left and outputs on the right. The elements of the table either can contain a simple "X," when we just want to show that the flow occurs, or can contain a value for the flow (for example, TRUE or FALSE; HIGH, MEDIUM, or LOW). Decision tables are just lists of all combinations of values the input signals can assume, together with the corresponding values of the output signals. In the special case in which all the inputs and outputs are binary, the transfer function may be expressed as a Boolean expression.

| CONTROL INPUT | | CONTROL OUTPUT | | |
|---|---|---|---|---|
| A | B | P | Q | R |
|  |  |  |  |  |
|  |  |  |  |  |
|  |  |  |  |  |
|  |  |  |  |  |
|  |  |  |  |  |
|  |  |  |  |  |
| CSPEC 0 | | | | |

*Figure 4.54: Generic Form of a Decision Table.*

The rows in decision tables must represent mutually exclusive logical conditions of the inputs—no two rows can be true simultaneously. For completeness, all possible combinations of input signal must be considered, but do not assign arbitrary outputs to "don't care" inputs; that is, do not over-specify.

The process activation table is a special kind of decision table in which the control flow outputs are replaced with the names of processes to be activated and deactivated. It is quite common to combine both functions into one table, having both control flows and processes as outputs. Alternatively, decision tables and process activation tables are often used together as different parts of one control specification, as shown in Figure 4.55.

| PROCESS / CONTROL | 1 | 2 | 3 |
|---|---|---|---|
| PC1 | 0 | 1 | 0 |
| PC2 | 1 | 0 | 1 |
| CCA | 1 | 1 | 0 |

CSPEC 0 : PART 2 OF 2

| CONTROL INPUT | | CONTROL OUTPUT | | |
|---|---|---|---|---|
| CCB | CCC | CCA | PC1 | PC2 |
| 0 | 0 | 1 | | |
| 0 | 1 | | 1 | |
| 1 | 1 | | | 1 |

CSPEC0 : PART 1 OF 2

*Figure 4.55: A CSPEC Combining Decision Table and Activation Table.*

Part 1 on the right-hand side is a decision table transforming two input control flows into three output control flows. The first row tells us that when both CCE and CCC have the value 0, the output flow CCA is set. The process activation table (Part 2 of 2) on the left shows that when the input flow CCA is set, Processes 1 and 2 are activated and Process 3 is deactivated.

Process activation tables can also be used in a single CSPEC with state charts, taking actions as inputs and transforming them into process activators. This is appropriate when the event list or the action list in the diagram would be too complicated (too many ANDs, ORs, NOTs, and so on). A table is often the easier way to express these logical combinations.

**Textual CSPECs**  It is unusual, but for simple functions, a CSPEC can consist of plain text instead of tables or diagrams. The only absolute rule for CSPECs is that they must map control input to control output and show process activation.

## 4.3.5 The Control Flow Model: Basic Elements

The control flow model is nearly identical to the data flow model, which we have already discussed, so there is not much to add. The only new element is a link to the control specifications, which we represent with a CSPEC bar. We discuss the graphical representation of control flows and CSPEC bars below.

### 4.3.5.1 Control Flow

**Definition**  A control flow, like a data flow, is a pipeline through which packets of information, material, or energy of known composition flow. While data flows represent inputs or outputs of processes, control flows are used, directly or indirectly, to activate or deactivate processes, or to exit from the system, as discussed in Section 4.3.4.2.

**Symbol**  A dashed vector with a name, as shown in Figure 4.56.

QUARTER

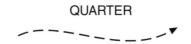

*Figure 4.56: Control Flow Symbol.*

**Naming Rule**  The name of a control flow must not imply any processing; that is, there must be no verbs in control flow names, only nouns and adjectives.

**Rules and Guidelines**  Identical conventions apply to both data and control flows:

- A control flow may consist of a single element or a group of elements.
- Each element or group must have a unique, descriptive name. The name of the flow must be indicative of its content. If you cannot find a good name for a group flow, you are probably grouping together unrelated elements.
- Every control flow *must* be defined in the requirements dictionary down to its primitive elements.

- If a group control flow enters a CSPEC, all of its elements must be used in that CSPEC.
- If you need to take a group flow into a CSPEC that does not use all the group's elements, form new groups, using only the necessary elements. In other words, "Starve your CSPECs."
- Control flows may split or combine. This is a mechanism for decluttering the flow diagram and for getting the right flows to the CSPEC.

### 4.3.5.2 CSPEC Bar

**Definition**  A CSPEC bar represents the interface between a CFD and the corresponding CSPEC. It is the sink for control flow inputs to the CSPEC and the source for the control flow outputs from the CSPEC.

Any number of instances of the CSPEC bar may appear on the CFD, but they together represent the one interface with the CSPEC associated with the CFD. The bars may be placed anywhere on the diagram, simply for convenience of layout. Since all instances of the CSPEC bar represent just one interface, they do not need labeling.

**Symbol**  A straight line of any length, at any angle, as illustrated in Figure 4.57.

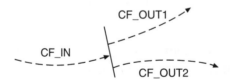

*Figure 4.57: A CSPEC Bar with Incoming and Outgoing Control Flows.*

## 4.3.6 Control Context Diagram

**Definition**  The control context diagram (CCD), as shown in Figure 4.58, establishes the control boundary between the system and its environment. It shows the terminators, the system function, and the control flows between them. It is the highest-level control flow diagram for the system.

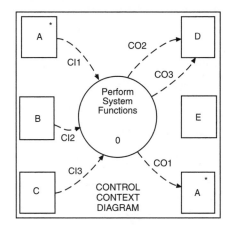

*Figure 4.58: Control Context Diagram.*

## Elements

- one process (representing the system)
- terminators (same as those on DCD)
- control flows
- optional: stores

**Rules and Guidelines**  All the rules and guidelines for the data context diagram, as described in Section 4.3.3.6, apply to the control context diagram.  Both diagrams should have the same terminators, even those that have only data flows or only control flows.

## 4.3.7 Control Flow Diagram

**Definition**  A control flow diagram (CFD) mirrors the processes and stores from the corresponding DFD, but it shows control flows instead of data flows.  The CFD simply constrains control flows to the same paths as the data flows.  An example is given in Figure 4.59.

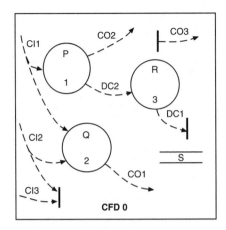

*Figure 4.59: Control Flow Diagram.*

## Elements

- process (same as a DFD)
- store (same as a DFD)
- control flow
- bar symbol (representing the control specification interface)

Figure 4.59 shows the child control flow diagram of the context process in Figure 4.58. Control flows entering and leaving processes follow exactly the same principles as data flows—flows in and out of the parent process must exactly match (subject to decomposition between levels) those in and out of the child diagram. Thus, CI1 in Figure 4.59 flows into Processes 1 and 2, and must therefore appear as an input to their child diagrams, CFDs 1 and 2.

A common misconception when first using the control model is that a control flow entering a process is a process activator, exercising some kind of control over the process. This is not true—the flow simply enters the child diagram, for use at some lower level in a CSPEC, where it *may* be involved in process activation. Similarly, CO1 flows out of Process 2 and must therefore be an output of CFD2, where it either comes from another process or comes from CSPEC2 via a CSPEC bar.

CI3 flows into a CSPEC bar, which means that it is an input to CSPEC0, where it might be used to activate processes on that level. CI3 is either an input to a decision table or an event in a state chart. Similarly, CO3 flows out of a CSPEC bar and is therefore an output from a decision table or an action of a state chart in CSPEC0.

**Naming and Numbering Rules**  The components (processes and stores) of a CFD, and the CFD itself, are named and numbered the same as the corresponding DFD.

**Data Condition**  Control flows may be generated in PSPECs through tests on data flows: Such control flows are called data conditions. The data flows are shown on the DFD, the resulting control flows are shown coming out of the same process on the corresponding CFD. Thereafter, they behave like any other control flows. Figure 4.60 illustrates the generation of a data condition.

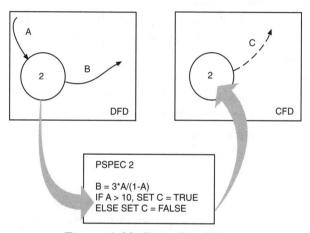

*Figure 4.60: Data Conditions.*

Since data flows cannot enter CSPECs, a data condition is required if a data flow participates in the activation or deactivation of some processing. The data condition can then enter the CSPEC in place of the data flow. If the condition is as simple as the one shown in Figure 4.60, you might alternatively use a guard for a transition—such as [A >10] ACTIVATE—instead of creating a control flow.

### 4.3.7.1 Rules and Guidelines for CFDs and CSPECs

- Each DFD may optionally have one CFD.
- Each DFD/CFD pair may optionally have one CSPEC. The CSPEC may have multiple parts. The DFD, CFD, and CSPEC have identical numbers and names.
- Control flows entering or exiting from a CSPEC bar are entering or exiting from the corresponding CSPEC.
- Every CSPEC bar in a CFD represents the corresponding CSPEC in its entirety. There is no indication on a CSPEC bar as to which part of a

CSPEC a flow goes to or comes from. Figures 4.50 and 4.51 in Section 4.3.4.2 show that control inputs and outputs can go to or come from multiple places inside a CSPEC.

- Control flows may not enter primitive processes, since there are no processes to activate or deactivate below the primitive level.
- Control flows, called data conditions, may be generated in PSPECs through tests on data flows.
- CSPECs may generate process activators that turn processes on and off in the corresponding DFD.
- CSPECs may also generate data flows, which will enter the corresponding DFD through CSPEC bars. These data flows will, of course, always be discrete-valued.
- Control flows into and out of CSPEC bars must be used as inputs and outputs in the corresponding CSPEC. They must be used either as the events and actions of state charts or as the inputs and outputs of decision tables or of any other construct used in the CSPEC.

From the CSPEC perspective, the following rules apply:

- An event in a state chart or an input to a decision table or other construct must come either from a control flow that enters a bar in the corresponding CFD, or from another part of the same CSPEC. In the latter case, it could be either an action from a state chart or an output from a decision table or from any other construct used in the CSPEC.
- An action in a state chart or an output from a decision table or other construct must be either an activator for a process on the corresponding DFD, or a control signal for use elsewhere in the CSPEC or elsewhere in the model via a bar. A CSPEC can only directly activate processes on its corresponding DFD. To activate processes in other parts of the model, the CSPEC must create control flows and send them via CFDs to the right places.

## 4.3.8 Separation of Data and Control

The requirements method explicitly separates processing from control of the processing. This distinction is clear in, say, large industrial control processes, where you need to know the process before you can control it. The distinction between processing and control in the requirements model is not always so obvious, so Figures 4.61 and 4.62 provide some hints and guidelines for distinguishing data flows from control flows, and information/material/energy processing from control processing. The rule of thumb for the classification of a flow is that if it involves any continuous-valued data, then it must be a data flow; otherwise, the classification depends solely on the flow's usage and the type of processing that will be performed on it.

The rule of thumb for the classification of processing is that if it contains any continuous-valued data, it must be a data process; otherwise, the classification depends solely on whether or not the processing is to be used in the model to activate and deactivate processes.

| Characteristic | Type of Flow |
|---|---|
| Continuous-valued signals representing continuous, physical quantities | Data flow |
| Many-valued discrete signal | Data flow or control flow depends on usage: If it is to be used as a process activator, then it is a control flow; otherwise it is a data flow. Some signals may need to be classified as both. |
| Binary signal | Usually control flow, but the same criteria as above apply |

*Figure 4.61: Hints on Distinguishing Data and Control Flows.*

| Characteristic | How to Model |
|---|---|
| Process with continuous-valued inputs and outputs | Process specification |
| Process with mixed continuous and discrete inputs and outputs | Process specification |
| Process with discrete inputs and outputs | Process specification or control specification, depending on utilization |
| Process that results in the activation/deactivation of processes, either sequentially or combinationally | Control specification |

*Figure 4.62: Hints on Distinguishing Processes and Their Control.*

## 4.4 REQUIREMENTS DICTIONARY

Although we discuss it late in this chapter, the requirements dictionary is one of the most important parts of the requirements model. It is an alphabetical list (these days, almost always a database) of all the items listed below that are used in the models, each with a definition of its component structure, its meaning, and other details. The requirements dictionary is as boring to read as a telephone book, but it is our most valuable resource for understanding terms that we do not understand by their names alone.

**Definition** The requirements dictionary defines all of the following:

- data flows
- control flows
- stores
- entity classes
- relationships
- attributes

Also defined are the components from which these elements are built, and other properties we need to capture.

**Notation** To define the composition of, and the relationships within, the items defined in the requirements dictionary, we use the symbols shown in Figure 4.63.

Groups of elements are structured using the operators shown in the figure. Primitive elements must have their properties defined, such as units, range, precision, resolution, and update rates. Sometimes, standard domain names are used to abbreviate these properties. Domains, such as currency or date, are defined once and then simply assigned to the elements.

For discrete elements, the value range should be made explicit. This is often done using square brackets to enumerate the alternative values. Figure 4.64 shows a more complete schema for all the primitive properties we want to describe in the requirements dictionary. The format is of less concern, and may differ between automated tools.

| Symbol | Definition |
|---|---|
| = | Separates the thing to be defined from its definition; can be read as: "is defined as" or "consists of" or "is composed of." (Does not mean "equals.") Often omitted in automated tools, because the symbols and definitions are in separate fields. |
| + | Collects members together in group being defined. Can be read as "and" or "together with." For example, "bread + butter." Does not imply addition or an ordered grouping. If ordering is required, use comments in the requirements dictionary or specify it in the PSPECs. |
| { } | Indicates any number of iterations of enclosed expression from zero to infinity, for example, {customer_record }. Note that we use the singular form inside the parentheses, since the parentheses indicates multiple instances. |
| M{ }N | Indicates any number of iterations from a minimum M to a maximum N, for example, 3{service_contract}7. |
| [ \| \| ] | Indicates alternative components: "exclusive-OR." At least two expressions, separated by vertical bars, must be contained in the brackets. In any given instance, exactly one of the expressions is included in the structure, for example, [red\|green\|blue\|black]. |
| ( ) | Indicates optional component: Can be read as "possibly" or "sometimes," for example, phone_number + (extension). |
| " " | Literal expressions: Appears in the system exactly as stated, as opposed to a variable that takes on a value. |
| * * | Enclose any comments needed to supplement the definition. Often omitted in automated tools, because comments are in a separate field. |
| \ \ | Enclose a primitive definition, not further structured or defined in the dictionary. Often omitted in automated tools, because primitive definitions are in a separate field, or are indicated by a flag. |

*Figure 4.63: Notation for Structuring Dictionary Entries.*

| Name | Meaning and Composition | Type | Units | Range/ Values | Accu- racy | Reso- lution | Rate |
|---|---|---|---|---|---|---|---|
| BARO ALT | barometric altitude | data | feet | 0 - 70.000 | ±10 feet | 1 | 1 per 100 msec. |
| SHAFT ROTATION | angular rotation of drive shaft | data | rads./ sec. | 0 - 20.000 | ±5 rads./ sec. | 0.1 | on demand |
| IN AIR | wheels off the ground | control | | ON, OFF | | | 1 per 200 msec. |
| FLIGHT PHASE | phase of vertical flight profile | control | | takeoff, climb, cruise, descent | | | 1 per 200 msec. |

*Figure 4.64: Properties of Basic Dictionary Entries.*

## Rules and Guidelines

- Every data flow, control flow, and store used anywhere in the DFDs, CFDs, and CSPECs must be defined in the dictionary.
- All components of group names must be defined.
- Eventually, everything must be broken down to primitive elements and their attributes, with a description of their meaning. The names of such elements often come close to a complete, though brief, definition: They are "self-defining."
- Primitive elements may have units, range or values, accuracy, resolution, and any other important attributes, in their definitions. However, only include those attributes that are essential to the requirements; leave to the architecture model any that are at the discretion of the designer.
- Special description templates are used for entity classes, relationships, and attributes, as discussed in Section 4.3.2. Nevertheless, they are considered part of the requirements dictionary. (Some of today's CASE tools keep these definitions in separate dictionaries. While this is a nice feature for separating the models, it is a source of trouble when attributes of entity classes can have definitions conflicting with elements in a data store. Ultimately, there is only *one* dictionary.)
- The dictionary should be created concurrently with the rest of the models. In fact, we recommend that you define the twenty to thirty most important items *before* you even start sketching any diagrams.
- The value of the dictionary cannot be overemphasized.

## 4.4.1 Timing Requirements

Our requirements models must include performance requirements, many of which are included in modeling elements we have already described: repetition rates, in the dictionary; functions of time and process-triggering rates, in PSPECs or CSPECs. Not included in any of these are the overall timing relationships between system inputs and outputs, and these relationships are an essential part of the system specification. *Strategies* provides details of timing specifications that capture these relationships, and they are further illustrated here in the case study in Part II.

There is an important facet of timing that affects the interpretation of the requirements model. The idealized nature of the requirements model appears to imply that processes, both data and control, perform their tasks in negligible time. This is true for tasks that are not functions of time, but for those that are, the tasks will take the amount of time determined by the function. We must, therefore, modify our interpretation of idealized operation: Instead of negligible time, we must think in terms of negligible error. The requirements model performs tasks precisely as specified, with negligible error in all specified parameters, including time. In contrast, the architecture model will perform those same tasks with non-negligible errors caused by tolerances in real-world devices.

For example, the task of either a data process or an STD action might be to generate a single sawtooth waveform, starting at 0 volts, increasing linearly in 10 seconds to 10 volts, and then returning to 0 volts. The requirements model will perform this function precisely as specified; the architecture model will perform it with tolerances in the time, the voltage, and the linearity.

A further effect of functions of time on the operation of the requirements model is that we cannot assume when a new input arrives that the model has completed all previous tasks. Both data and control processes are input-triggered, but if the processes' tasks are functions of time, then they may still be in operation when the next input trigger arrives. Generally, this means that the response of the process will depend on whether or not it is still active when a new input arrives. In the case of a sequential machine, it means that when an event causes both a new state and an action, the action—if it is a function of time—may remain in effect for part or all of the new state's duration. This is consistent with the convention we adopted in *Strategies* that actions remain in effect until the next transition occurs. It is quite usual to use the results of an action to generate the input trigger for the next state transition. If the action is not a function of time, this will cause two transitions with negligible time between them; if it is a function of time, the two transitions will be separated by whatever amount of time the function dictates.

## 4.4.2 Requirements Model Balancing

All flows and other links between elements of the model must have a source and a destination, and they must appear, explicitly or implicitly, in those places. Here is a summary of all the different kinds of balancing in the requirements model:

- **data flow diagrams**—flows into and out of a diagram and its parent process must balance.
- **process specifications**—inputs and outputs of a PSPEC and its parent process must balance. This includes PSPECs that are moved to the description or annotation fields as described in Section 4.3.3.8, "Detailing Diagrams."
- **control flow diagrams**—balancing in CFDs parallels that of DFDs; in addition, control flows into and out of CSPEC bars and the corresponding CSPEC must balance.
- **data conditions**—data conditions must appear on the CFD as outputs from the parent process of the PSPEC in which they are generated.
- **control specifications**—control and data flows in and out of the CSPEC must balance with corresponding flows in and out of the CSPEC bars. Process activators must activate processes only on the corresponding DFD, though not every process needs to have an activator.
- **timing specification (TSPEC)**—every primitive input and output included, either directly or as part of a group flow, among the input and output flows on the data and control context diagrams must appear at least once in the corresponding column of the TSPEC.
- **requirements dictionary**—every data and control flow on the diagrams must be listed and defined in the requirements dictionary. Elements of a group flow must also be listed and defined, including any that do not appear explicitly on the diagrams.

## 4.4.3 Architecture Template and Enhanced Requirements Model

The requirements models discussed so far should represent essential requirements only [McMenamin 84]. The process model should only include processes that add functional value to the inputs they receive. The control model should only show the required behavior, independent of how it is achieved. The entity model should only model things that the system needs to perform its job, independent of the technology used. These are highly idealized statements, difficult to achieve in practice. In one sense, requirements are never technology-independent, because they are always based on our knowledge of the capabilities of current technology. (Just imagine, for example, the reaction if, one hundred years ago, someone had written a specification for a system to accelerate a person from 0 to 60 miles per hour in 10 seconds!) Nevertheless, we must never state in our core requirements any specifics of that technology.

Before allocating the requirements to the architecture model, we take one step closer to reality. We consider the additional requirements needed as a result of the allocation process. To help us with this, we use the architecture template, as shown in Figure 4.65.

| Customer (User) Interface Requirements | | |
|---|---|---|
| Input Processing Requirements | Essential Requirements (Core Required Capabilities) | Output Processing Requirements |
| | Support Requirements | |

*Figure 4.65: Architecture Template.*

We discussed the template throughout Section 3.4, using it to classify system activities. There, we focused on categorizing system functions; here, we focus on categorizing requirements, and accordingly, the regions of the template have different names. For the methods, the architecture template is simply a means to an end, reminding us of five areas that we do not want to overlook as we develop the system:

- The central region contains the essential requirements: the process, control, and entity models discussed earlier.
- The four surrounding regions contain those processes, behaviors, and physical items needed for the physical interface with the outside

world—the system environment. The four system interfaces resulting from the application of the requirements are shown in Figure 4.66, clarifying the transformations that take place across the interfaces.

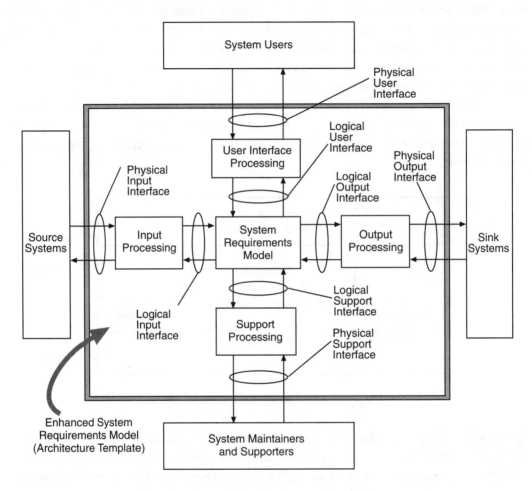

*Figure 4.66: Logical and Physical Interfaces.*

## Rules and Guidelines

- After mapping the essential DFDs and CFDs into the central region, consider each of the surrounding regions to determine if they need additional processes (data or control), stores, or modules.

- Do not be a slave to the architecture template: It is merely a guide to jog the memory and often one or more, or even all, of the enhancement regions need nothing added.
- The architecture template's second purpose is to clearly separate the core system, or business, requirements from those dictated by the required interfaces. Should the interfaces change, the contents of the outer ring will change, but not those of the core.

Applying the template produces the enhanced requirements model, which contains the complete set of requirements—core and interface—that must be allocated to the architecture model. The architecture template and the enhanced requirements model play an important role in the system development process, as we discuss further in Chapter 5 and illustrate throughout Part II.

## 4.4.4 Requirements Model Summary

The requirements model components integrate into a cohesive statement of the required system capabilities, independent of any particular implementation. We model three separate viewpoints:

- required processing capabilities in the process model
- required storage capabilities in the entity model
- required behavioral capabilities in the control model

These viewpoints are linked in multiple ways to each other and to the requirements dictionary, which serves as the central catalog of definitions.

Figure 4.67 shows the four major components of the requirements model and their major specifications and diagrammatic subcomponents. At the top and bottom are the data and control flows that connect to the system environment. Inside the requirements model are the model components and their most important links. Data flows link data flow diagrams to process specifications, where they are transformed from input to output flows; some of these are data conditions that cross over to the control model. Data conditions, together with external control flows, travel via control flow diagrams to control specifications or out of the system. Control specifications create new control flows, and they control processes via process activators.

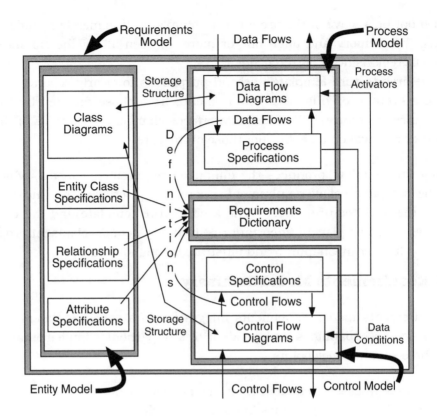

*Figure 4.67: Requirements Model Summary.*

On the left side of Figure 4.67 is the entity model, which defines the static structure of what the system stores, or remembers. The class diagrams link to the stores in the process and control models, as shown by the double-headed storage structure lines.

Central to the models, and therefore to Figure 4.67, is the requirements dictionary, which captures the definitions of all terms used in the three sub-models.

## 4.5 REQUIREMENTS/ARCHITECTURE RELATIONSHIPS

In Sections 4.2 and 4.3, we discussed the architecture and requirements models separately, but they are two views of the same system. We also used a multiple-viewpoint approach within the requirements model, looking at the process, control, and entity models as three separate but complementary views of the requirements. Similarly, we discussed the separate but complementary flow and interconnect views found within the architecture model.

In the next sections, rather than look at the differences, we consider the commonalities and relationships between the two main models. In Section 4.5.1, we discuss the scope of the two models; in Section 4.5.2, we introduce superbubbles as a graphical means to bridge the two; finally, in Section 4.5.3, we discuss a notation for traceability between the two models. All of these facets of the models play an important role in our process. This chapter introduces these ideas and gives some background for them, but Chapter 6 and the case studies in Part II and on-line demonstrate their application.

## 4.5.1 Scope Differences

We have discussed two different contexts: the requirements context, represented by the DCD and CCD, and the architecture context, represented by the AFCD and AICD. Can there be a difference between the requirements and architecture contexts? The answer is yes! As the models are developed, there can be several different versions of the requirements and architecture contexts as we progress toward their eventual versions.

When starting the requirements model, we often deliberately draw the boundary beyond where we expect the system scope actually to extend. This ensures that nothing is overlooked. It brings to the forefront, early in the development, any threat of "turf wars" over who is responsible for what. It is better to get these issues resolved early than to let them simmer throughout the project. Figure 4.68 shows a possible initial context boundary and the eventual boundary after resolving responsibilities. This eventual boundary might not be established immediately—some negotiation might be necessary—but as long as a boundary is there and clearly visible, it will be clear to everyone that, if nothing is done to change it, everything inside that boundary will eventually be part of the system.

We have seen, in Figure 4.66, that the application of the architecture template causes the architecture interfaces to be different from the requirements interfaces; the former are physical, while the latter are logical. There can be further differences: The addition of physical interfaces can require additional terminators in the architecture context diagrams, and entirely new flows not even considered in the requirements model. This is because the functions in the ring of interfaces in the architecture template might need external services beyond those called for by the essential requirements. These additional services are particularly common with the maintenance and support functions, which are not considered at all in the essential model.

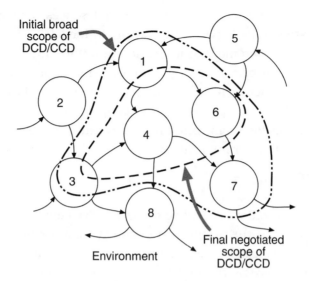

*Figure 4.68: Changing Requirements Scope.*

The architecture context diagrams eventually include all the terminators from the requirements context diagrams, with possibly some more needed to support the interfaces introduced by the architecture template. There is more work done in the architecture context than in the requirements context. Note that the parents of C/DFD0 are the CCD and DCD, but the parent of *enhanced* C/DFD0 (EC/DFD0) is the AFCD. This is because the flows in and out of the enhanced diagrams are the physical flows that also appear in the architecture model. The AFCD is also the parent of AFD0—it has two child diagrams—and no further context diagram is needed for enhanced EC/DFD.

## 4.5.2 Superbubbles

Allocating requirements to architecture is an important step in system development, and superbubbles provide a graphical way to do it. Figure 4.69 shows a generic, enhanced C/DFD superimposed with superbubbles, the thick black lines, each associated with an architecture module, grouping certain processes, stores, and bars.

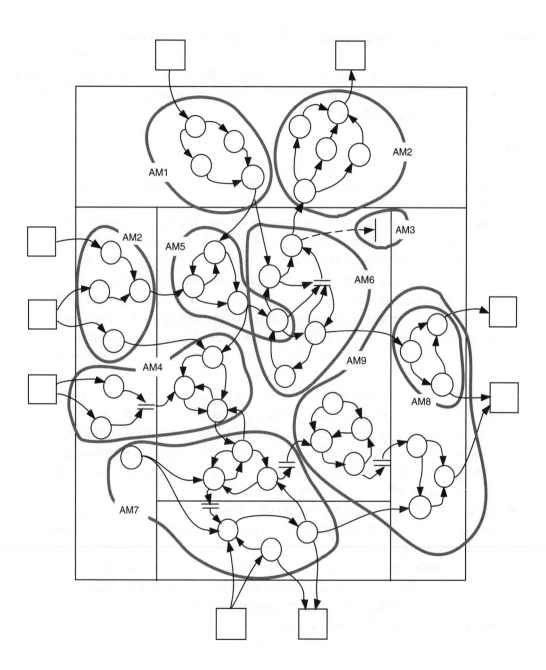

*Figure 4.69: Superbubbles.*

**Definition**  Superbubbles are heavy lines superimposed on enhanced C/DFDs, surrounding processes, stores, and CSPEC bars.  Their purpose is to allocate the elements they surround to architecture modules.  Each superbubble is associated with, and named the same as, a specific architecture module on the AFD associated with the enhanced C/DFD.

## Rules and Guidelines

- A superbubble can package any number of elements in the enhanced requirements model.
- Superbubbles may partially or completely overlap (as shown for AM5 and AM6, and for AM8 and AM9, in Figure 4.69), meaning that the multiply enclosed processes, stores, or CSPECs are multiply (or redundantly) allocated to more than one architecture module.
- For ease and convenience of layout, the superbubble for a given architecture module may be replicated on the diagram any number of times (see AM2 in Figure 4.69).  Everything enclosed by all replications of the superbubble is allocated to the one corresponding architecture module.
- When a process is allocated to an architecture module, all its descendants are allocated with it: its PSPEC or child diagram; any CSPECs on that diagram; and any further child diagrams, PSPECs, and CSPECs. This is also true for the allocation of stores:  A store is defined in the dictionary (or the entity model), and allocating it means allocating all its dictionary-defined components.
- Allocation is carried out on enhanced C/DFDs.  Sometimes, a process needs to be split between multiple architecture modules, as illustrated in the upper part of Figure 4.70.  Splitting a process necessitates going "inside" the process, to its child, and making the allocation explicit, as illustrated in the lower part of Figure 4.70.  If further processes are split in the child diagram, then the procedure must be repeated until the allocation is explicit.

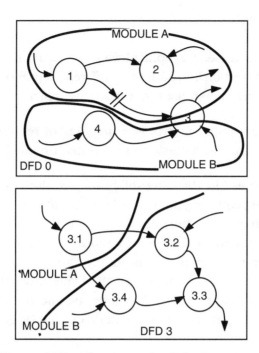

*Figure 4.70: Allocation of a Split Process.*

- If, at any stage of the above procedure, a primitive process is split between multiple architecture modules, then a design decision must be made on how those modules will implement the function defined by the PSPEC. This situation is one of the most common circumstances in which derived requirements, described in Sections 2.3.1 and 2.3.3, are created.

- Splitting a data store works the same way: The components of the store defined in the dictionary must be clearly allocated to the separate architecture modules and incorporated into new, child stores. The union of the contents of the child stores must balance with the contents of the original, parent store.

- Splitting a CSPEC bar means dividing the elements of the CSPEC between the architecture modules. The superbubbles must be repeated in the CSPEC guide to make the allocation of CSPEC elements specific. If the superbubbles split any of the CSPEC elements, then it is usually best to reorganize the CSPEC to eliminate this.

## 4.5.3 Traceability

Superbubbles provide a clear, graphical way to allocate requirements to architecture modules. This section introduces a different representation for the requirements/architecture relationships: the traceability matrix.

**Definition** The traceability matrix is a mapping of requirements model components—processes, stores, and CSPECs—to architecture modules.

**Rules and Guidelines** In the traceability matrix, illustrated in Figure 4.71, the vertical axis lists the requirements model components to be allocated to the architecture modules listed on the horizontal axis. An X in a matrix cell indicates that the requirements element in that row is allocated to the architecture module in that column. The traceability matrix is simply another way to represent the information that the superbubbles convey, so the same procedures apply: Allocating an element implies allocating all its descendants; allocations are first made at the highest level, and any split elements are made explicit by going to lower levels.

| ARCHITECTURE MODEL COMPONENTS / REQUIREMENTS MODEL COMPONENTS | AM1 | AM2 | AM3 | AM4 | AM5 | AM6 |
|---|---|---|---|---|---|---|
| P1 | X | | | | | |
| P2 | | | | X | | |
| P3 | | 2.1 | | | | |
| P4.1 | | 2.2 | | | | |
| P4.2 | | 2.3 | X | | | |
| P4.3 | | | | | | X |
| P4.4 | X | | | | | |
| P5 | X | | | | | |
| Store 1 | | | | | X | |
| Store 2 | | | X | | | |
| Store 3 | | | X | | | |
| CSPEC 0 | | | | | | X |

*Figure 4.71: Generic Traceability Matrix.*

There are some circumstances in which a simple X in a matrix cell provides insufficient information. First, since processes can be allocated to a single architecture module from multiple source diagrams, there can be conflicts in process numbering; in which case, the processes retain their original names but are renumbered in the newly constructed flow diagram. These new numbers are shown in place of the X in the traceability matrix, thus providing a cross-reference with the old numbers in the vertical axis.

Second, sometimes, especially in software, a process is not statically allocated: It is dynamically allocated to one of several architecture modules during operation. In such cases, a row in the matrix might contain or reference a function that determines the dynamic allocation. This allows us to model dynamic load distribution in networks, fallback strategies, and so on.

There are more examples and details of traceability matrices in Section 6.3 and in Part II.

## 4.5.4 Architecture Model/Requirements Model Balancing

We saw in Sections 4.2.9 and 4.4.2 that balancing pervades both the architecture and requirements models, but equally, it pervades the combined models through the links between them. The traceability matrix represents some, but not all, of those links. Here is a summary of all the links:

- requirements model elements to architecture modules—these are the links represented by the traceability matrix, the processes, stores, and CSPECs allocated to architecture modules. The links are recorded in the traceability matrices, and through the requirements models for each architecture module that result from the allocations.
- data and control flows to architecture flows—every data and control flow in the essential and enhanced requirements models must be mapped to an architecture flow, either between architecture modules or within a module. This is recorded by transferring all requirements dictionary entries to the architecture dictionary and ensuring that every architecture dictionary entry has a matching flow somewhere in the architecture model, either explicitly or as part of a group flow.
- timing specification to architecture module—every requirements model includes a TSPEC that is allocated, with the rest of the model, to an architecture module. As requirements to architecture allocations

progress through modules, sub-modules, and so on, new TSPECs are created that jointly satisfy the higher-level TSPECs for the parent module. Thus, there is eventually a TSPEC for every architecture module, each one obeying the balancing rules for an individual TSPEC, and jointly satisfying the requirements of the top-level TSPEC. Note that the process of creating these TSPECs is a central part of the engineering analyses and trade-offs that go into developing the system. The architecture and requirements methods simply capture the results of this engineering work; they do not actually do the work.

## 4.6 A NOTE ON OBJECT ORIENTATION

The latest initiative in object orientation is the Unified Modeling Language (UML), largely spearheaded by Grady Booch, James Rumbaugh, and Ivar Jacobson. In the summary description of UML found on Rational Inc.'s Website at the time of this writing (www.rational.com), the following statement appeared:

> Structured methods clearly separate data from functions, decreasing their cohesion. Object-oriented (OO) methods take a different approach. They unify data and the functions that operate on them into software components called objects. In the real-time world, objects are models of things such as sensors, motors, and communication interfaces.

To address this distinction between structured methods and object-oriented methods, it is worth answering the question: What is a method? In its broadest sense, a method is a prescribed set of techniques to facilitate the achievement of some desired goal. In development work, a method consists of a notation (graphical or textual), a syntax that defines how the notational elements may be used together, a set of semantics that defines the meaning of the notation when used in accordance with the syntax, and a set of heuristics and guidelines on how to apply the method to real-world problems. Both structured and OO methods possess all of these properties, so we can conclude that this common definition of methods applies to them both, and there is no distinction on that score.

Next, what does "structured" mean in the context of structured methods? It means that the method, when used according to the prescribed heuristics and guidelines, has some kind of well-defined (and presumably useful) structure. Do OO techniques possess this property? As we discuss elsewhere, some do and some do not, but there is a very laudable effort in the OO community to define such structures on a scale that is larger than single objects. It seems apparent then, that, even if OO methods do not currently possess higher-level structures, they soon will.

So, what can we conclude from all this? Dare we say it? Object-oriented methods *are* structured methods, just like all the others that preceded them! We are sure this will be construed as heresy by some of our readers, but if you can see a flaw in our argument, we would love to hear about it.

To address the UML statement further, we have shown in this chapter that by using the requirements and architecture methods in combination (which is how they should to be used), the separation of data from function goes away. We have also shown that OO methods blend very nicely with the requirements and architecture methods.

Why are we making such a big deal of this issue? Because it is time to acknowledge that software development techniques did not begin with object orientation, as some OO advocates would have us believe. Object orientation brings some extremely valuable additions to our toolbox of software techniques, but the techniques that preceded it were hardly worthless. In fact, a great deal of OO is founded on principles developed within these earlier techniques. Moreover, some of those earlier techniques have benefits not enjoyed by OO: Object orientation does not maintain a clear separation of requirements from design; there is no consensus so far in the OO community on large-scale OO structures; and it is not clear that OO methods will be as applicable at the higher system levels of multidisciplinary systems as they are within software. These are all important issues, and we demonstrate in this book that they are all solved by using OO in conjunction with the requirements and architecture methods, and that doing so does not violate any sacred OO principles.

In summary, then, OO is a major and valuable new step in the progression of structured methods; much of it is founded on earlier structured methods; in spite of its benefits, it has some deficiencies, at least in its present form(s); using it in conjunction with the requirements and architecture methods overcomes those deficiencies.

## 4.7 SYSTEM MODELS SUMMARY AND FURTHER READING

This chapter has provided an overview of the models used in our system development approach. We have described various components, elements, and views of the architecture and requirements models. We did not attempt to reinvent the wheel, but only to use well-known and proven approaches wherever possible, making minor changes to bring the notations up to date.

We have concentrated on the essentials of the notations and added some hints, guidelines, and rules, especially in areas where we have seen difficulties in applying the methods and notations in practice. Here are descriptions of some publications, listed in the Bibliography, that we recommend for further reading on the individual components of our models:

- [Hatley 88] builds on Tom DeMarco's process model. It serves as the definitive text for the control and the architecture models, except for the changes described in the Appendix of this book.
- [Robertson 98] is the best book on the current state of the art of the process model, the entity model, and their integration. An extensive case study shows the details of working with these two models.
- [DeMarco 78]—a classic: the introduction of the process model. Still a highly recommended book, it illuminates the motivation for analyzing systems using models.
- [McMenamin 84] is the definitive cookbook: a step-by-step procedure on using the process model to represent essential requirements. It introduces event-oriented decomposition (nowadays called USE CASE modeling).
- [Booch 99 and Jacobson 99] both present the Unified Modeling Language (UML), which is the most widely used object-oriented software development notation, mainly based on the OMT approach of Rumbaugh et al. [Rumbaugh 91], the Booch method [Booch 94], and Jacobson's OOSE [Jacobson 94]. UML provides insight into the thinking of today's OO community, and it is suggested as a follow-on method as the architecture model progresses into software design.

# Chapter 5
# The System
# Development Process

## 5.1 PROCESS, METHODS, AND TOOLS

In *Strategies for Real-Time System Specification*, we introduced a diagram titled "The Total System Life Cycle," little realizing at the time just how significant it was. An embellished version of that diagram is shown in Figure 5.1. In the years since we wrote *Strategies*, a great deal of attention has been focused on the development process, initially on the software development process, but recently on the more general system development process [CMM]. A common conclusion of this work is that a well-defined process is an essential prerequisite for effective methods and tools. The development process defines what development is to produce (the deliverables) and the standards those deliverables must meet. The deliverables include not just the end products of development, but also all the intermediate products, such as requirements analyses, trade-off study reports, design justifications, test plans and procedures, quality assurance reports, and so on. This process, then, is the focus of this chapter, and indeed, of this entire book: PSARE—the process for system architecture and requirements engineering.

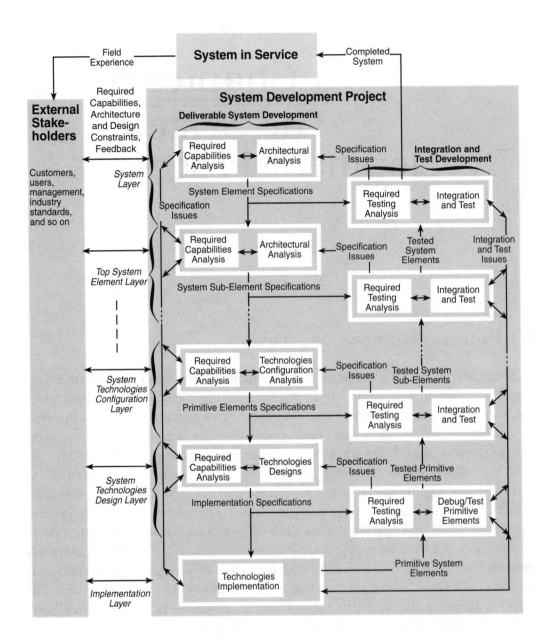

*Figure 5.1: The Total System Life Cycle.*

The purpose of a system development method is to provide support for a defined process; without such a process, it is difficult to know what the method will do for us. Likewise, the purpose of an automated tool is to automate some or all of a defined method; without a good understanding of the underlying method (if any), it is difficult to know what a tool will do for us. This order of precedence is depicted in Figure 5.2. Because this message has not been well understood, most CASE tools sold in the past decade are now shelfware. Watts Humphrey, founder of the Software Engineering Institute's development process program, is fond of saying that "If you have a chaotic process and you automate it, you will have a very fast, chaotic process!"

# PROCESS $\Longrightarrow$ METHODS $\Longrightarrow$ TOOLS

*Figure 5.2: Order of Precedence: Process, Methods, Tools.*

Does this order of precedence mean we should not use automated tools until we have a fully mature process and set of methods in place? Of course not. But it does mean that we should embark on the use of a tool with our eyes open, realizing that we will not get maximum value from it until our process and methods are mature. This invariably means ignoring much of what tool vendors tell us, and doing our own assessments of the tools, of how we can best use them, and of what they will or will not do for us. The same cautions apply when adopting methods—including those described in this book—prior to having a mature process in place.

## 5.2 THE NATURE OF THE DEVELOPMENT PROCESS

In the following sections, we describe the history of the efforts to define the development process, from early sequential models to today's concurrent models. We describe the concurrent process and its advantages over earlier approaches.

### 5.2.1 The Evolution of the Development Process

One of the earliest attempts to define a development process was the waterfall model, in which requirements analysis, design, build, integration, test, and deployment follow each other in a simple sequence, with some limited feedback and concurrency between successive activities but little or no provision for other interactions. This model worked rather well when systems were relatively small and simple, and when a whole system could be envisaged by one or just a few developers. It certainly made life easy for project managers, who could lay out a simple milestone chart based on the waterfall, with each activity closed—never to be revisited—shortly after the succeeding activity started.

Unfortunately, the waterfall model started failing as systems grew larger and more complex, interactions between all activities became significant, and a small team could no longer envisage the whole system. Increasingly, unexpected problems arose in the later stages of a project, which would throw the simple model and the schedule into disarray. A useful attempt to overcome these problems was the spiral model [Boehm 86], in which the requirements analysis, design, prototype, integration, and test activities are repeated several times on increasingly refined prototypes until the final prototype is replaced with the production system. This is a good approach, allowing for the progressive elimination of problems and conflicts as each iteration proceeds.

Although the spiral model is a big improvement, it suffers difficulties similar to those of the waterfall model because it remains sequential within each iteration. In recent years, the emphasis has been on concurrency in development. This trend started with concurrent engineering [SOCE], in which manufacturing engineers assist in the hardware development to ensure that the product is easily manufacturable. This principle is now being extended to include all development disciplines, so that interactions between different parts of the design are taken into account wherever they occur.

## 5.2.2 The Concurrent Development Process

Figure 5.1 is a comprehensive illustration of a concurrent development process. Notice that no sequence is implied anywhere in the diagram—as far as the diagram is concerned, the activities inside the various blocks can occur all at once or in any sequence. Flows between blocks travel in both directions, so no block is superior or inferior to any other: The diagram is a network model in which all the elements have equal status.

Figure 5.1 is quite similar to the V model used in several US military standards. The big difference between Figure 5.1 and the V model is that in the latter, the two sides of the V diverge from the bottom up (hence the V) with minimal links shown between them, whereas in Figure 5.1 the two sides are vertical and side-by-side, with strong interactions linking them.

Overall, Figure 5.1 consists of three major blocks: the System Development Project, the System in Service, and the External Stakeholders. These three blocks form a closed loop in which field experience is gained from a system in service, external stakeholders of the system modify their requirements or produce new ones, and requirements of numerous kinds—as described in Chapter 2—are applied to the current system development project. This is an endless cycle that produces both modified systems and new systems as needs and technology evolve.

The External Stakeholders of the system are all of those described in Chapter 2. They produce all of the different types of external requirements discussed in that chapter, and, consistent with the principle that not all requirements flow top-down through the layered structure, the requirements are shown in Figure 5.1 flowing directly into the appropriate layer. The figure also shows feedback along those same paths, representing issues arising from the various received requirements. It is evident that this system development structure is very complex, with many interrelated concerns. Keeping track of them is usually referred to as *traceability*, and it is an essential part of a well-constructed development process. Later in this chapter, we discuss how the requirements and architecture methods provide the comprehensive traceability needed.

All of the layers in Figure 5.1, except the Implementation Layer, involve some Deliverable System Development, as well as some Integration and Test Development. The Deliverable System Development includes an analysis of the required capabilities for each layer and, in the top two layers, an analysis of the architecture. The Architectural Analysis takes account of the architecture constraints received from outside the project, and of those generated from architectural decisions in the layers above and from technology constraints in the layers below.

All of the layers in Figure 5.1, except the Implementation Layer, also involve some analysis of what testing is required in that layer and some actual integration and test (or debug and test, in the lowest layer). Again, we emphasize that, while the layered structure is a true representation of the system and its development, it is particularly true of integration and testing, which may not follow any sequence corresponding to the layers. It is common for certain parts of the system to be fully integrated and tested right up to the System Layer before integration of other parts of the system is even started. This occurs for various reasons, including the availability (or unavailability) of system elements or the need to verify certain critical parts of the system as early as possible.

The System Layer in Figure 5.1 represents the whole system, its interfaces with its working environment, and its integration and test. The major architectural decisions that determine the overall structure of the system are made in this layer. Here, too, the overall integration and test strategy is developed, with particular emphasis on testability needs in the Deliverable System Development. Among the principal deliverables of the System Layer are the System Element Specifications. These go to the Top System Element Layer and to the Integration and Test Development in the System Layer (so that it will know what is to be integrated and tested). These specifications consist of requirements, either passed through the System Layer or derived within it, and black-box descriptions of the highest-level system elements. Notice again that there are feedback paths from the recipients of these specifications that facilitate problem resolution.

The Top System Element Layer in Figure 5.1 essentially repeats what the System Layer does, but for each top system element individually. In fact, the whole diagram could be applied to just one of these system elements, treating it as a self-contained system that has the rest of the system as its environment. This, in fact, is often done when a particular system element is subcontracted out to another department or to an outside developer.

There can be any number of layers similar to the Top System Element Layer, but it is unusual to have more than two or three of them. Each layer represents a further decomposition of the system into finer elements. What distinguishes the system layers from the lower layers is the fact that the specific configurations of the separate system technologies have not been established. It may be known that a certain system sub-element will include, for example, some mechanical devices, some hydraulics, and some software, but the exact role each will play is not determined in the system layers.

The lowest system layer, then, is the one in which these roles *are* established, labeled in Figure 5.1 as the System Technologies Configuration Layer. In this layer, specific system functions are allocated to specific system technologies or groups of technologies. The specifications from this layer go to the specialists in the corresponding technological areas, who proceed with their designs and implementations.

As shown in Figure 5.1, the Deliverable System Development layers progress downward from Architectural Analysis, to system technologies configuration analysis, to system technologies designs. In one sense, all of these constitute designs, but there are major qualitative differences between them. We use the terms "architecture" and "architecting" in the system layers, because in these layers we are dealing with the overall concepts and structure of the system without addressing the actual physical details (but remember, if there is any question about the ability of the physical details to support the higher-level concepts, then they must be investigated before proceeding further). The system technologies configuration is treated as the lowest system layer because it maps the architectural structure into real physical technologies. Below this layer, there may still be some architectural considerations, especially in the configuration of digital processors, but the work mostly consists of detailed design.

Note that Figure 5.1 shows in each layer a single instance of each activity, but there are actually separate threads within each layer for each system element, sub-element, and so on. The number of layers may differ from one thread to another, and in particular, the System Technologies Configuration Layer may be at different levels in different threads.

The System Technologies Design Layer is shown as a single layer in Figure 5.1, but like the Top System Element Layer, it can contain multiple layers of its own, according to the number of elements and sub-elements within each set of technologies.

Every one of the layers includes analysis of the required testing and the testability requirements for that layer, and addresses the integration and testing of the elements received from the layer below. Part or all of that integration and testing may be done in conjunction with parts of the integration and testing of other layers, as described earlier in this section.

For convenience, we have described Figure 5.1 in a top-down sequence, but remember that in practice nothing has to be carried out in this or any other particular sequence. Consider, for example, the case of an existing system element, perhaps containing various types of hardware and software, that is to be reused in the current system. In this case, it makes sense to plug that element into the appropriate layer and to work from there upward to merge with the higher layers.

Finally, notice the flows on each side of the System Development Project block in Figure 5.1. They indicate that there is opportunity for multifarious communication between any of the layers. They represent the reality that any technical specialty may be needed at any layer of the model. For example, the availability of a new technology, with much greater capabilities than its predecessors, may have a profound influence on the overall, top-level system structure.

## 5.2.3 The Meaning of Concurrent Development

Does concurrency mean that we throw everyone who will ever work on a project into a big room on day one and tell them to do everything, together, right away? Certainly not! It does mean we must define a process that can support multiple, concurrent, interacting activities, using cooperating, multidisciplinary teams as needed by the particular task.

For any given project, then, the areas of the system that will need concurrent, interactive problem-solving—and the teams that will address them—must be defined in a project plan. These team efforts can then be put together to form a project plan that calls for concurrency where needed and for sequence elsewhere. The plan itself must be flexible, and it must be reviewed regularly to adapt to unexpected results arising from the problem-solving efforts, and to new strategies based on achieved results.

Notice again that there is no predefined sequence in this model. It can (and often does) happen that an activity that would have occurred last in the waterfall model happens first in the concurrent model. For example, if an entirely new technology is being considered and it is very uncertain whether it will meet the requirements, the applicable requirements would need to be analyzed, and those parts of the system involving the new technology would need to be built and tested as quickly as possible to arrive at a sound decision on its use. Of course, intelligent project management would take this approach anyway, even with the waterfall model, but that would require a major deviation from that model. With the concurrent model, it fits as well as any other approach and requires no deviations.

The principles underlying the concurrent model are as follows:

- Any project activity is potentially in effect at any time in the project life cycle.
- Everyone on the project has some responsibility for the whole project, and may be called at any time to participate in any activity in the project life cycle.

Starting from this foundation, the project plan must establish exactly which activities will take place when and who will conduct them.

Notice that as the development models have evolved, life has become increasingly difficult for project management. In contrast with the simplicity of the waterfall model and its nice sequential milestones, we now have a model that has no prescribed sequence and must be customized for every project. No one said life should be easy for project management!

Figure 5.3 illustrates the concept of how the concurrent development process works. Note that this figure is not based on any real data—it is a concept diagram only. (Gathering the data to construct such a diagram for a variety of different system and process types would make an excellent research project.  Some work has been done in this area by Shenhar [Shenhar 97]).

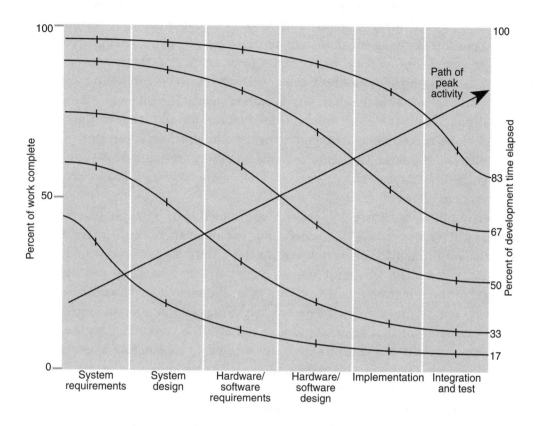

*Figure 5.3: Concurrent Work Flow*

The columns in Figure 5.3 represent the typical activities that are shown sequentially in the waterfall model.  Each column can be thought of as representing the total amount of work that needs to be done in the corresponding activity through the whole development process.  The left-hand vertical axis represents the percentage of the work completed at any given time.  The curved lines that run across the diagram represent the percentage of development time elapsed, as labeled on the right-hand vertical axis; they divide the project time into six approximately equal time divisions.  Consider the lowest of these curved lines—17 percent (about one sixth) of the development time elapsed.  The intersections of these lines with the centers of the columns—indicated by the vertical marks—represents the percentage of the work in that column that has been completed at that point in the development time. So, when the development time is about one sixth elapsed, roughly 40 percent of the system requirements activity has been completed, 30 percent of the system design, and progressively lesser amounts of the succeeding activities. Similar readings can be taken from the other curves. When about five sixths of the development time has elapsed, a small percentage of system requirements activity still remains to be done and there is progressively more of the following activities remaining, with about 40 percent of the integration and test still to do. This diagram shows rather clearly the difference between the waterfall model and the concurrent model. In the former, each of the activities would be done in sequence; in the concurrent model, there is certainly a path of peak activity that follows the same sequence as the waterfall model—indicated by the diagonal line across the diagram—but all of the activities are in progress to some degree at all times.

Referring back to Figure 5.1, we can see immediately some areas where concurrency will almost always be needed. For example, there is an Integration and Test development activity in every layer. In the waterfall model, we would proceed sequentially down the left-hand side of Figure 5.1 and back up the right-hand side, so that the Integration and Test activity in the highest layer would take place at the very end of the schedule, whereas the requirements analysis and architecture development for that layer would take place at the beginning. In the concurrent model, everything in a given layer can be started together. For example, the integration and test team and the development team analyze the requirements together, establish a system integration and test strategy, and resolve any issues arising right away—issues that may affect the architecture in that layer. In this way, we will be assured of having a testable system, rather than finding out too late that inadequate test features have been included in the design.

## 5.3 THE PROCESS AND THE METHODS

The previous sections in this chapter have discussed general development process principles. This section and those that follow describe the role that the requirements and architecture methods, described in Chapter 4, play in the process. Both methods produce layered models that fit well with the natural structure of systems and the development process. Generally, one layer of the architecture model corresponds to one system layer and one process layer and contains several layers of the requirements model.

## 5.3.1 System Specification Models

The combined requirements and architecture methods provide support for concurrent development by defining an integrated requirements/architecture/design model that is nonsequential, meaning that it can be populated using any combination of concurrency and sequence as needed. Although it is beyond the scope of this book to discuss it in detail, the methods also provide support for the Integration and Test parts of Figure 5.1: The structure of the requirements, architecture, and design can be used directly to provide a structure for integration and test.

Figure 5.4 provides a generic view of the models used to represent a given system or subsystem, and of the transitions between these models. This figure relates to the left-hand side of the System Development Project block of Figure 5.1. Instead of showing the layers separately, it shows them as a single iterative loop that can be traversed in either direction. Moving counterclockwise around the loop is equivalent to moving down through the layers of Figure 5.1; moving clockwise is equivalent to moving up through the layers. Let us walk around this iterative loop in both directions to see what it means.

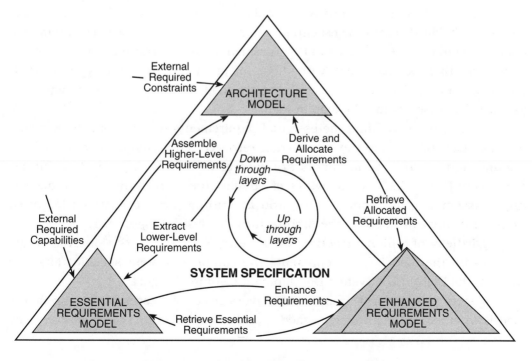

*Figure 5.4: System Specification Models.*

Picking as a starting point the essential requirements model (an abstraction/detailing model), in the lower left corner, we see that the system receives its top-level requirements from outside sources (External Required Capabilities). Proceeding counterclockwise (downward), we see that the requirements model is enhanced to account for the interfaces introduced by architectural decisions, which leads to the enhanced requirements model shown on the lower right (another abstraction/detailing model). The enhanced requirements and any derived requirements are allocated to the chosen architecture modules in the architecture model (an aggregation/decomposition model) at the top of the figure. External Required Constraints limit the choices and characteristics of the architecture modules. For each architecture module, the essential requirements can now be extracted, giving rise to an essential requirements model in the layer below and completing our journey counterclockwise around the loop.

Consistent with the nondirectional nature of the development process and of the methods, this procedure can be reversed. If an existing system or subsystem is to be reused (or if, for whatever reason, some part of the lower-level design took place early in the project), it can be inserted at the appropriate layer in the model, where it will appear as an existing architecture module. From here, its allocated requirements can be retrieved (or deduced, if they were not properly recorded), moving us clockwise to the enhanced requirements model. The allocated requirements can be divided into the essential requirements and enhanced requirements; allowing us to retrieve the essential requirements model. These essential requirements can then be assembled with those for other modules, taking us to their parent module and back to the architecture model. This, then, completes our journey clockwise around the loop in Figure 5.4.

The activities of building the essential requirements model (from the External Required Capabilities and the extracted or retrieved requirements) and of enhancing and deriving the requirements are equivalent to the Required Capabilities Analysis of Figure 5.1. The activities of building the architecture model, allocating or assembling its requirements, and accounting for the External Required Constraints are equivalent to the Architectural Analysis of Figure 5.1.

Regardless of which direction we take in Figure 5.4, the outer triangle encloses all the models and represents the complete system specification—the whole of the Deliverable System Development column of Figure 5.1.

A system with several architecture layers needs an essential requirements model, an enhanced requirements model, and an architecture model for every one of its elements and sub-elements, as well as for the system as a whole. Figure 5.5 shows several layers of a system hierarchy for an aircraft and its subsystems. As discussed earlier, this hierarchy can be described as an aggregation/decomposition model—each layer is an aggregate of the subsystems in the layer below, which result from the decomposition of the layer above. It can also be described by some aliases: whole/part—a given element is the whole of which the sub-elements are parts; context/content—each layer provides the context in which the layer below must work, and is the content of the layer above; composed-of—each layer is composed of the sub-elements in the layer below; or assembly/subassembly/component—an element is an assembly of subassemblies in the layers below, which are subassemblies of components in the lowest layer. The structure illustrates in practical terms the principle we discussed in Chapter 2, that every system (below the whole universe) is part of a higher-level system, and that every system (above the elementary physical particles) is made up of lower-level elements. When specifying a system of any kind, it is important to identify its proper place in this overall hierarchy of things, so that its proper context and content are known.

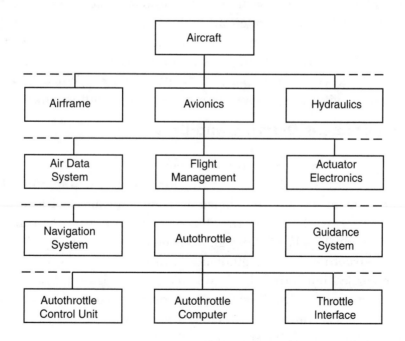

*Figure 5.5: Avionics Hierarchy.*

## 5.3.2 Requirement Enhancement and Allocation

Figure 5.6 provides a more detailed look at the enhancement and allocation relationships in the avionics hierarchy of Figure 5.5, showing the locations and mappings of several of the model's components. In effect, Figure 5.6 illustrates two iterations around Figure 5.4, equivalent to three layers in Figure 5.1. Each of the boxes in Figure 5.6 is a system element or sub-element with its requirements model, enhanced requirements model, and architecture model illustrated in accordance with Figures 5.1 and 5.4. The three models together form the system or subsystem specification. Each specification includes a traceability matrix that records the linkages between the requirements elements and the architecture modules.

In Figure 5.6, requirements that are enhanced and allocated to a given architecture module are divided up and once more enhanced and allocated to a module in the layer below. Some requirements are passed directly through a layer to layers below, but the enhanced requirements (and another type of derived requirements, described in the next section) arise through design decisions. This is the reason for the confusion that often arises between requirements and design, and for the old adage: One person's requirement is another person's design. We make design decisions, and they result in derived requirements, which are requirements imposed on other parts of the development. When we make a decision, it is design; when it is received elsewhere, it is a requirement.

## 5.3.3 Requirement Deriving and Detailing

Enhanced requirements arise from the new interfaces created by architectural decisions, but another kind of derived requirement arises from other design decisions. These might include the choice of a mechanical, electrical, or hydraulic mechanism to operate a valve, or the choice of a particular numerical algorithm to solve an equation. This kind of design decision can be made anywhere in the layered system structure, but the guideline is to make it in the layer where it will actually be carried out (otherwise it will have to be passed down unnecessarily through one or more higher layers). These derived requirements are created as part of the architectural and technologies configuration analyses of Figure 5.1 and appear in the system element specifications.

Requirements *must* be derived when a primitive requirement is allocated to more than one architecture module. When this happens, it means the primitive

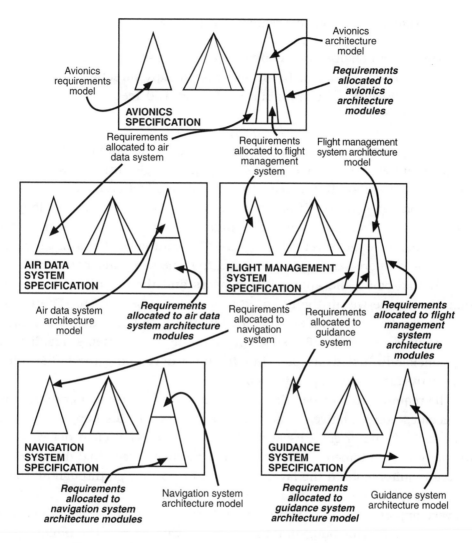

*Figure 5.6: Mappings Between Specification Layers.*

requirement must be split between those modules. However, by definition, a primitive requirement cannot be split. The only solution is to decide *how* the primitive requirement will be carried out (a design decision) and to split the resulting design between the modules. We call this a *split primitive requirement*. It can occur in any system layer, simply depending on where the primitive is multiply allocated.

As an example, consider this requirement:

> The system shall estimate aircraft ground position, using all available position sensors, to an accuracy in any direction no worse than 100 feet with probability .95, and 150 feet with probability .99.

This is the system-level requirement for an aircraft navigation function. It is a primitive requirement, in that it calls for just a single function with its performance requirements. It can lead to a number of different design solutions, depending on the sensors chosen and the accuracies required. As long as the requirement is entirely assigned to one architecture module, it remains as written and may pass through several layers intact. Eventually, it will have to be allocated to one or more sensor modules, and to some computer hardware and software. At this point, the appropriate sensors and the algorithm for making an optimum estimate within the given accuracies must be chosen. The navigation algorithm can be very complex and lengthy, and it can give rise to a whole subsystem of its own. That subsystem, including its requirements, result from the design decisions just described, but to those developing the subsystem, the requirements are essential requirements.

In the requirements model, the above scenario gives rise to a primitive process that becomes non-primitive. It is very important when this happens to retain in the model both the original PSPEC and the newly created child diagram so that traceability is maintained. Processes in the newly created child diagram become essential requirements in the layer below, and they may go through all the usual allocations, enhancements, and further derivations.

A very important facet of requirement deriving and allocating is the accompanying timing and error budgeting that must go with them. The timing specification (TSPEC) included in the methods defines input-to-output timing for a whole system or subsystem, and so there is one TSPEC for every architecture module. When requirements are partitioned between architecture modules, the corresponding TSPECs, and the corresponding accuracies and any other performance parameters, must be partitioned with them. These partitions are made through timing and error budgets. No simple rule can be given for the derivation of these budgets, except that taken together, the budgets must meet the timing and performance requirements specified in the layer above; they are very dependent on the functions being allocated and the nature of the modules. In software, queuing theory can play a significant role in timing analysis; in all technologies, simulation can be a powerful aid. The timing and error budgeting process is an intrinsic part of the architectural design process, and it plays a major role in trade-offs between different candidate architectures.

Requirement deriving, which we have just described, is distinctly different from requirement *detailing*, which is simply the process of adding to an abstract requirement statement the detail necessary for a design decision to be made—it often consists of definitions of words and terms used in the abstract statement. The distinction between the two is that in requirement detailing, no design decisions are made; they are made, of course, in requirement derivation. This distinction is very explicit in the requirements and architecture methods. The layers in a single essential requirements model simply represent layers of increasing detail of description—they do *not* represent design: If they do, you have a bad requirements model. As requirements are allocated to architecture modules, enhanced and derived requirements are generated from them. All of these are design steps that lead to further essential requirements for each architecture sub-module. These subsequent essential models also consist purely of layers of increasing requirement detail, even though some of them were derived from design decisions. As we discussed in Chapter 3, the requirements model is an abstraction/detailing model, whereas the architecture model is an aggregation/decomposition model, and we can now see how very important it is to keep these two properties distinct.

## 5.3.4 Traceability

We stated earlier the need for a development process to record complete traceability between all the various development concerns. It is, perhaps, worth asking why comprehensive traceability is so important. The simplest answer is to look at the mess that projects get into when they do not have such traceability: It is not possible to verify either that every requirement has been met or that every piece of design resulted from a legitimate requirement. Consequently, it is not known if the system will meet the users' needs or if it has features that go beyond those needs or differ from them.

Our methods provide complete traceability within and between the requirements and architecture models by applying the layered structure, the traceability matrix (contained within a module specification), and the architecture dictionary's allocation of flows to channels. All of these relationships are illustrated in Figure 5.7.

This figure takes some of the information from Figure 2.3 (the entity model of requirements) and some from Figure 5.1, and it presents that information from the particular viewpoint of traceability.

Starting at the top left of that figure, External Stakeholder Needs (from any sources) are assigned either directly or as part of the requirements model to an architecture module, giving rise to an Architecture-to-External-Requirement Trace that is recorded by external references in the indicated requirements or architecture specifications, depending on where the requirement appears.

Another possibility, as shown in Figure 5.7, is that the requirement may pass through that module, and may then be decomposed into its constituent parts, giving rise to a Requirement-to-Requirement Trace that is captured through process or dictionary parent/child relationships (in the generic sense described in Chapter 3). Some of the constituent requirements may be given added detail or used to produce derived requirements (through design decisions). In either case, child requirements are produced that trace back to their parent requirements through the various process parent/child relationships in the requirements model, or through the traceability matrices (part of the architecture module specifications).

When a requirement is assigned to an architecture module, as shown in the figure, the resulting Architecture-to-Requirement Trace is again captured in a traceability matrix or in the architecture dictionary (through the flow-to-channel allocations). New interface requirements are introduced through enhancements, using the architecture template, giving rise to a Requirement-to-Architecture Trace, which is captured in the Allocated, Enhanced Model for that module. Finally, an architecture module is decomposed, giving rise to an Architecture-to-Architecture Trace that is captured through the architecture model parent/child relationships.

In this way, all types of traceability are captured somewhere in the models. This means that

- every incoming requirement can be traced to every piece of design created to satisfy it, allowing a check on the completeness of coverage
- every piece of design can be traced back to the requirement(s) that justify its existence, allowing a check on superfluous design
- there is complete visibility into the impact of a change, both in terms of identifying the parts of the system that are affected and in estimating the resources required to make the change

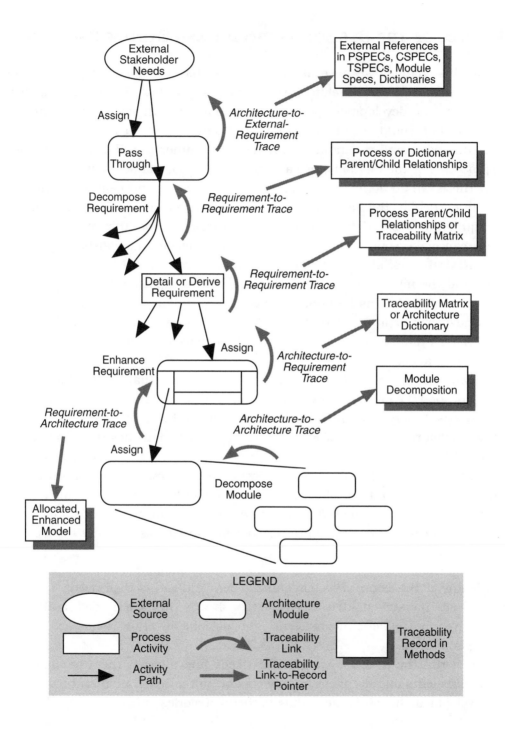

*Figure 5.7: The Traceability Tree.*

## 5.4 ROLES OF THE SYSTEM ARCHITECT AND SYSTEM ENGINEER

So far in this chapter, we have described the system development process and how the requirements and architecture methods support it. There are innumerable activities and development products that go along with system development, many more than could be fully described in a single book. It is worth stepping back at this point and reminding ourselves that neither a well-defined development process, nor the methods, nor any automated tool will actually do the work for us. These can do no more than make the work easier and help us organize it better. In particular, the methods simply define a repository for the results of the work required by a well-defined development process. A tool that automates the methods can make populating the repository and checking its consistency much easier. Nevertheless, all the actual thinking, the problem-solving, the trade-off studies, and the myriad other development activities must be done by you, the system developer. In this section, we look at a sampling of those activities and discuss how they fit into the process and the methods. Our hope is that discussing these examples will motivate the proper placement of other activities as they arise in practice.

One way to approach this summary of the actual work that must be done is to ask the question, "What does a system architect or a system engineer do?" The glib answer is, "Everything included from the System Layer to the System Technologies Configuration Layer of Figure 5.1." But what activities do those layers include? The following list is a reasonable summary. (See [Sheard 96] for another attempt to categorize the roles of system engineers. Although our categorizations differ in detail from Sheard's, it is not difficult to map one to the other.) *Remember, in accordance with the concurrent development principles, all of these activities are, in principle, ongoing throughout the development. Only the level of effort changes.*

- Identify all the external system stakeholders and gather their needs.
- Evaluate the stakeholders' needs, establish why they are needed, and resolve any conflicts, inconsistencies, omissions, or other issues arising from them.
- Categorize the external stakeholder needs and allocate them to the requirements and architecture models and to the integration and test development structure, according to their categories.

- Evaluate the top-level required capabilities and constraints with regard to possible system architectures that might satisfy them.
- Perform analyses, trade-off studies, and prototype evaluations as needed to determine the architecture that best meets the top-level requirements uncovered in the previous step.  The architecture includes the system's overall structure and its major technologies.
- Establish the overall system integration and test strategy, and ensure that integration and test requirements that affect the deliverable system are included in the deliverable system specifications.
- Complete the top-level architecture; enhance, derive, and detail the requirements, and allocate them to the major system elements and interconnects.  This will result in a requirements specification and design rationale for each of the elements and interconnects.
- Develop the requirements, architectures, rationales, and justifications for all system elements, down to the system technologies configuration layer (which may be at different levels in different system threads).
- Prepare integration and test plans for all system layers in accordance with the integration and test strategies.
- Prepare requirements specifications and design rationales for each of the system technologies in cooperation with the specialists in those technologies.
- Work with the technologies specialists to coordinate their efforts, and assist them in interpreting the system needs and in evaluating their designs.
- Integrate and test the implemented technologies in accordance with the integration and test plans.
- Integrate, test, and deliver the entire system in accordance with the integration and test plans, working as needed with the customer to integrate the delivered system into its working environment.

These, then, are the principal activities of the system architect and system engineer.  They are not all immediately obvious from Figure 5.1, but all of the results of these activities have a place in that figure; more particularly, they have a place in the requirements and architecture methods.

In the following sections, we look at a selection of these activities in more detail.

## 5.4.1 Requirement Management

Requirement management is one of the major responsibilities of the system architect and engineer. As the above list shows, and as we discussed in Chapter 2, requirement management consists of six major parts: requirement gathering, requirement integrity analysis, requirement feasibility analysis, requirement detailing, requirement deriving (which includes enhancing), and requirement decomposing and categorizing. Ultimately, our goal is to allocate the requirements resulting from these activities to architecture modules, and this allocation itself plays a role in the activities, serving as a reality check. All of this must be done to the derived requirements as well as to the external requirements, so requirements management continues as a major system activity throughout development. The requirements drive everything else in development, so their central role in the process is hardly surprising.

It should now be very clear why the detailed requirements categorization that we described in Chapter 2 is necessary, and it is made clearer still in the case study in Part II.

## 5.4.2 Feasibility Analyses, Trade-Off Studies, and Prototypes

Another major system responsibility is the choice of the overall system architecture and the major technologies it will include. If the system is simply an upgrade of an existing system, with no major changes in technology or function, then this responsibility is straightforward; but if major new technologies are to be used or if the system is entirely new, then this responsibility becomes a major part of the system development.

Principal tools in making architectural and technological decisions are feasibility analyses, trade-off studies, and prototypes. They will normally be carried out in that order, only proceeding to the next one if a firm conclusion has not already been reached. Their results are vitally important project records; they must be included or referenced in the architecture and design rationales passed down from layer to layer. They are also vital for future projects that will upgrade the system. Without these records, architects and engineers on future projects will not know the reasons the particular architecture or design was chosen, and they may change it in inappropriate ways or be forced to repeat the work.

In conducting these feasibility analyses, trade-off studies, and prototype evaluations, it is important to establish in advance criteria that will be used to choose between the various alternatives. Often, these criteria can be weighted according to their relative importance, and a figure of merit can be established for comparing the alternatives. These criteria are not all technical. Cost, schedule, and resource availability are always factors, and organizational politics—such as personality issues, pet projects, and turf wars—often come into play. While engineering purists may deplore them, these considerations are a part of the real world; the best way to keep them from getting out of hand is to include them, with their weighting factors, in the evaluation criteria.

### 5.4.3 Project Coordination

Members of long-established system engineering groups tend to develop a culture in which they consider themselves the Great Gurus of the organization (a view rarely shared by others in the organization). This attitude produces many negative results, including system specifications that get passed down as decrees to the technology specialists and a deep resentment among those specialists toward the system engineers.

Our view is that, if system engineers should be considered any one thing in particular, it should be the Great Coordinators. This is particularly true when development is carried out concurrently, as we advocate. In such an environment, numerous multidisciplinary teams must work together harmoniously. It is the system engineer's responsibility to ensure that the right teams are brought together, that they have clear descriptions of the tasks they are to perform—in terms they can all understand—and that conflicting demands of the different technologies are resolved to everyone's mutual satisfaction. These are no small tasks, and carrying them out effectively requires extraordinary people skills. It requires getting into the trenches with the technology specialists to work out any difficulties in as much detail as needed. Quite a contrast with the Great Guru image!

### 5.4.4 Manual Procedures and Other Operator Functions

We have pointed out that the system operator can, and often should, be considered an intrinsic part of the system. This can be realized in practice by treating the operator procedures as one of the technologies in the System Technologies Configuration Layer in Figure 5.1. The procedures will then become one or more architecture modules, allowing us to allocate system functions to the operator procedures just as we would to any other module. If the operator procedures are extensive and divide naturally into several sub-procedures, then the operator procedures module can be divided into sub-modules corresponding to those sub-procedures. In general, the division between manual and automated procedures can occur in any system layer, and if the operator procedures module is divided into sub-modules, then it can occur in several layers. Eventually, the requirements allocated to the operator procedures will be translated into text and illustrations in the actual procedure documents, instead of being translated into hardware and software designs as in the other modules.

Exactly the same approach can be taken with maintenance and support functions, which can be allocated to maintenance and support procedure modules and then translated into text and illustrations in the corresponding maintenance manuals.

This approach provides, for the manual procedures, all the built-in traceability and consistency checking that the methods provide for the rest of the system.

In addition, the system operators can serve other roles in the models: as terminators, when they are the sources or recipients of system inputs or outputs; or as architecture channels, when they provide the means for moving materials into, out of, or within the system. There is no contradiction in having operators serve more than one of these roles in one system—they function in the different roles at different instants in time, or different operators fulfill the different roles.

### 5.4.5 Companion IR&D Projects

Sometimes, a development project will depend on an independent research and development (IR&D) project for some of its elements. In such cases, it is the responsibility of the system engineer to ensure that the results of this IR&D are available at the right time, which may require close coordination between the two project schedules. Another responsibility is to ensure that the development project needs are conveyed to the IR&D project, and that the IR&D project plans call for the results actually needed by the development project.

## 5.5 SYSTEM DEVELOPMENT PROCESS SUMMARY

We have looked at the nature of the development process and at the meaning and benefits of concurrency in the process. We have shown how the requirements and architecture methods support a well-defined development process, especially a concurrent one. Finally, we have described the roles of the system architect and engineer in the development process and how the process and the methods, while not actually performing the work, make that work much easier and provide an organized repository for its results.

# Chapter 6
## Applying the Models to Development

## 6.1 OVERVIEW

We have now described systems, the system development process, and ways to model both. What remains is to describe the practical application of these models to actual systems, which is the primary focus of this book. In Part II, we present a comprehensive case study that illustrates this practical application, but first, in this chapter, we introduce simpler illustrations of the fundamental concepts.

Briefly, to summarize what we have seen so far,

- Systems and their requirements naturally form layered structures (Chapters 2 and 3).
- Models are devices that represent certain aspects of the real world in a useful and understandable way (Chapter 3).
- The requirements and architecture methods produce models that exploit the layered natures of systems, of system requirements, and of the development process (Chapter 4).
- The system development process can be modeled around the layered system structure (Chapter 5).

This coalescence of requirements, architecture, system structure, and the development process makes these methods unique and gives them broad applicability.

## 6.2 UNDERSTANDING THE GENERIC DEVELOPMENT STRUCTURE

In Chapter 5, we used the simplified diagram in Figure 5.4 to illustrate the application of the methods. It is now time to elaborate on this diagram and to look more closely at the structure and application of the methods. Figure 6.1 shows the components of the methods and the links between them for the architecture context level and for architecture Level 1. The latter is typical of all lower levels. In Figure 6.1, the various incarnations of the requirements model are shown on the left, and those of the architecture model are on the right. Because of this layout convention and to save space on the diagram, we have omitted the word "requirements" from the models on the left, but we use it in the text for clarity.

Although Figure 6.1 may seem complex, it is a useful guide to the methods, and we will use it as a reference throughout the rest of this chapter. Any complexity it has merely reflects the real nature of systems—everything you see in Figure 6.1 represents a real and essential part of a system or its development.

Another benefit of the comprehensive illustration in Figure 6.1 is that it reemphasizes the fact that the models have no intrinsic sequence built into them—a property we discussed in Chapter 5. Figure 6.1 shows a static structure, with bidirectional links. This structure must be populated with actual diagrams and specifications for a given project; however, it can be populated in any sequence. The plans for a given project must establish a sequence of development, but there is no a priori reason why another project should follow the same sequence.

The architecture context level includes an essential requirements model (a set consisting of a process model, a control model, and an information model), architecture flow and interconnect context diagrams (with their module and interconnect specifications), and an enhanced requirements model (comprising the same set as the essential model). All of these are directed at satisfying external stakeholder needs (both required capabilities and required constraints). At this level, there is just one architecture module (the architecture context module, representing the whole system), so the entire enhanced requirements model must be allocated to that module. The enhanced requirements model is needed to take account of the interfaces with the system's environment.

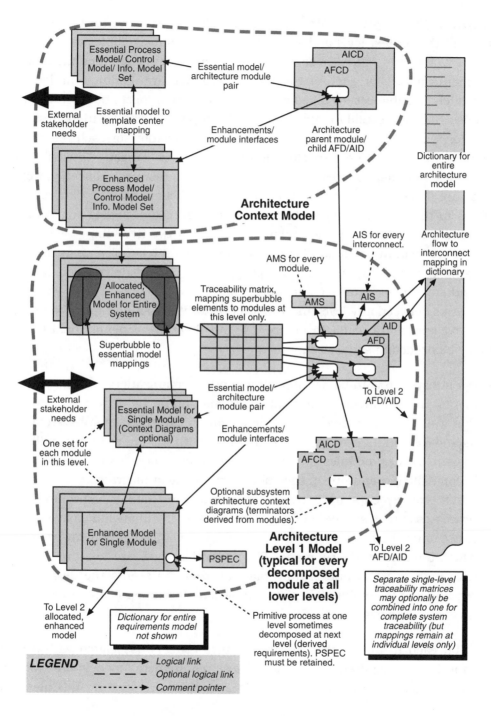

*Figure 6.1: A Roadmap for the System Specification Model.*

As shown in Figure 6.1, the Architecture Level 1 Model inherits the enhanced model from the context level and allocates it through superbubbles to modules in the Level 1 AFD and AID. These superbubble allocations produce an essential requirements model for each of the Level 1 architecture modules, and each of these models is enhanced to take account of the interconnects between the Level 1 modules. The traceability matrix reflects the superbubble allocations in a more concise form. There is an architecture module specification for each module and an architecture interconnect specification for each interconnect. The definitions, physical descriptions, sources, destinations, and interconnect allocations of the architecture flows are captured in the architecture dictionary. The data and control flows in the requirements and enhanced requirements models are defined in the requirements dictionary (not shown in Figure 6.1). Everything at this level aims to meet—within the limitations of the underlying technologies in the levels below—the required capabilities and constraints passed down from the level above and any further external stakeholder needs.

The links between any level and the level below it are similar to those between the context level and Level 1 in Figure 6.1, but there are some optional features that may be needed in some situations:

- If a subsystem is to be developed by another organization, its requirements and architecture context diagrams should be generated. In this way, the other development organization can treat its subsystem as a system in its own right, but the links with the larger system still remain. Other modules on the AFD and other processes on the DFD become the terminators on the subsystem's context diagrams.

- When requirements are derived, as described in Chapter 5, primitive processes can be sources of derived requirements. In such a case, the PSPEC must be retained as a record of the original requirement from which the derivation was made. This retention gives rise to a process with both a PSPEC and a child diagram that represents the derived requirement (a combination that was strictly forbidden in the original Structured Analysis method).

Notice that each module within an architecture layer is associated with a complete, multilayered requirements model. These requirements models are linked to each other through the traceability matrices and the architecture modules, but each one is usually just a few layers deep. This is a major benefit of using both methods, rather than the requirements method or Structured Analysis alone, as has too often been the practice in the past. Without use of the architecture model, developers tend to construct huge, monolithic requirements models that quickly become unmanageable. This unfortunate situation has been aggravated by the fact that, so far, most CASE tool developers have chosen to automate only the requirements model. When both models are used, the total volume of requirements is no less, but the requirements model is divided into bite-size chunks by the architecture model, providing a well-organized and manageable combined structure.

It is important to remember that although we have described above just the eventual content of the models, every item shown in Figure 6.1 is the result of extensive analysis, trade-off studies, and design decisions. Our description of the models is not meant to trivialize the intensive engineering work that goes into the system development process, but the models do provide a convenient and comprehensive way to capture the results of the process.

System development is a difficult and complex process, but the good news is that the Level 1 structure of Figure 6.1 applies to all levels. The basic structure remains the same whether it is for a higher system level, the hardware/software level, a level within the software, or a level within some other technology—a hydraulic subsystem, for example. Certainly, there are unique considerations in each of these different levels and technologies, but they can all be represented by this one, generic development structure.

## 6.3 EXAMPLE: A PATIENT-MONITORING SYSTEM

In the following sections, we describe the development of a hospital patient-monitoring system, using the generic development structure in Figure 6.1 as a reference and pointing out the unique issues at each level of development. The patient-monitoring system serves as a vehicle for illustrating various aspects of the system development process. Since the focus in this chapter is on the process, not on the model, we make no attempt to complete the model. To keep this illustration simple, we proceed in a top-down manner. Other sequences are illustrated in Part II.

## 6.3.1 Problem Statement: Nurses' Tasks

Nurses on a typical hospital floor are responsible for carrying out numerous tasks. In this example, the hospital administration would like to automate some of these tasks to ease the burden on the nurses, allowing them to more effectively assist doctors and perform other tasks. The administrators interviewed many nurses and came up with the following composite picture of nurses' tasks that might be automated.

The doctors provide the nurses with a list of patient's vital signs and the frequency for checking them. This information varies, depending on the patient's condition—for example, numerous vital signs at high frequency right after surgery, fewer vital signs at a lower frequency when the patient is past the critical stages of recovery. Currently, the nurse makes up a monitoring schedule based on the doctors' inputs and checks the patient's vital signs at the appropriate times. The collected data is tagged with the time and with the patient's ID, which is assigned upon entry to the hospital. The nurse stores the data in a filing cabinet after comparing the current vital-sign readings to some safe ranges prescribed by the doctor for that patient. If a vital-sign reading is out of the safe range, the nurse issues an alert, and a doctor is called for consultation to determine further action, if any. Additionally, from all the data collected, doctors may instruct the nurses to look up medical data to assist in making diagnoses, gauge the effects of certain drugs administered over certain time periods, or perform analyses of trends or fluctuation percentages between day and night readings. The nurses would prepare these reports and provide them during the doctors' rounds.

## 6.3.2 Modeling the Environment

When developing the context-level model, we must look beyond the system itself, to its environment. The boundary between the environment and the system defines the system context, and establishing it is a vital and often difficult task. Often, a customer specification does not explicitly exist, and our job is to identify the required capabilities and constraints of the customer and other stakeholders. There are many ways to do this, such as by conducting customer surveys, investigating the end environment in which the system will be used, or studying existing systems that will be enhanced by or integrated with our work. Using this information, we can establish a model of the system's environment, locate within it the area of development, ensure that the needs of the environment are addressed, and clearly identify the interfaces between the environment and the system—essentially, satisfying some of the basic system premises we established in Chapter 2.

Using the problem statement in the previous section, we can generate a model of the environment, as shown in Figure 6.2, in which nurses, doctors, and patients are identified.

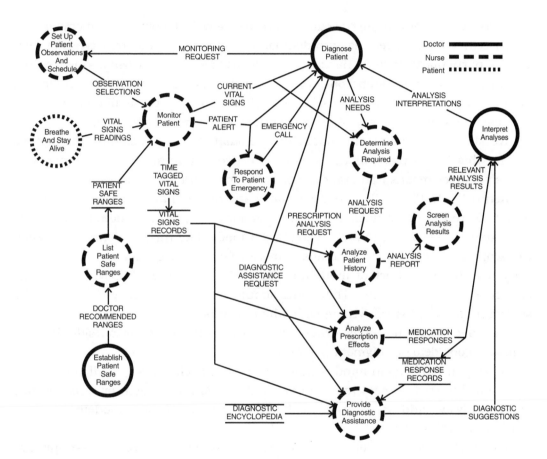

*Figure 6.2:    Environment Model for Nurse's Patient-Monitoring Task.*

Before proceeding further, we should point out some conventions that are used in all of our models throughout this book:

- Flows and stores (the information, material, and energy that the system processes) have fully capitalized names.
- Processes, modules, and interconnects (the functional and physical elements of the system) have names with all first letters capitalized.
- Other text, in PSPECs and AMSs for example, have normal capitalization.

We chose these conventions because they are easy to follow and remember and because they make it very easy to distinguish between the different types of text. This is particularly true in narrative specifications, such as PSPECs, where the capitalized flow names stand out clearly from the rest of the text. We emphasize, however, that these conventions simply reflect our own particular preferences; you may know of or discover other conventions that work just as well.

We should also point out that many automated tools—including the one we use for this book—place restrictions on the use of non-alphanumeric symbols. This sometimes means that standard punctuation cannot be followed.

Returning to Figure 6.2, we note that many details have been left out of this model: Surely, a nurse does more than this, for example. But there are two considerations to keep in mind while creating a model like this: The first is to keep the scope large enough to encompass more than the target for automation; the second is to stop short of modeling the entire universe! So, what is "large enough"? Tough question! The model should include everything we believe the system must do, plus everything with which it must directly interact. Of course, at this stage, we do not know exactly what is or is not inside or outside the system, so a good deal of judgment is required.

A key point to keep in mind is that nothing is chiseled in stone. If you draw a picture of the environment and find you did not go far enough, or went too far, you can always add or subtract model components. System modeling is very much an *iterative* process.

The environment model should be supplemented by narrative descriptions. Each process should have a task description (a candidate PSPEC), and each inter-task communication (the task's deliverables) should have a description (a candidate dictionary definition). For example, the task description for the process Set Up Patient Observations And Schedule should include the criteria for interpreting the input MONITORING REQUEST, the information that is to be transferred as OBSERVATION SELECTIONS, and the frequency with which the schedules are to be updated. Similarly, the deliverable description for PATIENT ALERT should precisely identify the content of the alert: this could range from a simple statement that an unusual condition has occurred, to a detailed description of the condition.

### 6.3.3 Building the Context-Level Model

Using the environment model, we can start creating the system specification with a context-level model like the one shown in Figure 6.1.

First, define the context of the system under consideration by selecting out of the environment model the portion that is to be included in our system, as shown in Figure 6.3.

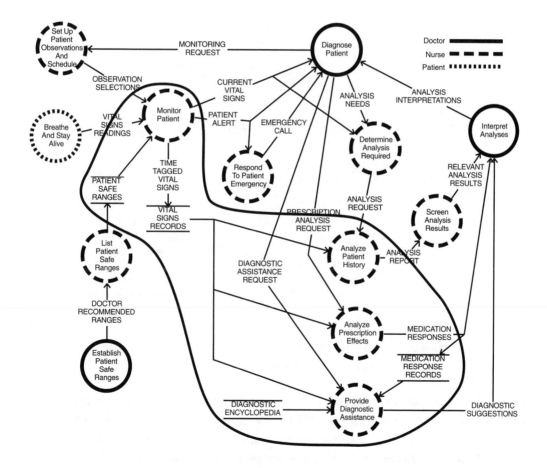

*Figure 6.3:*   *Environment Model with Superbubble for Context Definition.*

The superbubble, described in Chapter 4, shows our selection for the context of the patient-monitoring system. Superbubbles are among the features added to the methods since *Strategies for Real-Time System Specification* was written, and you will see a lot more of them in the rest of the book: They are our way of graphically showing a selection of components for allocation to a system or subsystem. Based on the superbubble selection of Figure 6.3, Figure 6.4 shows the requirements context diagram for the system. The context process is obtained by collapsing everything inside the superbubble into one process. The terminators are the physical agents that perform the processes outside the superbubble.

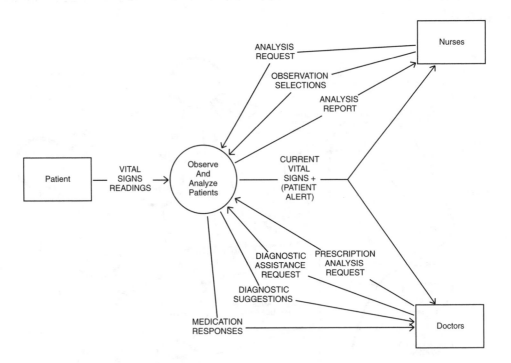

*Figure 6.4:  Requirements Context Diagram for Patient-Monitoring System.*

Notice that the context diagram in Figure 6.3 omits several communications between the doctors and nurses. Why? Because when we select a particular set of activities within a superbubble, some communications are entirely outside the superbubble and therefore outside the scope of our system. A good system engineer will be aware of these external communications and will understand any subtle influences they might have on the system, but the system design does not have to account for them.

Also, note that only nurses' activities are selected for automation. This reflects the wishes of the hospital administrators (who pay the nurses' salaries), but if the doctors had been involved in the system selection, they might have included some of their activities. Selecting the context is not always straightforward: Technical and other (mostly political) considerations all play a part.

One way to deal with these contentious issues is to go beyond the expected scope of the automated system, as illustrated in Figure 6.5. There are several reasons for doing so:

- to keep the boundary flexible until a decision is made about what should be inside and outside the context. For example, if the system is to automate some manual tasks, it is worthwhile to leave open the question of where manual functions should end and where automated functions begin, initially including within the system all tasks that could possibly be automated.
- to permanently include some manual tasks in the context of the system. Obviously, we are not going to build the operators who perform these tasks, but we do need to write operator and maintenance manuals that describe the tasks and how to perform them.
- to better understand the manual environment and to help specify the system's ability to respond to that environment.
- to better understand the interfaces between the system and the environment.

Depending on which of these reasons applies, the system context either will remain as originally specified, will be reduced to just the functions for automation, or will be expanded to include manual functions and existing automated systems. These issues are usually resolved when the architecture context diagram is developed.

Sometimes the customer or management will leap to an early—often premature—conclusion regarding the system boundary in an attempt to avoid the iterative process described above. Even if the system boundary is predetermined in this way, a little flexibility is needed to allow for some iteration. Too often, we find projects that become too rigid too early, for no obvious reason. We have even seen a very early context iteration put under formal configuration control. You know what it takes to change things then? Moses has to come down from the mountain! So, whatever you do, please don't put your system specification under configuration control too soon.

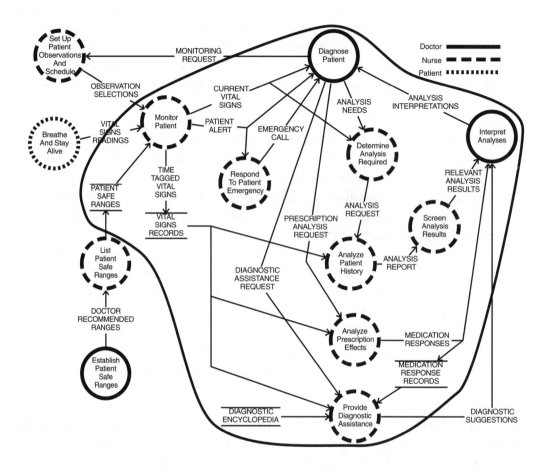

*Figure 6.5: Option for an Expanded Context.*

After the system requirements context is captured, at least tentatively, the next step is to describe the system's functionality and to define any flows not defined in the environment model. Figure 6.6 shows DFD0, which corresponds to the tasks we included within the system context. Figure 6.7 shows some dictionary entries for flows in DFD0. Figure 6.8 shows process specifications (PSPECs) for the processes in DFD0.

Note that in DFD0, one of the flows from the environment model (Figure 6.3) is missing: the flow that updated the PATIENT SAFE RANGES store. That flow will be accounted for a little later; for now, just note that we have omitted it.

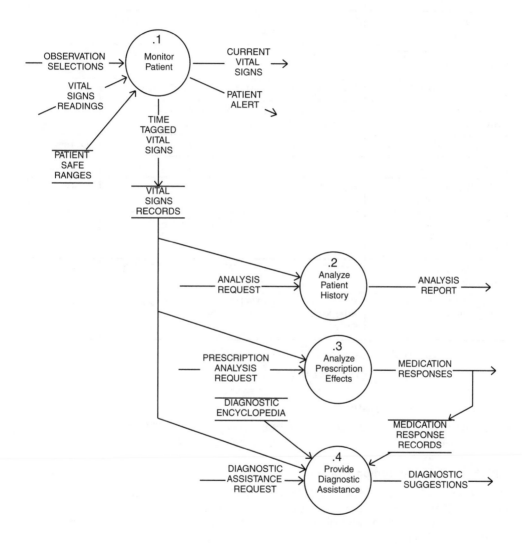

*Figure 6.6:* DFD0, *Observe And Analyze Patients.*

| Name | Composed of | Type |
|---|---|---|
| OBSERVATION SELECTIONS | PATIENT ID + PATIENT SCHEDULES + SELECTED VITAL SIGNS | Data |
| VITAL SIGNS READINGS | { BED ID + SENSOR OUTPUTS } | Data |
| PATIENT SAFE RANGES | { PATIENT ID + { VITAL SIGN LOWER LIMIT + VITAL SIGN UPPER LIMIT } } | Data |
| TIME TAGGED VITAL SIGNS | VITAL SIGNS READINGS + TIME OF READING | Data |
| PATIENT ALERT | PATIENT ID + VITAL SIGN OUT OF RANGE | Data |
| CURRENT VITAL SIGNS | SELECTED VITAL SIGNS READINGS + PATIENT ID | Data |
| ANALYSIS REQUEST | PATIENT ID + 1{ VITAL SIGNS } | Data |
| ANALYSIS REPORT | PATIENT ID + 1{ VITAL SIGNS RECORDS } | Data |
| PRESCRIPTION ANALYSIS REQUEST | PATIENT ID + { VITAL SIGNS } | Data |
| DIAGNOSTIC ASSISTANCE REQUEST | PATIENT ID + { LIKELY DIAGNOSIS } | Data |
| DIAGNOSTIC SUGGESTIONS | { DIAGNOSIS + DIAGNOSIS PROBABILITY } | Data |
| MEDICATION RESPONSES | PATIENT ID + { AVERAGE VITAL SIGN + MINIMUM VITAL SIGN + MAXIMUM VITAL SIGN } | Data |

*Figure 6.7:    Selected Requirements Dictionary Entries for Flows on DFD0.*

**PSPEC2: Analyze Patient History**

For the PATIENT ID in ANALYSIS REQUEST, select the VITAL SIGNS RECORDS that correspond to the VITAL SIGNS in ANALYSIS REQUEST and list them, to produce ANALYSIS REPORT.

**PSPEC3: Analyze Prescription Effects**

For the PATIENT ID in PRESCRIPTION ANALYSIS REQUEST, find the VITAL SIGNS in PRESCRIPTION ANALYSIS REQUEST listed since the previous request for VITAL SIGNS RECORDS. Determine the average, maximum, and minimum values for this set of VITAL SIGNS, and list the results as MEDICATION RESPONSES.

**PSPEC4: Provide Diagnostic Assistance**

Use VITAL SIGNS RECORDS and MEDICATION RESPONSE RECORDS to search DIAGNOSTIC ENCYCLOPEDIA for the most probable diagnosis or diagnoses for the patient specified in DIAGNOSTIC ASSISTANCE REQUEST. Concentrate first on any LIKELY DIAGNOSIS in DIAGNOSTIC ASSISTANCE REQUEST. Use the results to generate DIAGNOSTIC SUGGESTIONS.

*Figure 6.8: Process Specifications for Processes in DFD0.*

## 6.3.4 Technology Constraints for the Patient-Monitoring System

In addition to the required capabilities of the system, the customer has some pre-conceived ideas on the desired implementation—a common situation in system development. The hospital administrators have decided (after an evaluation of available technologies) that the nurses will enter schedules and analysis requests via a data-entry mechanism, and the alerts and analysis reports will be displayed on a screen. Additionally, the nurses will need to print the analysis reports for the doctors.

The vital signs will be measured by sensors that are mounted beside the patient's bed. These sensors must be of very high reliability, and their readings must be validated to identify malfunctions. The system must compare the sensor readings to the equipment's normal operating ranges recommended by the manufacturer. If the sensor data is out of range, the nurse is given an equipment alert, which signifies that the system could not proceed with the monitoring because the equipment had a fault. The nurse then either calls the sensor maintenance people and takes the vital-sign readings manually, or replaces the sensor. (Note that while checking the range limits provides a gross measure of sensor integrity, errors within the operating ranges will not be detected. More sophisticated techniques are needed to overcome this difficulty, such as using multiple redundant sensors. Regular sensor calibration checks would also minimize the risk.)

The doctors sometimes change the patient's safe ranges, and the equipment manufacturers, who are constantly trying to improve their equipment, may change the equipment's normal operating ranges. The system must be able to adapt to these changes.

A dilemma arises at this point in planning the system: When an alert is flashing on the central display, how will the nurse know the patient's location?

Earlier, we noted that a patient ID is associated with the patient's safe ranges, so that the alert message reports when one of the safe ranges is exceeded. However, nothing has been said so far about telling the nurse where the patient is located.

Accordingly, the hospital administrators decided that each of the bed locations will be given an ID number, and the alert will display both the patient ID and the bed location ID. As a result of this, our system must contain a bed-location-ID/patient-ID file, so that when alerts are issued, the system will access this file to find the patient's location.

This, in fact, turns out to be a good solution to the hardware design problem as well as to the patient location problem. Because the sensors will be mounted on the beds and plugged into a data link at each bed location, the data link connector location will not change with relocation of a bed or of a patient. The system will simply read the data link connector location (in much the same way that a telephone number is determined by the phone line, not by the instrument plugged into that line).

One final technology constraint: To aid in the diagnostic assistance function, a database containing a comprehensive diagnostic encyclopedia will be included in the system. This, too, will need to be updated as medical research progresses.

## 6.3.5 Creating the Enhanced Requirements Model

Taking into account all of these technological constraints, we apply the architecture template to create an enhanced requirements model, EDFD0, as shown in Figure 6.9. (Remember, we are still building the context-level model of the generic development structure shown in Figure 6.1.)

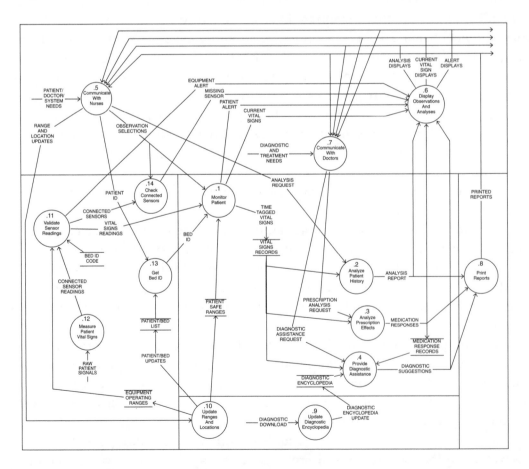

*Figure 6.9: Enhanced DFD0 Patient-Monitoring System.*

To create this enhanced model, processes are added into each of the surrounding buffers of the architecture template, as needed. We do not have a CFD0 in this model; if we did, that too would have to be enhanced. The enhancement processes are just like the processes in the essential requirements model—they can be given further detail by adding child diagrams. For example, Figure 6.10 shows the child diagram of Enhancement Process 5: Communicate With Nurses. When the appropriate level of detail is reached, the enhancement processes must be described in PSPECs. In addition, any flows added to the enhanced model must be defined in the requirements dictionary.

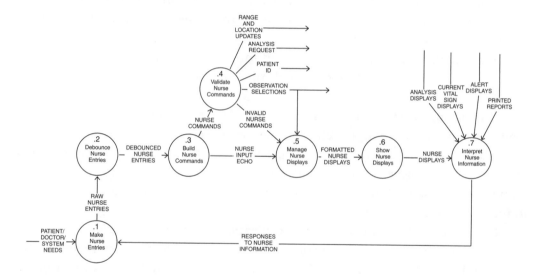

*Figure 6.10:* DFD5, *Communicate With Nurses.*

The placement of processes in the architecture template is sometimes open to question. For example, the Print Report process in Figure 6.9 is in the output processing buffer; however, since nurses and doctors will be reading the reports, shouldn't it be in the user-interface buffer? People have even suggested that the formatting of the printout information belongs in the user-interface buffer, while the actual printing process belongs in the output-processing buffer.

First, we should point out that, no matter which process is put into which buffer, the system will not self-destruct. The worst that can happen is that problems of understanding or maintenance might be created, but even then, there will be plenty of chances to reconsider the placement. In the meantime, some simple heuristics are available for the enhancement process: The user-interface buffer is intended for interfaces that use special technologies to meet human factors needs; the input and output processing buffers are intended for all other operational interfaces, especially those between automated systems; the maintenance and support buffer is intended for nonoperational interfaces and functions that keep the system running reliably.

The processes in the essential requirements model perform technology-independent transformations, while the enhanced model processes perform technology-dependent processing—they transform flows that are either received or transmitted by the system. (Some people like to think of enhancement processes as *transducer* processes.) In addition, the maintenance and support buffer sometimes contains functions that are internal to the system, such as those for self-test and redundancy management.

In the previous section, one flow used in the environment model was omitted from the technology-independent model: the flow that updated the PATIENT SAFE RANGES store. Since updating the store is a system setup or maintenance function that is highly dependent on the particular technology used, the flow was omitted from the essential model. The goal of the essential requirements model is to capture only the essence, or core processing, of the system: those functions that must be performed regardless of what technology is used. This flow has now reappeared in Figure 6.9, flowing from the Update Ranges And Locations process in the maintenance buffer.

With the exception of the timing specification, which we will defer until Part II, we have now completed the essential and enhanced system requirements models in the architecture context level of Figure 6.1. To complete the remainder of that level, all that remains is to create the architecture context diagrams using the flows from the EDFD as the architecture flows on the AFCD. The result is shown in Figure 6.11.

Notice in Figure 6.11 that apart from the new Medical Research terminator, the terminators are the same as those in the essential requirements context diagram of Figure 6.4. However, some of the flows to and from those terminators are different. This is a practical illustration of the enhancement principle described in Chapter 4, Figure 4.67, whereby the core model and the terminators remain constant, but new enhancement processes are added between them. The original, essential flows remain attached to the essential model, which is now buried inside the system module, and some new, physical flows are added between the enhancement processes and the terminators. A specific example is the RAW

PATIENT SIGNALS flow from the Patient terminator in Figure 6.11, replacing the
VITAL SIGNS READINGS flow in Figure 6.4.  In the essential model, we identified the
fact that we need PATIENT VITAL SIGNS from the patient, and we assumed for the
moment that these signals would just magically appear.  When we physicalized
the system with enhancements, we recognized that these signals must be derived
from raw, microvolt-level electrical impulses from the patient's body, requiring
special sensors and signal processing, as shown in the enhancements of Figure 6.9.

To create the AICD, we need to establish the interconnects over which the
architecture flows will travel.  In this case, as in many others, we will need to
delve into the next architectural layer before we can establish these channels.
The following sections describe how this is done.

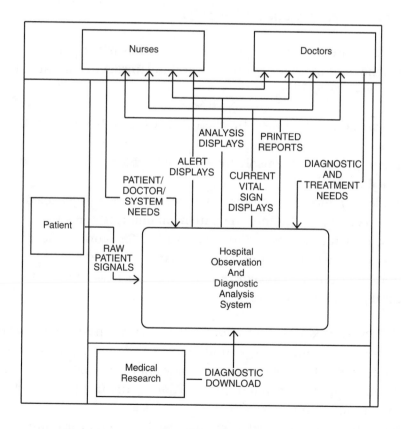

*Figure 6.11: AFCD, Patient-Monitoring System.*

## 6.3.6 Building the Architecture Level-1 Model

Since, for the sake of this illustration, we are proceeding in a top-down fashion, we are now ready to start building the Architecture Level 1 Model shown in Figure 6.1. From the context level, we can now use the enhanced requirements model and the AFCD.

We must allocate all the requirements—those that were part of the essential requirements model, plus the enhancements added using the architecture template—to real, physical entities. This is accomplished by developing the Architecture Level 1 Model, which will provide processors to perform the processes of the requirements model. At the system level, these processors may consist of hardware alone, hardware and software, or people, and they will need to be defined.

### 6.3.6.1 Architecture Model Allocation

We will assume here that the proper trade-off studies of the available technologies have been done, and that as a result, the architecture is to consist of the following system elements:

- a sensor module mounted by each bed, with probes to attach to the patients
- a patient-monitoring console by each bed, which will include the sensor validation
- portable monitoring computers that can be carried or wheeled around the wards and plugged into the patient-monitoring consoles
- a central monitoring computer and printer, for storing and retrieving all the permanent patient and system data
- doctors' and nurses' procedure manuals, which will be treated as an integral part of the system

These architecture modules will be connected wherever possible via standard data buses, but because the hospital is quite large—and running a cable to each bed would be quite difficult—a decision was made that the sensors will communicate with the main computer via radio links. That is, the computer and sensor sets will all contain radio transceivers.

Based on our new knowledge of the Level 1 system architecture, we can deduce the channels over which the main system inputs and outputs will flow and construct the architecture interconnect context diagram, as shown in Figure 6.12.

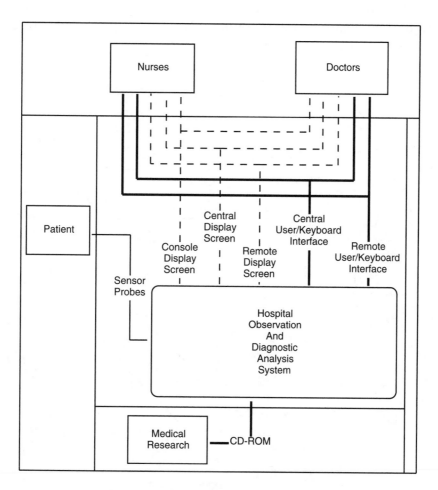

*Figure 6.12: AICD Patient-Monitoring System.*

In the course of the architecture trade-off studies, tentative requirements assignments would inevitably have been made—because, of course, the architecture is largely based upon the requirements—but now that the architecture modules and channels have been established, these assignments can be firmed up. We accomplish this by forming superbubbles on the enhanced requirements model, as illustrated in Figure 6.13. Each superbubble represents a module (a processor) in the architecture. In principle, there are no restrictions on the manner in which the requirements may be allocated to the architecture; while good black-box design will tend toward a one-to-one mapping of processes to modules, there are often sound, practical reasons for having a more complex mapping. Regardless of the simplicity or complexity of the mapping, we need to capture the traceability between the two models, as we describe later in the chapter.

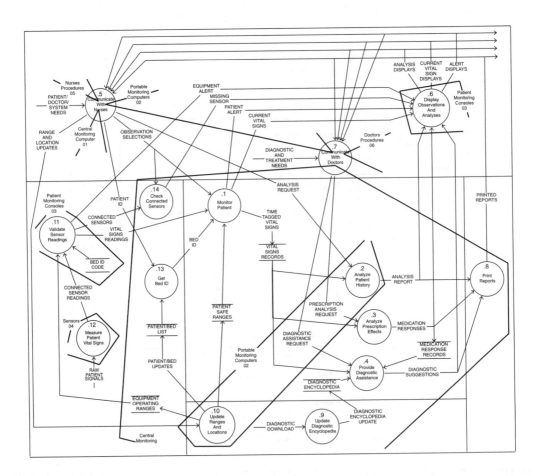

*Figure 6.13: Enhanced DFD0 with Allocation Superbubbles.*

In Figure 6.13, one of the processes, Communicate With Nurses, has been split between three architecture modules. Since allocations must be explicit, we must go down to the child diagram (and lower, if necessary) to make them explicit. Figure 6.14 shows the decomposition of the split process and the superbubble allocation of its child processes to architecture modules.

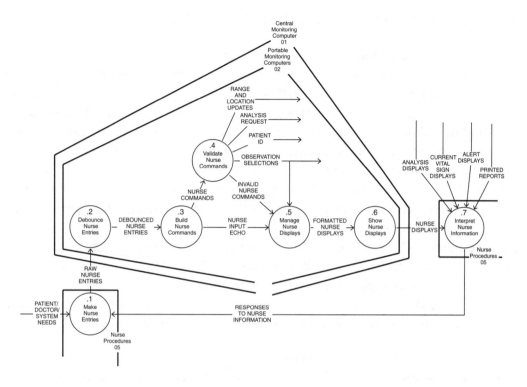

*Figure 6.14:  DFD5, Communicate With Nurses, with Super-*
*bubbles for Allocation.*

The superbubbles used in the child diagram must correspond to those used to split the parent process.  Accordingly, processes that are *not* split do not have superbubbles in their child diagrams.

Notice that in Figures 6.13 and 6.14, some processes are allocated to more than one architecture module.  For example, Processes 2, 10, and 5.2 through 5.6 are allocated to both the central monitoring computer and the portable monitoring computer.  This allocation is realized by surrounding one or more processes (or stores or CSPECs) with more than one superbubble.  Furthermore, in this particular system, some of the architecture modules are replicated on the architecture diagrams—namely, the sensors (one set per bed), the patient-monitoring consoles (one per bed), and the portable monitoring computers (any number).  Although only one superbubble is shown for each of these replicated modules, the processes enclosed within the superbubble are replicated the same number of times as their modules.

## 6.3.7 Interconnects and Further Enhancements

We have now established a set of architecture modules, and we have allocated requirements from the enhanced system-level requirements model to these modules. It is tempting to start constructing the Level 1 architecture flow diagram by simply connecting the flows that cross the superbubble boundaries to their corresponding modules. However, before making these connections, further enhancements are required: Every architecture module requires its own enhanced requirements model, as shown in Figure 6.1. The newly created architecture modules have physical interconnects between them, and some of the flows may need to be enhanced for compatibility with these interconnects. So, we must map the allocated requirements to each module and use the architecture template to enhance them. Wherever necessary, a modified version of the flows crossing the superbubble boundaries is created, and these modified flows appear on the AFD in place of the flows crossing the superbubble boundaries.

To review, the steps needed to complete the top system-level model, with much concurrency and/or iteration between them, are as follows:

- Establish the Level 1 architecture modules.
- Take the enhanced requirements from the context level and use superbubbles to allocate them to the architecture modules.
- Construct the architecture interconnect diagram to establish the channels between modules.
- Enhance the requirements allocated to each Level 1 module.
- Construct the architecture flow diagram, using the flows from the enhanced requirements models for each module.
- Construct the Level 1 traceability matrix from the allocated, enhanced model.

These activities are intimately dependent on each other, and they will normally be carried out concurrently, with numerous intermediate models before a firm model is built. Even the firm model will be a compromise between many conflicting factors, and will be open to revision.

## 6.3.8 Completing the Architecture

We can now complete the architecture flow diagrams (AFD) and architecture inter-connect diagrams (AID) of the Level 1 model. Figures 6.15 and 6.16 show AFD0 and AID0, respectively, for the patient-monitoring system. The AFD shows the system processors and the information (and the material and energy, in the general case) that flows between them. The AID shows the same system processors, but with channels along which the architecture flows travel. These channels are actual, physical interconnections between the modules and the outside world. The interconnect channels can be electrical, mechanical, optical, radio, hydraulic, or any other type of linkage mechanism.

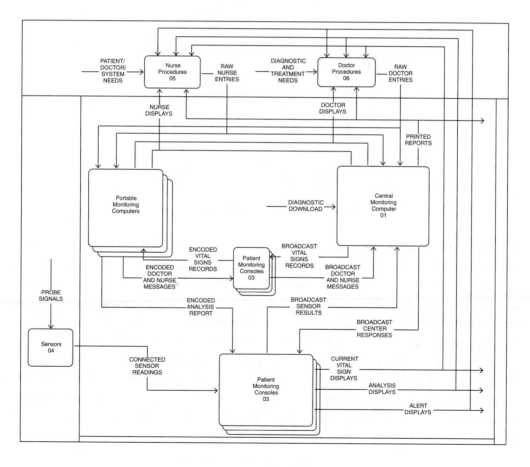

*Figure 6.15: AFD0, Patient-Monitoring System.*

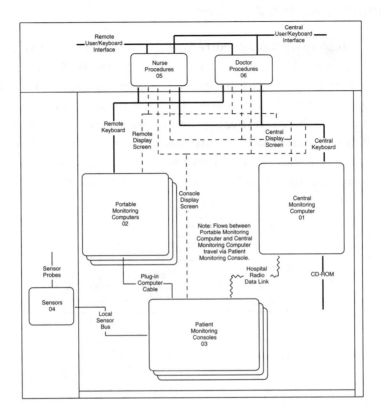

*Figure 6.16: AID0, Patient-Monitoring System.*

The architecture model is supported by written specifications. Every processor in the AFD has a specification (an AMS) that describes the processor and any reasons for its particular requirements allocations. Every interconnect on the AID has a specification (an AIS) that defines its characteristics: for example, the transmission protocol of a radio link between two processors. You may have noticed that we have been calling the entities on an AFD *processors*, and those on a DFD, *processes*. This terminology emphasizes the complementary roles of the two models; the usual term for an AFD processor is *architecture module*, or simply, *module*.

Although superbubbles provide a good graphical view of the allocation of requirements to architecture modules, a more concise representation is provided by a traceability matrix, as shown in Figure 6.17.

| Requirements Component | Architecture Component | | | | | |
|---|---|---|---|---|---|---|
| | Central Monitoring Computer 01 | Portable Monitoring Computers 02 | Patient Monitoring Consoles 03 | Sensors 04 | Nurse Procedures 05 | Doctor Procedures 06 |
| Make Nurse Entries 5.1 | | | | | X | |
| Interpret Nurse Information 5.7 | | | | | X | |
| Debounce Nurse Entries 5.2 | 6.8.1 | 6.8.2 | | | | |
| Build Nurse Commands 5.3 | 6.8.3 | 6.8.4 | | | | |
| Validate Nurse Commands 5.4 | 6.8.5 | 6.8.6 | | | | |
| Manage Nurse Displays 5.5 | 6.8.7 | 6.8.8 | | | | |
| Show Nurse Displays 5.6 | 6.8.9 | 6.8.10 | | | | |
| Build Doctor Entries 7.3 | 6.8.11 | 6.8.12 | | | | |
| Validate Doctor Entries 7.4 | 6.8.13 | 6.8.14 | | | | |
| Manage Doctor Displays 7.5 | 6.8.15 | 6.8.16 | | | | |
| Show Doctor Displays 7.6 | 6.8.17 | 6.8.18 | | | | |
| Debounce Doctor Entries 7.2 | 6.8.19 | 6.8.20 | | | | |
| Analyze Patient History 2 | X | X | | | | |
| Update Ranges And Locations 10 | X | X | | | | |
| Measure Patient Vital Signs 12 | | | | X | | |
| Display Observations And Analyses 6 | | | X | | | |
| Validate Sensor Readings 11 | | | X | | | |

*Figure 6.17: Traceability Matrix for the Patient-Monitoring System (Continued).*

| Requirements Component | Architecture Component | | | | | |
|---|---|---|---|---|---|---|
| | Central Monitoring Computer 01 | Portable Monitoring Computers 02 | Patient Monitoring Consoles 03 | Sensors 04 | Nurse Procedures 05 | Doctor Procedures 06 |
| BED ID CODE | | | X | | | |
| Make Doctor Entries 7.1 | | | | | | X |
| Interpret Doctor Information 7.7 | | | | | | X |
| Monitor Patient 1 | X | | | | | |
| Analyze Prescription Effects 3 | X | | | | | |
| Provide Diagnostic Assistance 4 | X | | | | | |
| VITAL SIGNS RECORDS | X | | | | | |
| Get Bed ID 13 | X | | | | | |
| EQUIPMENT OPERATING RANGES | X | | | | | |
| PATIENT SAFE RANGES | X | | | | | |
| MEDICATION RESPONSE RECORDS | X | | | | | |
| DIAGNOSTIC ENCYCLOPEDIA | X | | | | | |
| Print Reports 8 | X | | | | | |
| Update Diagnostic Encyclopedia 9 | X | | | | | |
| PATIENT/BED LIST | X | | | | | |
| Check Connected Sensors 14 | X | | | | | |

*Figure 6.17: Traceability Matrix for the Patient-Monitoring System.*

In this matrix, the vertical axis lists the requirements from the enhanced requirements model, and the horizontal axis lists the modules from the Level 1 AFD. In this particular case, we chose to skip the control and information models and to include only the process model components from the requirements model: processes, process specifications, and stores. Otherwise, had we included the control and information models, the matrix would have shown control specifications along the vertical axis, and many of the entities and attributes would have been identified as flows and defined in the requirements dictionary.

When a process is allocated to a column of the traceability matrix (or, equivalently, enclosed within a superbubble on an EDFD), all the details underlying that process go along with it, right down to the process specifications. Allocating a process, therefore, is a convenient way to allocate many process specifications.

When a process is split between architecture modules, its child processes are shown on the traceability matrix, not the process itself. For example, in this particular case, Process 5 from EDFD0 was split between three processors. Hence, the allocation of Process 5 was made using its child processes, 5.1 through 5.7, which are specifically shown in the traceability matrix.

Finally, just as the allocation of processes, process specifications, and stores has been recorded, the allocation of flows also needs to be recorded. As described in Chapter 4, this is done in the architecture dictionary, which includes all the information from the requirements dictionary, with additional information on the physical nature of the flows and on their allocation.

## 6.3.9 Developing the Lower-Level Models

At this stage in the architecture model development, we have defined just one level of the system's physical configuration and allocated the requirements from the enhanced requirements model. However, like the requirements model, the architecture model consists of multiple levels. In the requirements model, the levels are conceptual and can be repartitioned to create fewer or more of them, but in the architecture model, each module in a given level must correspond to a real, physical entity within the system. This distinction relates to the categorization of layered structures, described in Chapter 3. The requirements model is an abstraction/detailing structure, and the architecture model is an aggregation/decomposition structure.

Each architecture module's requirements can be determined either by inspecting the traceability matrix or by physically cutting out each superbubble of the enhanced requirements model, and pasting it onto a data flow diagram for the corresponding architecture module. Again, had we specified the control and information models, the requirements allocated to each module would have included components from those models, too.

The requirements allocated to the portable monitoring computers are illustrated in Figure 6.18. As you may recall, the superbubble for this particular module encloses processes from EDFD0 (Figure 6.13), DFD5 (Figure 6.14), and DFD7 (not presented here, but implicit from Figure 6.13, because Process 7 is split by multiple superbubbles). Not only do the requirements for this module come from three different places, they are also reorganized in the new diagram: The processes from DFD5 and from DFD7 are abstracted into two new processes, numbered .20 and .30 respectively. (The child diagram of Process .20 is identical to the processes enclosed in the two superimposed superbubbles in Figure 6.14.) This merging of multiple levels into a single DFD and any reorganization of a module's DFD can lead to numbering conflicts, where process numbers have the same last digit or different numbers of digits. If a conflict arises, processes can be renumbered when they are mapped to an architecture module. The renumbering conforms with the numbering of the architecture modules, which can be similar to that of the requirements model. In this case, the context module is numbered 0, the modules in its child AFD are numbered 01, 02, 03, and so on. Accordingly, the DFD for Module 01 is numbered 01, and its processes are numbered .1, .2, and so on. Although these numbers duplicate those in the original requirements model, the DFD and process *names* serve as their unique identifiers. Furthermore, with careful arrangement of the diagrams in a specification tool, there will be little chance for confusion.

The processes' original numbers can be found by referring to the traceability matrix. Remember, there were numbers for the central monitoring computer and the portable monitoring computer in their columns of the matrix shown in Figure 6.17. The columns list the newly assigned numbers, while the vertical axis lists the enhanced requirements model components and the original numbers. This arrangement allows complete forward and backward traceability.

Using the enhanced requirements for a module, we can proceed with the process of architecting that module by continuing the trade-off process used with the whole system architecture. This will result in a set of sub-modules and interconnects for each subsystem module. Then we can use superbubbles (one for each sub-module) to allocate the EDFDs to the sub-modules.

The process of architecting, allocating, and enhancing is repeated in this way, module by module; each string of modules is terminated when the appropriate level of detail is reached; a traceability matrix is created for each module, so that there is traceability throughout the entire structure. Note that different strings of modules can terminate at different levels: A typical system will contain strings of two, three, four, and five levels, depending on the nature of the various parts of the system. It is unusual to create strings of more than five levels—at that point, the resulting modules are sufficiently detailed for final design and implementation by the detailed designers. Identifying the proper level of detail is something of a judgment call, requiring the involvement of people with detailed knowledge of the related disciplines. Often, the hand-off point is reached when the module contains only one technology, but this is by no means the only criterion.

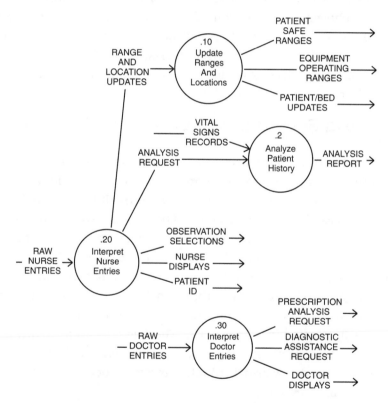

*Figure 6.18:* DFD *for Requirements Allocated to the Portable Monitoring Computers.*

Software is almost always treated separately from the other technologies, so that a complete software subsystem can be handed off, but in some cases, it may be appropriate to hand off multiple-technology modules if they are sufficiently detailed. For example, a hydraulic subsystem with electromechanical valves employs two distinct disciplines, but since they are intimately interconnected and only exist to support each other, it would not make sense to break them apart. The detailed design would be carried out by a team of hydraulics and electro-mechanical engineers.

Conversely, even a single-discipline module may require systems work if the module is complex. This is often the case with software systems, since software encompasses more and more of the functionality of modern systems. The software structure can have a profound influence on the overall system structure. For example, the number of microprocessors in a system is intimately linked with the load the software will place on those processors; once a multiprocessor configuration has been chosen, the question of how to allocate the software to those processors—and whether the allocation will be static or dynamic—is not just a hardware or software issue, but a true systems issue.

The following sections discuss issues that are unique to certain system levels, and how these issues affect the models.

## 6.4 CONFIGURING SOFTWARE AND COMPUTER HARDWARE

In a system that includes software, one or more architecture modules must include some form of computer hardware and software. The child model of such a module consists of separate hardware and software modules and their interfaces. This closely resembles the system decomposition process described earlier, but what makes the partitioning of hardware and software different is that software does not have a real, physical form like other technologies. The only structure that software has is the one we give it, not anything that exists in nature. Software is more like an amorphous blob that can be stuffed inside one hardware module, or spread among several, or divided and then stuffed inside one or spread among several, as illustrated in Figure 6.19. There is one simple truth underlying this rather complicated situation: Regardless of its form, software always communicates with the outside world through hardware, because operational software only exists within hardware.

The above statements may seem like mere truisms, but they have profound implications on the characteristics and development of software. All other technologies are naturally constrained by the laws of physics; their practitioners learn very early not to violate those laws, because the results simply will not work. Software, on the other hand, is not constrained by the laws of physics, and this is both good news and bad news. The good news is that it gives us the freedom to do just about anything we want; the bad news is that it gives us the freedom to do just about anything we want! An example of the good news is that we can make digital filters with powerful characteristics that are physically impossible with analog filters. An example of the bad news is that we can make software that runs just fine—that is, without crashing—but still attempts to make the hardware it is controlling go beyond its physical operating range. In the worst case, the results can be disastrous—a plane crash, for example. Adding to the hazards of software is the fact that most of the complexity of today's increasingly complex systems resides in software. So, here we have a technology that includes no natural physically-imposed constraints, yet in this technology, we have the greatest need for the discipline that physical constraints impose. No wonder, then, that software development continues to be so problematic.

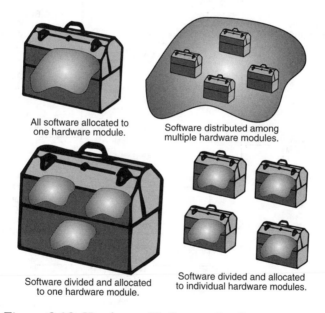

All software allocated to
one hardware module.

Software distributed among
multiple hardware modules.

Software divided and allocated
to one hardware module.

Software divided and allocated
to individual hardware modules.

*Figure 6.19: Hardware/Software Configurations.*

Because of the abstract nature of software, models are the *only* way to represent it. Software methods do nothing more than create models. Software prototypes— or rapid prototypes, one of the software silver bullets of the late 1980's—are only models, though fairly close to the "real" end product.

The simplest configuration is a hardware/software module that has just one processor and one software subsystem. This hardware/software module simply decomposes into a two-module architecture. The patient-monitoring computer module in the patient-monitoring system may decompose this way, as illustrated in the AFD and AID of Figures 6.20 and 6.21, respectively. As these figures show, all links with the world outside the computer pass through the computer hardware, and the computer hardware and software link through channels, such as registers, interrupts, and DMAs (direct memory access).

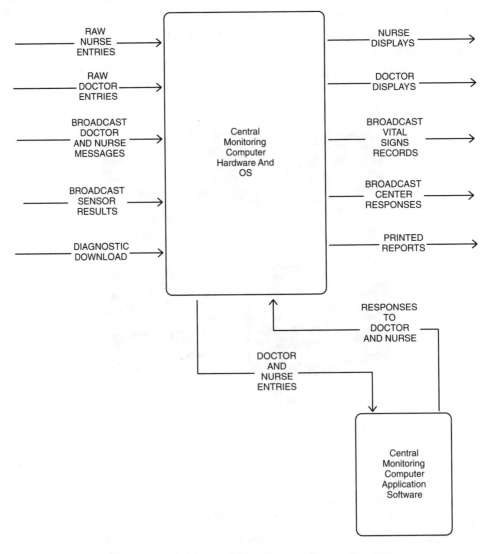

*Figure 6.20: Central Monitoring Computer AFD.*

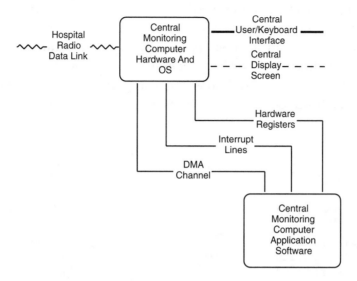

*Figure 6.21: Central Monitoring Computer AID.*

Even with the simple one-to-one hardware/software configuration, there are significant variations depending on whether the computer hardware is custom or off-the-shelf. The hardware/software interfaces might be very different for these two possibilities, but in either case, they would be specified in architecture interconnect specifications.

There are two configurations that are more complex than the single-module hardware/software form: the single-hardware/multiple-software and the multiple-hardware/single-software configurations, as seen in Figure 6.19.

## 6.4.1 Single-Hardware/Multiple-Software Configuration

The single-hardware/multiple-software configuration can occur if the software for a system is very large and naturally divides into more than one major function. Such a hardware/software module can be decomposed into a configuration with one (very powerful) processor hardware module and several software modules, as illustrated in the AFD and AID of Figures 6.22 and 6.23, respectively.

In this configuration, the links with the outside environment pass through the computer hardware, as usual, and the links between the computer hardware and software retain the same form as before. Now, however, links may exist between the separate software modules in the form of architecture flows. The means by which these flows pass can be represented as architecture interconnects between the software modules. Often, however, these interconnects are not explicitly represented, because they are an intrinsic part of the whole software package. For example, software modules running on a common processor share data in common memory locations, so we could show the computer memory as the channel between software modules, but we generally do not.

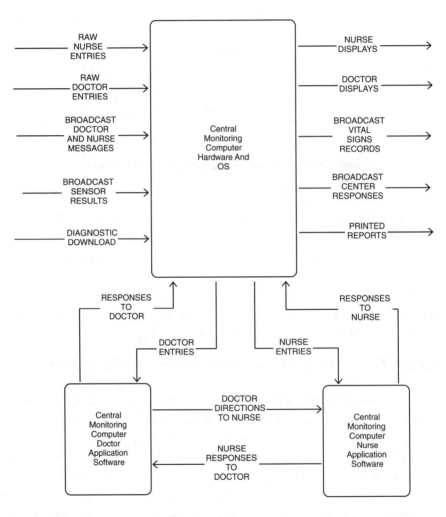

*Figure 6.22: Single-Hardware/Multiple-Software Module Configuration AFD.*

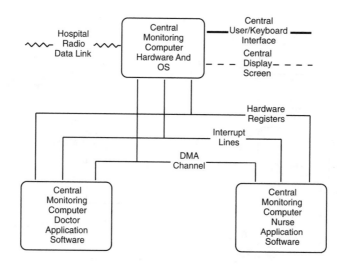

*Figure 6.23: Single-Hardware/Multiple-Software Module Configuration* AID.

## 6.4.2 Multiple-Hardware/Single-Software Configuration

The multiple-hardware/single-software configuration has one software subsystem running on several processors. This is common in large software systems in which multiple concurrent processors are used—either of the same or of different types—instead of a single, very powerful processor. There are two possible scenarios for this configuration: Either the software subsystem is divided and each part is allocated to a specific processor, or the subparts are dynamically allocated to the processors at run time. These scenarios could also be used in combination—some of the software subdivided, and some dynamically allocated.

The first of these scenarios can be viewed as multiple cases of the single-hardware/single-software configuration. A hardware/software module can be decomposed one more time before the hardware and software are separated, or all the hardware and software modules can be separated at once, as illustrated in Figure 6.24.

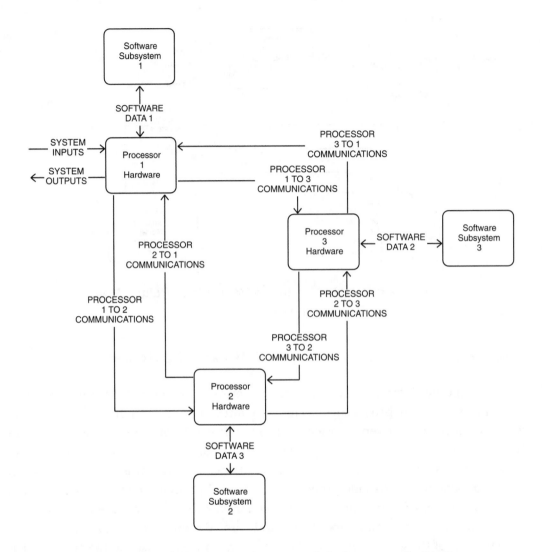

*Figure 6.24: Multiple Hardware and Software with Static Allocation.*

The second scenario is trickier, as shown in Figure 6.25. To enhance the requirements for this configuration, we will need to manage the dynamic allocation with a new process in the maintenance and support region of the template, as illustrated in Figure 6.26. This process will define the allocation algorithm to be used. In addition, we must modify the form of the traceability matrix, as illustrated in Figure 6.27. The matrix allocates all of the essential software to all of the hardware modules, and it references the dynamic allocation process that was added during enhancement.

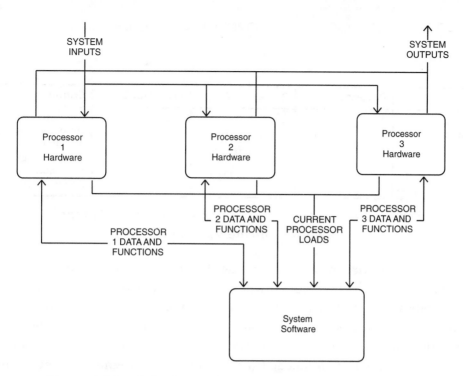

Figure 6.25: *Multiple-Hardware/Distributed-Software with Dynamic Allocation.*

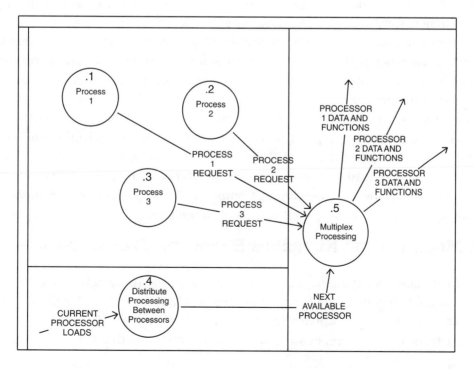

Figure 6.26: *Software Enhancements for Single-Hardware/ Multiple-Software with Dynamic Allocation.*

| | Processor 1 | Processor 2 | Processor 3 | Comments |
|---|---|---|---|---|
| Processes 1, 2, 3 | X | X | X | Allocated at run time by Process 4, "Distribute Processing Between Processors." |

*Figure 6.27: Traceability Matrix for Single-Hardware/ Multiple-Software with Dynamic Allocation.*

The dynamic allocation process in the second scenario is not the only special enhancement that may be required when hardware and software are partitioned. Support software may be required for the operational software to which system-level functions are assigned. Often, an operating system (OS) is needed to perform the dynamic allocation function and other software management functions. If a custom-designed OS is needed (as it often is with embedded systems), it should be specifically shown as a process in the maintenance and support region of the template. If a standard, off-the-shelf hardware and software platform is chosen, however, it should be treated as a "black box" reusable module; its internal components, such as the OS, should not be identified separately in the model.

In summary, hardware/software partitioning follows essentially the same procedure as any other partitioning, except for some special considerations regarding software's abstract nature. Once again, we emphasize that the requirements and architecture methods produce models that capture merely the *results* of the partitioning process. The decisions required by the hardware/software partitioning process are extremely complex: whether to use single or multiple processors, which processors should be used, how to allocate the software to them, how to assess the software load under different circumstances, and many others. In fact, at the time of writing, Engineering of Computer-Based Systems is the name and sole topic of a major, ongoing IEEE technical committee.

## 6.5 MODELING THE NUMEROUS HARDWARE TECHNOLOGIES

One of the most satisfying aspects of working with the architecture and requirements methods has been the frequent challenge of applying them for the first time to another technology or application and achieving success. There are so many different types of hardware, of such varied characteristics, that it would be utterly impossible to treat each of them in detail here. Instead, in this section, we describe a few typical cases—electrical, electronic, electromechanical, mechanical, hydraulic and pneumatic, optical, chemical, manufacturing, mixed technologies, and detailed hardware design—to show how the methods apply to the chosen cases and to give guidelines on applying them to other cases.

All of the technologies listed below are mature, and their practitioners have developed their own notations, models, and tools over the years. We do not attempt here to illustrate all of those techniques, but note that the engineering block diagram—in which the architecture method is firmly rooted—is used almost universally in engineering technologies. It is, therefore, usually quite straightforward to adapt the architecture method or a technology-specific method—or both—to make them fully compatible with each other.

There is a tendency these days, when hardware is mentioned, to think only of computer hardware. The following paragraphs remind us that this is far from the only type of hardware, and that for systems to work in the real world, many types will always be needed.

## 6.5.1 Electrical

Electrical hardware includes lighting, electrical heating, batteries, power supplies, power distribution, ignition systems, and more.

With the major exception of the national power generation and distribution system itself, purely electrical systems are uncommon. Electrical systems are usually part of electronic or electromechanical systems, in which they provide the primary power source. As such, electrical power generation and distribution within a system is very much an implementation-specific function, usually added as an enhancement once the detailed system architecture is chosen. At that point, power sources and power distribution around the system can become a critical design issue. An important variation on the architecture method is to use interconnects on architecture interconnect diagrams for specifying power and ground distribution. The interconnect specifications then describe in great detail how the distributions should be configured. These particular interconnects are unique in that they have no flows allocated to them. Figure 6.28 shows an AFD and its AID with power and ground distribution.

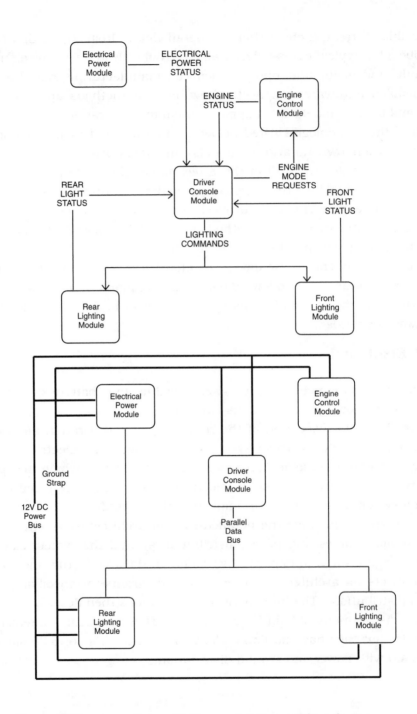

*Figure 6.28: AFD and AID with Power and Ground Distribution.*

## 6.5.2 Electronic

Electronic hardware is used in telephony, radio, television, navigation, communication, and more. This is a subset of electrical systems and a superset of computer systems (which, these days, are almost always contained in electronic systems).

In modeling electronic systems, the processes in the requirements model become the functions allocated to the amplifiers, mixers, sensors, transmitters, receivers, and other active electronic components. Architecture modules represent individual components or groups (assemblies) of them. The flows become electronic signals of various kinds, passing between the components. The architecture interconnects are the wires, cables, printed circuit conductors, electromagnetic waves, and other media over which the signals pass.

## 6.5.3 Electromechanical

Electromechanical hardware includes electrically driven mechanical transports, electric motors and generators, domestic appliances, electric vehicles, relays, solenoid actuated valves, and more.

The typical electromechanical device will have an electrical signal as an input and some kind of mechanical motion as an output (although, in the case of a generator, it works the opposite way). The electrical input appears as the usual flow, with wires, cables, or buses for interconnects. The electromechanical device itself will be a module with the allocated function of, say, pumping water into a dishwasher. The output, in this particular example, will be a water flow traveling through a plastic hose interconnect. An illustration of this is shown in Figure 6.29.

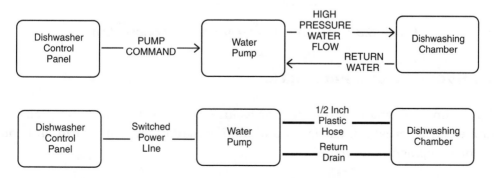

*Figure 6.29: AFD and AID of an Electromechanical Device.*

## 6.5.4 Mechanical

Mechanical hardware includes engines, transmissions, conveyors, bicycles, paper feed mechanisms, and more.

A good example of a mechanical system is the automobile (of course, it is also a good example of electrical and, these days, electronic systems). Figure 6.30 shows a model of an automobile's accelerator pedal, power unit, transmission, and wheels and suspension.

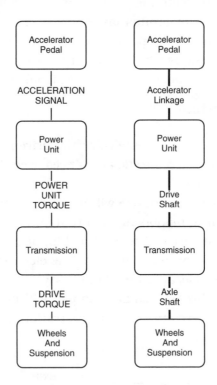

*Figure 6.30: AFD and AID of a Mechanical Subsystem.*

## 6.5.5 Hydraulic and Pneumatic

Hydraulic and pneumatic hardware devices include brake actuators, some aircraft control surface actuators, car jacks and lifts, actuators for heavy farm and construction equipment, and more.

Hydraulic and pneumatic devices generally provide actuation and linkage between mechanical devices, though they can be used in much more sophisticated ways, as illustrated in the Part II case study of the groundwater analysis system and in the real system from which the case study was derived. Requirements that call for hydraulic linkages typically require a force or motion to be transferred between two locations. A data flow in the requirements model would represent the force or motion; an architecture flow would specify that the same force or motion is a hydraulic flow; the architecture interconnect would show a hydraulic tube with an AIS that defines the tube's material, dimensions, and pressure rating.

## 6.5.6 Optical

Optical devices include fiber-optic data links, laser speed detectors, spectral and scatter detectors in medical diagnostic equipment, and more.

With the advent of lasers, light-emitting diodes, and optical fibers, optical devices are playing an increasingly important role in modern systems. They are commonly used as data links in communication systems, and there is promising research on optical computing. For example, the groundwater analysis system in Part II includes a light source that is projected through a chemical sample, and the diffraction and scatter are analyzed to determine the sample's content.

## 6.5.7 Chemical

Chemical devices include automatic chemical analysis systems, chemical manufacturing plants, and more.

When chemicals and chemical processes are used in a system, they usually represent the central purpose of the system rather than a means to some other end. Once more, the groundwater analysis system in Part II provides a fine example of chemicals and a chemical process in a system (we chose that system for this book because of its diversity of technologies). There, the groundwater passes through hydraulic tubes to containers where it is mixed with chemical reagents. The mixture is heated and agitated, and then light is transmitted through it for analysis. This system provides a rich collection of different types of processes, flows, modules, and interconnects, and it illustrates how the methods support such diversity.

## 6.5.8 Manufacturing

Manufacturing systems include automobile assembly lines, food processing plants, integrated-circuit production lines, and more.

Manufacturing processes lend themselves well to the application of the architecture and requirements methods. We have stressed throughout the book that data and architecture flows represent information, material, or energy, and there is no better example of materials processing than manufacturing. Raw materials are received as inputs; processes in the requirements model describe what must be done to them; the architecture modules define how it will be done; architecture interconnects show the mechanisms by which the materials are passed from one processing module to another; and the final products appear as requirements and architecture flows leaving the system. An illustration of the AFD and AID for a typical manufacturing process appears in Figure 6.31.

## 6.5.9 Detailed Hardware Design

Detailed design techniques for the above technologies are mature disciplines with established methods and tools. The use of sophisticated computer-aided engineering (CAE) tools is almost universal, and nothing in the methods described in this book supersedes them. Instead, the methods can be used up to the point of detailed design, when technology-specific methods and tools take over. The link between the two approaches is provided by cross-references that link the architecture module and interconnect specifications with the design drawings and CAE models. In effect, with these links, the detailed design drawings and CAE models become part of the AMSs and AISs at the lowest architecture levels.

It is our hope and intention that tools that support the architecture and requirements methods will eventually be interfaced or integrated with CAE tools so that both the techniques and the tools will work together seamlessly.

## 6.5.10 Mixed Technologies

The preceding examples have treated each technology separately, but almost all systems involve multiple technologies that must work together smoothly if the system is to succeed in its overall mission. In fact, the technologies described can be used together in any combination, as the groundwater analysis system in Part II illustrates.

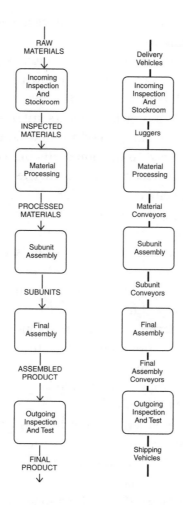

*Figure 6.31: A Manufacturing Process.*

By now, it should be evident that you may need to adapt the architecture and requirements methods further, perhaps in unforeseen ways, as you apply them to future systems. The good news is that they have proven adaptable to every situation we have encountered in industry so far.

## 6.6 COMPUTER HARDWARE LAYERS

Having pointed out the many important types of hardware besides computer hardware, it is now time to acknowledge that computer hardware plays a huge role in virtually all modern systems. Indeed, most modern systems would not be possible without it. One might think that computer hardware models would therefore be a major part of the overall system models, but often this is not the case. Computer hardware is often what is known in military jargon as COTS (commercial off-the-shelf) hardware, and is therefore treated like any other reusable module—as a black box, with only its interfaces and overall function known. Commercially available computers are now so powerful and comprehensive that there is usually no need to develop a custom computer. In these cases, the computer hardware will decompose no further than the level shown in Figure 6.20. The AMS will specify the particular computer chosen, why it was preferred over other choices, why it is expected to meet the required performance, and then simply reference the manufacturer's data for further details.

If a custom digital-processing configuration *is* chosen, the black box is opened, and the configuration is specified with one or more additional layers below what is shown in Figure 6.20. There are numerous configurations available, and it is particularly important to recognize that not all digital processing has to involve software. Hardware technologies include ASICs (application-specific integrated circuits), FPGAs (field programmable gate arrays), and DSPs (digital signal processors) that can be customized for frequent, computationally-intensive tasks with much higher throughput than would be achieved using a software-programmed general purpose processor.

In Figure 6.32, we use the patient-monitoring system as an example of a typical computer hardware configuration. Here, CAE tools would be used for further detailed design, as they would in models of the other types of hardware, usually at the next level below the one depicted in Figure 6.32. For detailed integrated-circuit design, VHDL—a hardware design language in widespread use and very similar to a software language—is often used. VHDL stands for VHSIC Hardware Description Language; VHSIC stands for Very High-Speed Integrated Circuit [Navabi 93].

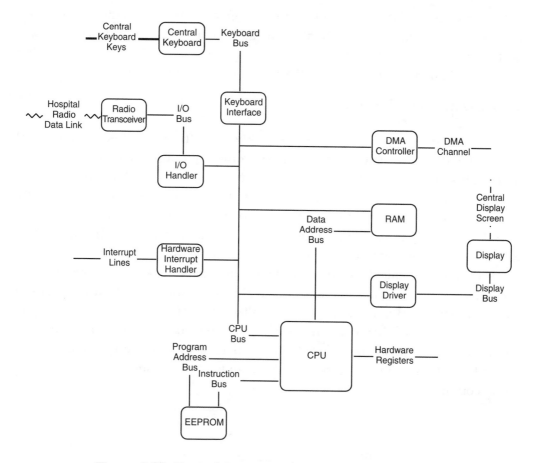

*Figure 6.32: Typical Computer Hardware Configuration.*

## 6.7 SOFTWARE LAYERS

Software is a powerful tool for solving almost any problem that can be digitized. The trouble is, no one has quite figured out how to use it. So far, every time we find a good way to handle systems of the current complexity, computer hardware becomes an order of magnitude more powerful and we have to start all over again.

As we mentioned earlier, software's lack of physical structure allows us to give it any structure we want. Whether or not a given software structure is good—if such a quality can be defined—we do have extraordinary flexibility, and if we so choose, software can adopt the layered structure of the architecture method.

Over the years, several generations of software design methods have been developed, each taking a slightly different approach. Before we describe how to use the architecture model for software design (or for the transition to modern software design), we review some of the more popular approaches below.

### 6.7.1 Structured Design

Structured Design (SD) has become the workhorse software method. It was developed in the 1970's by Edward Yourdon and others [Yourdon 75; Page-Jones 88], and remains one of the most widely used software-specific method. A factor contributing to its success is its widespread automation by various CASE tools. The central construct of SD is the structure chart, illustrated in Figure 6.33. Unlike an architecture flow diagram, which represents a network, a structure chart forms a hierarchy—a controlling/controlled structure, as discussed in Chapter 3. The rectangles are called *modules,* although *functions* might be the better name for them. Like architecture modules, SD modules contain a specification that provides a rationale and a justification, but unlike architecture modules, they do not decompose: Instead, they contain the actual source code. SD modules call other modules below them, as shown by the invocation vectors, and they exchange data and control information with modules above and below, as shown by the data and control couples.

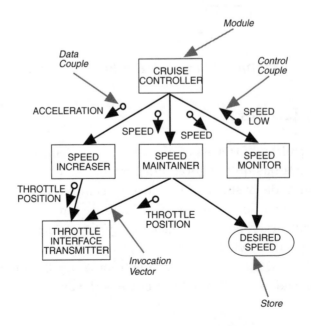

*Figure 6.33: Typical Structure Chart.*

A structure chart represents a single-thread activity, which further distinguishes it from an AFD; by default, only one thing can happen at a time in a structure chart, and this is its biggest constraint. However, structure charts and AFDs can complement each other if AFDs are used for concurrent processes and structure charts are used whenever a module contains only a single thread. We then have a set of concurrent, single-thread processes.

The concepts of coupling and cohesion were first introduced in the context of Structured Design [Page-Jones 88]. Coupling is a measure of the interdependence of two modules as a function of the amount and type of information passed between them. In most cases, coupling should be low. Cohesion is a measure of how closely the elements within a module are related as a function of the tasks they perform. In most cases, cohesion should be high. Coupling and cohesion have turned out to have much broader application than just SD. They have application to any modular structure, including those created by object-oriented methods and the requirements and architecture methods. It is almost universally true that we would like the building blocks—whatever they may be—of our models and systems to be independent (with low coupling), and for each block to serve a simple, clear purpose (with high cohesion). There are good reasons to deviate sometimes from these criteria, but even so, they serve as a yardstick for measuring how compelling those reasons really are.

## 6.7.2 CODARTS

CODARTS (Concurrent Design Approach for Real-Time Systems), was developed by Hassan Gomaa and is particularly useful for representing software in embedded real-time systems, in which multiple concurrent tasks must meet severe timing constraints [Gomaa 93]. CODARTS was preceded by DARTS (Design Approach for Real-Time Systems) and ADARTS (Ada-based Design Approach for Real-Time Systems).

CODARTS and its predecessors are founded on four earlier methods: Real-Time Structured Analysis and Design, such as the methods described in this book; Jackson System Development (JSD) [Jackson 83]; the Naval Research Laboratory's Software Cost Reduction Method [Parnas 86]; and object-oriented design. The steps in using CODARTS are as follows [Gomaa 99]: Develop a real-time analysis model; if applicable, structure the system into distributed subsystems; structure the system into concurrent tasks; structure the system into information-hiding modules; if applicable, develop Ada-based architectural design; define component interface specifications; and proceed with incremental development of the system. CODARTS has an extensive notation and syntax [Gomaa 93].

## 6.7.3 Object Orientation

Object orientation (OO) may be remembered as the software silver bullet of the 1990's [Brooks 87]! Since the late 1980's, every new software design method has been called "object-oriented" [Coad 91; Booch 94; Booch 98; Jacobson 92; Rumbaugh 91; Shlaer 88]. Yet, all of them emphasize different things when it comes to software architecture.

It seems as if the majority of people using or advocating OO do so because "Everyone else is doing it, so it must be good." At the time of this writing, the actual adoption and use of OO in industry lagged far behind its popularity in the software community. It remains to be seen how widely OO methods will be used in the long term.

Object orientation takes encapsulation and information hiding to a new level. An object is a software structure that represents a real-world entity and contains all the data, behavior, and functions (often referred to as *methods* in OO terminology) that pertain to the entity. In OO design, objects also have interfaces through which they send and receive messages to and from other objects. Other objects only know our object's name, its interfaces, and what to expect from it in response to a message. Other objects do not know what functions it contains, nor the data or other resources it uses to perform them.

Objects are therefore very similar to our lowest-level architecture modules, which are not further decomposed. As mentioned above, messages are the links between objects. A message is a request from the sending object for a service from the receiving object. In most OO design methods, no restrictions are placed on the routing of messages. That means the overall structure of the software is a network, where any object can potentially send messages to any other object.

Besides messages, OO has introduced another powerful mechanism for coupling objects: *inheritance.* Inheritance is the OO term for the subtype/supertype hierarchies described in Chapter 3: It is used not only for abstraction purposes, but for defining attributes, functions, and behavior in the supertype only, so that the subtypes inherit all these features. This reduces the amount of code, whenever similarities are found in the real world, and makes maintenance much simpler.

At the time of this writing, there is no agreement among the OO design gurus about packages larger than objects. However, many approaches have been suggested, from nesting objects within objects, to forming subsystems, categories, modules, and so on.

An anticipated benefit of OO's high encapsulation and inheritance is its reusability. These highly self-contained pieces of software, in well-defined and useful classes, are expected to serve as "plug in" software in multiple applications. This potential has not yet been realized, at least not on a broad, industry-wide scale, but it is certainly worth seeking.

How do OO methods and the methods in this book relate? One aspect of their relationship is that the architecture model can transition to an OO model at a chosen level within the software. Object-oriented methods represent the design of a software subsystem, and as such, they have a close correlation with the architecture method: Architecture modules can be considered objects or groups of objects. In Chapter 4, we demonstrated how flows can change to messages, emphasizing control instead of information/material/energy flow and further supporting the transition from the architecture method to OO.

One of the weaknesses of most OO methods is that requirements and design become inextricably intermingled. Using OO in conjunction with the requirements and architecture methods overcomes this weakness: The requirements mapped into an object module represent the functions that module must perform, and the architecture template can be used in the usual way within the object module to account for the interfaces with other objects. The stores within the requirements model are also mapped into the object module, and they represent the hidden data the object uses to perform its functions. The control model can be used to express the behavior of objects and to package it into the architecture module that implements the behavior. The aggregation/decomposition hierarchy of the architecture module can be used to form larger packages of objects, allowing scope control and life-time control that is not yet offered by most OO design methods. Thus, the best of both methods can be used together to produce a very powerful approach to software development.

Some might argue, based on the heuristic that form should follow function, that the intermingling in OO of requirements and design is a strength, not a weakness. Our position, as we have described above, is that this heuristic can be followed when appropriate, without the inextricable intermingling.

There are some who believe that OO will become the technique of choice for all system development. While this is certainly possible, we do not believe it is likely. Object orientation is an abstract approach that fits well with the abstract nature of software, but it is hard to relate to the real world. A real automobile, for example, does not "know" all the things it can do (its methods), and then perform them independently of any other objects. It does them in close interaction with people, other automobiles, and the highway system. In the abstract world of software, the idea that objects contain and perform their hidden methods, using hidden data, can work well, but in the real world of nuts and bolts and sheet metal, it is a rather obscure notion. Most importantly, the users of our systems are unlikely to think in terms of objects of the OO variety. Certainly, everyone thinks of objects—the whole world is full of them—but not of the hidden methods and abstract data types that OO demands.

Chapter 1 of [Page-Jones 95] has probably the best overview to date of the essentials of object orientation. It is highly recommended for those seeking a quick introduction to the subject.

## 6.7.4 Lessons from the History of Software

The preceding brief history of software development shows our need for software design methods that allow us to create building blocks of any size and complexity, from the small functions of Structured Design to the large blocks required for a first separation of client and server parts, for example.

The blocks need a versatile glue to combine them. A simple controlling/controlled structure, such as the calls in Structured Design, is not sufficient. We also need network communication, aggregation/decomposition hierarchies, inheritance hierarchies, and controlling/controlled hierarchies. In summary, we need all the properties of the architecture model described in Chapter 4.

The emphasis shifts when we go from system and subsystem modeling to software modeling. On the higher levels, we need network structures (as used in architecture flow diagrams) and channel structures (as used in architecture interconnect diagrams); for software, we need inheritance structures and message diagrams—which are closer in style to today's programming languages—in place of flow diagrams.

## 6.7.5 Software Categories

When we create architecture models on system or subsystem levels, the criteria for selecting requirements elements to be packaged into an architecture module are often determined by external constraints. In engineering systems, we might use existing processors as architecture modules; in organizational systems, we might use departments or groups of people. The resulting modules are usually visible and recognizable in the real world.

For software, we are generally free to choose the structure of the architecture modules, as mentioned in the introduction to this section. The original criteria for identifying requirements that should be packaged were suggested by David Parnas when he created the term "information hiding" [Parnas 71]. The original examples were at a very low architectural level, often close to the implementation. Since then, we have learned a lot about what to hide and how to do it. But the original goal is still the same: To keep each part of the software architecture independent of design decisions made in other parts. Therefore, we try to hide as much as we can, allowing more freedom to change design decisions without affecting other parts of the software system.

In Section 3.6, we suggested various categories of components to consider when developing larger systems. Here, we will be more specific. For software architectures, many hiding categories are available, based on existing software designs that have achieved many of the design goals: easy maintainability, flexibility and stability with respect to change, extensibility, reusability, stability, and many of the other "-ilities."

The design of software packaging starts with those parts of the enhanced requirements model that have been assigned to software. How do we arrive at a good software design? We want to form highly cohesive, loosely coupled modules, as indicated in Figure 6.34, and the principal criterion for forming them is information hiding. Even packages that are already hidden can have further secrets inside, as indicated by the nested structures in the user-interface region in Figure 6.34. So, information hiding is a concept that can be applied on as many levels as desired.

What do we hide? First of all, we stick to the grouping suggested by the architecture template. Hiding the *essential core* and the *physical ring* of the architecture template is a strong heuristic. In many cases, we try to separate each of the four regions in the physical ring and treat them as separate information-hiding modules.

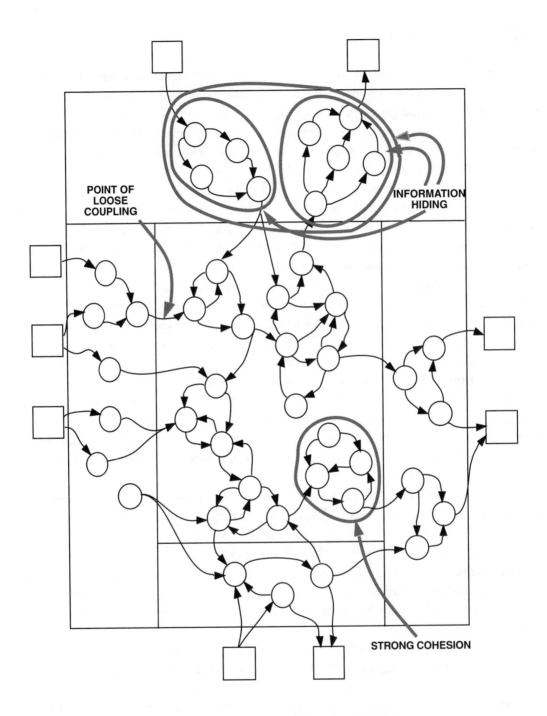

*Figure 6.34: Forming Architecture Modules.*

The template was originally used in the requirements model to help us remember needs that might otherwise be forgotten. We used it to separate the physical processing (and the corresponding storage and control structures) from the logical processing (with *its* storage and control structures). At the system levels, the allocation of this processing to architecture modules often cuts across the template boundaries, but when designing software, we try to conform to the template's structure. In other words, we want to have separate architecture modules for the essential core and the four surrounding regions. Of course, some design constraints can lead to violations of these guidelines. If, for performance reasons, we have to accept data from an input device and immediately work on it—because any separation of physical and logical data would be too slow—we will need to cut across template boundaries. But in our first attempt, we should always try to create architecture modules that conform to the template.

In a large, multilayered software system, a high-level architecture module may cross the template boundaries (even, possibly, encompassing the whole template), but inside that module there may be smaller modules that do conform to the template boundaries.

The heuristics suggested so far would only give us five information-hiding modules, one for each region of the template. But we can go beyond that: Each region of the template can be further subcategorized to provide guidelines for grouping, partitioning, hiding, and producing maintainable architecture modules.

Figure 6.35 shows the architecture template with hiding categories within each region. In all four outer regions, there are abstract interface modules. Generally, these are used to hide characteristics of the outside world—such as device characteristics—from the kernel of our software system. Messages from the environment are received in a device-dependent format and transformed into a standard internal format by an abstract interface module. As a result, our software does not have to know the format of the original message. Similarly, on the output side, an abstract interface module can hide the format of the output device. It translates the formats of the software kernel system into any format needed by the receiver.

Abstract interface modules are also needed in the user-interface buffer. They hide the features of the devices that communicate with the user: keyboard receivers, display drivers, switch interfaces, or any other interfaces between the user and the software system.

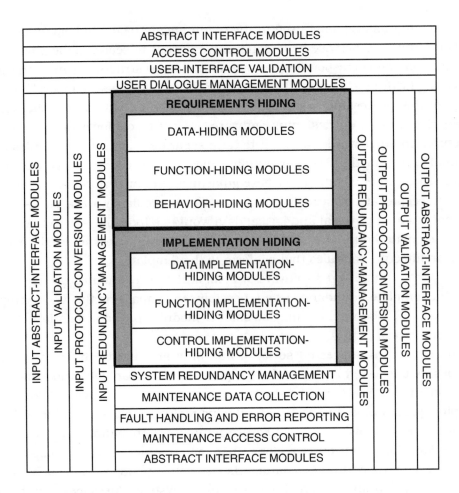

*Figure 6.35: Suggested Information-Hiding Categories.*

In the support buffer, the devices are often different from those in the other buffers. Maintenance personnel usually access the system through less ergonomic, but more efficient, interfaces.

Data received from or transmitted to external devices are either

- in a standard format, but used by the system in an internal format
- in a nonstandard format, such as a synchro signal, but converted by the system to some internal format

In both cases, abstract interface modules perform the conversions.

To summarize, we can say that abstract interface modules are buffers that shield the essence of the system from external devices and make the system independent of modification or replacement of these devices.

These interfaces are shown graphically in Figure 6.36, where Abstract Interface 1 might represent a low-speed bus for printers and scanners (Device 1), and Abstract Interface 2 a high-speed bus for remote disks (Device 2). The setup allows a printer or external disk to be changed to another model without affecting the essential system software.

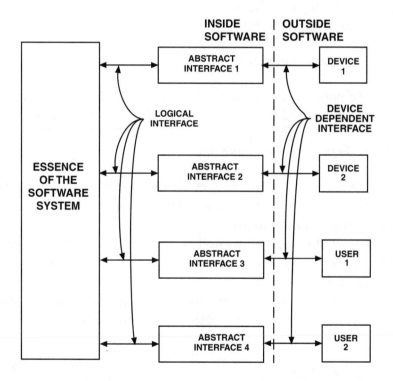

*Figure 6.36: Illustration of Abstract Interfaces.*

Having considered the ring of abstract interface modules in general, let us take a more detailed look at the four outer regions of the template.

In the support area at the bottom of Figure 6.35, there are five suggested groups for hiding requirements. Within each of these groups, architecture modules such as the following may be hiding design decisions:

Abstract interface modules may hide

- maintenance user interfaces (as discussed above)
- maintenance data-entry interfaces (any data-entry function, with its behavior and its local data, can be hidden here)
- maintenance display interfaces
- automated test equipment interfaces

Maintenance access control may hide

- maintenance personnel validation, especially provided for the support staff. (We shall find similar hiding units in the user-interface region.)

Fault handling and error reporting may hide

- fault monitoring in special architecture modules specifically for this purpose. (How often and when this is done is also hidden. The rest of the system does not have to know.)
- graceful degradation algorithms and strategies. (These provide for as much functionality as possible when parts of the system fail.)
- system error annunciations.
- fault data collection and analysis. (Here we hide the structure of the log files, the way fault data is collected, and the data analysis algorithms.)

Maintenance data collection may hide

- maintenance log files
- self-test analysis and error reporting
- maintenance data display

System redundancy management may hide

- redundancy management algorithms
- system reconfiguration algorithms

In the user-interface region of the template, there are four categories of typical architecture modules, as shown in Figure 6.35, with subcategories as follows:

Abstract interface modules, discussed above, may hide

- keyboard receivers
- display drivers
- switch interfaces

Access control modules, which manage security for the core system, may hide

- user validation tables
- password verification
- user priority levels
- access parameter settings
- access validation according to system state

User-interface validation modules may hide

- prompt structures
- syntax checking
- input reasonableness checking
- entry error handling
- output validation

User dialogue management modules: In user-interface-intensive systems, this can be a large part of the design. There are books devoted entirely to user-interface strategies; just a few of the items that user dialogue management may hide are

- particular display formats
- scheduling and updating of displays
- human factors details
- user input formats

Finally, to complete the physical ring illustrated in Figure 6.35, we discuss the input and output buffers, which usually hide the same kinds of things:

Abstract interface modules may hide

- handshake modules
- device interface modules

Input or output validation modules may hide

- data reasonableness checking
- maintenance interface for devices
- interrupt handlers
- data rejection and error reporting
- input or output collection and scheduling

Input or output protocol conversion may hide

- receivers or transmitters
- communication protocol drivers
- protocol configuration management

Input or output redundancy management may hide

- redundancy management algorithms
- input or output fault detection and management

Many of the suggestions so far are technology-specific and do not depend on the application area of the system under study. The essential core is specific to the project and domain, so it is more difficult to give detailed suggestions for hiding. However, we can define two broad items that should be encapsulated and hidden: The first is the essential requirements; the second is their implementation. Figure 6.35 shows these two categories in the center region, with their subcategories.

Why would we want to hide requirements? During analysis, we did not try to hide anything; our goal was to establish requirements with the system stakeholders, and everything we discussed was relevant. During design, we have to package all the required features into structures that are maintainable and extensible, in case the requirements change. We hide as many requirements as possible inside architecture modules and make the interfaces between the modules as lean as possible.

In Chapter 4, we discussed three categories of requirements and their models: process, control, and data. We can hide all three of these categories, but by far the most important is data hiding. Architecture modules should have functions (processes from the enhanced requirements model) in their interfaces, and the data for the functions should be hidden from other architecture modules. Others know how to access the functions, but their data is secret. In this way, data hiding allows the data structures to be changed (for example, attributes can be added or regrouped) without affecting other parts of the system.

Not all functions from requirements model processes need to be visible and accessible at the architecture module interface. Some functions provide internal support for others and can be hidden, making the functional interface as lean as possible.

In some cases, instead of hiding an entire function, we can just hide its decisions. From the outside, we know that the function will produce a certain result but the criteria it uses are hidden. This form of hiding allows us to change the decision algorithm inside the function without changing other parts of the system.

The third and last of our requirements hiding categories concerns the control model, representing the behavior of the system or subsystem. States and transitions can be kept secret within an architecture module. When functions in the interface are called, the caller does not have to know the internal behavior of that architecture module: The module is free to organize its internal work according to its own state machine. It can change this internal organization without affecting other modules.

Besides requirements hiding, we are also interested in implementation hiding to keep design decisions local and to hide the implementation of every requirement possible: both core and enhancement requirements.

Starting with data hiding again, this can include the implementations of entities' attributes, of relationships, of functions controlling access to data, of integrity checks performed on the data, and of derivable attributes (for example, whether they are stored or recalculated every time they are needed). Even if an architecture module does not hide the data itself, it can hide how it manages the data.

We can also hide the implementation of PSPECs, that is, we can hide the algorithm chosen to implement the functionality specified by the requirements model. This allows us to exchange the algorithm, find a better one, or buy one, for example.   Other architecture modules only know the name of the function and its interfaces, not its internal workings.

The third category of software implementation hiding concerns how we transform the decision tables, process activation tables, and state transition diagrams of our control model into software.  Architecture modules should hide whatever implementation we choose, so that other modules know what states and transitions are possible, but not how they are implemented.  Again, this allows us to change the implementation without affecting other modules.

The amount of implementation hiding we do depends on whether we are using sophisticated operating systems, database management systems, and advanced programming languages, or using something closer to assembly language.  When we simply define our data structures in a DDL, its implementation is already hidden in the DBMS.  On the other hand, if we create records, arrays, lists, and stacks in our favorite programming language, we have to make sure that these decisions are not visible to too many other modules; otherwise, we are losing flexibility.

If our programming language supports concurrent processing (often implemented as activities, tasks, or threads), we will use these features and not worry about process communication algorithms and process synchronization.  If we simulate such concurrent processes right on top of our operating system, we should hide them in standard architecture modules.  Hiding will allow us to port our software to another operating system without recoding everything.

The same is true for task scheduling, resource scheduling, and foreground/background processing—including priority handling, exception handling, and so on. All such aspects can be hidden from the rest of the system by creating special architecture modules.  The more we can isolate, the more flexibility and maintainability we will build into our software architecture.

## 6.7.6 Software Architectures

The hiding categories described above are just one part of the software structure. Once we have these categories, a question arises:  How are they related?  Our answer lies in the larger issue of software architecture.

In this chapter, we have reviewed the progression from Structured Design, with very strict controlling/controlled hierarchies, to CODARTs, with network structures using delegation among peers, to object orientation, emphasizing inheritance structures.  The body of knowledge about software architectures is not yet very large, but there has been progress in recent decades. In the following, we discuss this evolution and its consequences for software design.

In early software systems, there was little information hiding and therefore little structure, as illustrated in *a* and *b* of Figure 6.37. The software was often built as a monolithic block. Changes were not easily achieved. Some classical programming languages may have contributed to this; COBOL, for instance, led us to separate data (in the data division) from functions (in the procedure division), while user interfaces were everywhere in the code.

Next, we learned that "layers" gave us more flexibility. High-level pictures of a typical software architecture looked like diagram *c* of Figure 6.37. The layers indicated control hierarchies: The user interface was separated from the application, which in turn was separated from the database. In time, standard user-interfaces and databases evolved. Whenever we could not trust the operating system or our programming language with tasking or exception handling (for example, there is no parallel tasking in MS-DOS, and many languages do not have the exception handling of C), an additional software component (called technical support in Figure 6.38) was added as a partition for use by all three hierarchical control layers. Since the application layer is positioned inside a U-shaped framework, this structure is often called a "horseshoe architecture."

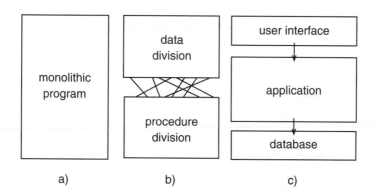

*Figure 6.37: Early Software Architectures.*

Figure 6.39 shows an alternative view of software architectures, a four-layered hierarchy. The four typical layers pictured here make the software architecture more flexible and maintainable. The top layer of this controlling/controlled hierarchy is labeled Control Modules, reflecting the idea (from Structured Design) that management of work should control the execution of work. Any top-level control from the analysis is usually packaged into this layer. The next layer is called Application Modules. It contains the processes found in the requirements model. Skipping the third layer for a moment, note that the bottom layer contains Basic Storage Structures (derived from the data stores of the process model or the class model) and access functions (not shown in the figure); it also hides the implementation of our logical data structures. Returning now to the third layer, it is created in the course of our software design, and contains support data structures and support algorithms that make life easier for the application modules in the layer above. Any special structures that are introduced for performance reasons are kept and maintained in this layer.

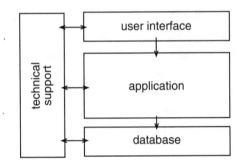

*Figure 6.38: Horseshoe Architecture.*

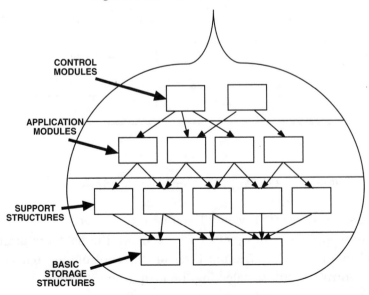

*Figure 6.39: An Alternative View of a Control Hierarchy Architecture.*

In our experience, controlling/controlled hierarchies are easier to manage than network structures. Within each layer (or within each component in a layer), networked cooperation among peers works well, but on a larger scale, we recommend a control hierarchy. The overall system shape should be onion-like or mosque-like, as in Figure 6.39; this keeps us from having too many bosses and not enough workers, but also encourages shared resources and reuse at the bottom of the hierarchy.

Next in the evolution of software architecture came workflow management systems. Their manufacturers told the astonished software world that only one component is needed to coordinate the software modules: the workflow engine. User-interface processes, algorithms, data storage, and all the other layers are slaved below the workflow engine. It will coordinate everything in the software system (and also discipline the user in front of the screen). The overall architecture is shown in Figure 6.40.

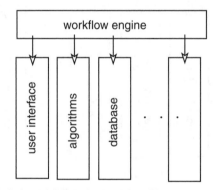

*Figure 6.40:  A Workflow-Centered Architecture.*

In contrast to the workflow engine approach, object orientation (or at least some brands of it) brought us back to the idea that the developers should decide the structure. Also, OO methods stress that real-world structures should dominate the software architecture. This is often called "structuring by business objects" today [Eeles 98]. A business object is a package of related processes, data, and behavior from our essential requirements model. There are packages dominated by the data structures (Jacobson, in [Jacobson 92], calls them "entity objects;" Taylor, in [Taylor 95], calls them "resources") and packages dominated by the control structure ("control objects" in OOSE terminology, or "processes" in Taylor's OPR model). These business objects (that is, architecture modules created from the essential requirements model) can and will use any support module, including user-interface technology, data-storage technology, communication technology, task management technology, infrastructure technology, factored reusable functions, and any of the other information-hiding approaches discussed earlier.

A modern software architecture shaped in this way might look like the one in Figure 6.41. Business layer objects are always the bosses, using technology layer objects to serve their needs. Technology layer objects should never call business objects: Their only role is to send responses when asked. Thus, the two layers form a controlling/controlled hierarchy.

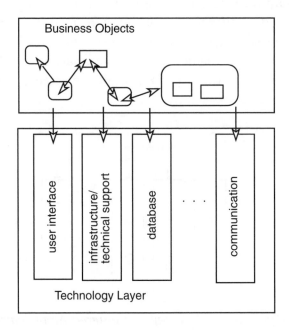

*Figure 6.41: Business Object-Oriented Architecture.*

Within both layers, other forms of cooperation between the components are used:

- inheritance hierarchies simplify the design when similar components are discovered
- aggregation hierarchies control scope and visibility
- abstraction/detailing hierarchies help to create conceptual clarity
- lower-level controlling/controlled hierarchies delegate work to subordinates
- network relationships delegate work to peers

Business object architectures are different from architectures that are user-interface-driven or workflow-driven because *none* of the technology modules is the boss: The business logic alone is the boss. Before such architectures, user interfaces not only exchanged data with the user, they often contained the central control functions. Whenever the user interface sensed a mouse click or a key stroke, it called the appropriate application function. Instead, the philosophy now is that the business application calls the user-interface driver with requests such as: "Send me the input when the user hits any key." (Of course, the user interface still senses the input, but it does so only after being told this is its job.)

Another example of the business object architecture approach is that a database should never initiate a business function: Databases are limited to storing and retrieving as instructed by the business functions. Of course, a business function can instruct a database to "Wake me up whenever this stored attribute changes." In that case, the database sends a message to the application, but it is the business function, not the database that initiates the interaction.

The software architect is responsible for determining the overall structure, rules, and guidelines. The detailed designers cooperate with the architect (who certainly should consult them on his or her work, because concurrent, cooperative development principles apply within software, too). The architecture will stabilize as software design progresses. If all the hiding categories mentioned above are utilized, the design will survive a lot of business and technology changes.

## 6.8 SUMMARIES

In this chapter, we have shown how to apply the diagrams, the rules, and the modeling concepts that we introduced in Chapter 4. We have shown their application to the systems and the software domains, and in this section we summarize these two application domains.

### 6.8.1 System Summary

We have seen that the architecture and requirements methods encompass systems of all kinds, sizes, and technologies. The methods can be used down to the level of detailed design or can transition smoothly to other, technology-specific methods. They support the layered nature of systems and of system development. They provide a framework for recording all the complex decisions made in the course of system development, and in so doing, they act as a reminder of what needs to be done. No particular sequence of development is imposed by the methods; they can support any sequence that is appropriate to the needs of the project. Numerous consistency checks are provided, as well as traceability throughout the requirements and architecture structure. Figure 6.1 provides a useful guide to the overall structure of the methods, and it should be referenced frequently, especially when the methods are being used for the first time.

## 6.8.2 Software Summary

Our architecture model offers all the constructs needed to build a sound software architecture. Architecture modules, regardless of their size or how abstract they are, are glued together in a variety of ways, depending on their positions in the overall software architecture:

- We can, on the higher levels, use network structures to delegate work among peers, or controlling/controlled hierarchies to establish client/server behavior early in development.
- We can model conceptual similarities using inheritance structures.
- We can apply abstraction hierarchies to cope with complexity.
- We can start informally, linking architecture modules via the flows they exchange, and gradually switch to messages. Over time, we can formalize the structure by adding message parameters that facilitate a smooth transition into programming languages.

# Chapter 7

# System Development Overview Using a Meta-Model

## 7.1 INTRODUCTION

In the preceding chapters, we have discussed the nature of systems, and we have shown how to use models to specify them. Also, we have shown that the development process and the models have similar structures: They are multilayered, and they can accommodate concurrent processes.

Most overview chapters simply summarize what has been said earlier. We take a different approach here, by using the architecture and requirements methods to model the system development process. This strategy serves two purposes: First, it provides a review of earlier material, in a form that adds new insight; second, it introduces the practical use of the methods, which will be greatly expanded in Part II.

The model we develop in this chapter provides a different view of the information in Figure 6.1. Here, we present a requirements model of the development process (a *what* model), using data flow diagrams of activities, their inputs, and their deliverables. We use the architecture template (in a slightly modified form, as explained later) to form an enhanced requirements model.

To develop a system, we must first develop a project structure (a *how* model), using the activities in the requirements model mentioned above. To represent this, we use the architecture model to package activities into phases, define milestones, allocate activities to resources, and map the resulting packages to a timeline. We use the idea basic to these methods: The essential requirements model, the enhanced requirements model, and the architecture model serve significantly different roles.

## 7.2 A META-MODEL FOR DEVELOPMENT PROJECTS

In Chapter 3, we showed how the architecture template can be adapted to suit any kind of system. Figure 7.1 shows such an adaptation to suit a system development project, which is itself a system. Used in this way, the architecture template becomes a meta-model of the specific class of system for which it is adapted—in this case, a development project.

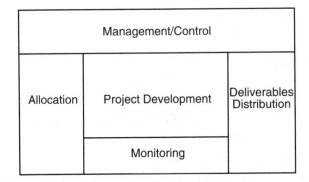

*Figure 7.1:*     *The Architecture Template, Adapted for a System Development Project.*

The user-interface region becomes the Management/Control region, because project management is the user of a system development project. The input-processing region becomes the Allocation region, because incoming resources and requirements must be allocated to activities in the central region. The output-processing region becomes the Deliverables Distribution region, because the outputs of a project are deliverables to be received by various external entities. The maintenance and support region becomes the Monitoring region, reflecting the importance of observing and measuring project activities and progress. Finally, the essential model region becomes the Project Development region, reflecting the particular application of this version of the template.

## 7.3 AN ESSENTIAL MODEL OF THE DEVELOPMENT PROCESS

Figure 7.2 is a requirements context diagram for the system development process, showing just those interfaces that are essential to that process. Later in this chapter, we will add much more, using the enhanced and architecture models. Figure 7.2 includes only those terminators that are essential to the development process in an ideal world. Consider each of them:

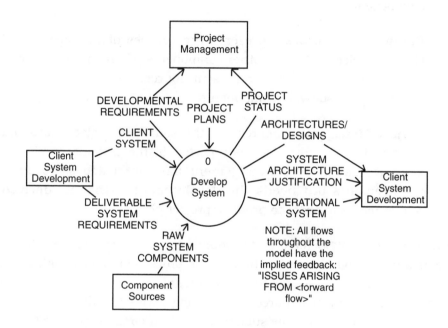

*Figure 7.2: Development Process Requirements Context.*

**Client System Development** indicates that our system is to be embedded within the client system, which is consistent with our earlier layered-system diagrams showing that all people-made systems are part of larger systems and must work harmoniously with them. Here, deliverable system requirements come directly from the client (remember, this is an "ideal world" model).

We will need to integrate our system into the client system, so the latter is shown as an input to our system development. (Of course, in the real world, our process will probably go to the client system for integration. One of the nice features of flow diagrams is that this makes no difference to the model.)

The operational system is the main output of the development process to the client, but other outputs are architectures, designs, and system architecture justification. Not all clients require these other outputs, but many do, for reviews and records; even if they are not requested, we should certainly have them available for our own benefit.

**Component Sources** represents the sources of the mechanical, electrical, electronic, and other components of which the system is constructed. It may also represent sources of external, reusable hardware and software components.

**Project Management** represents the source of project plans and the recipient of project status reports. In the essential model, we assume that project management has direct access to client requirements but needs the developmental (that is, derived) requirements in order to produce project plans.

Figure 7.3 shows DFD0 for our development process model. At this level, the model is quite straightforward: There is one process for specifying the deliverable system and three processes for building, integrating, testing, installing, and field-testing it. The extent of required field testing varies greatly, the most extensive being for safety-critical systems such as those that control commercial aircraft.

In Figure 7.3, the build, integrate, and test activity is where developmental testing takes place. Testing system compliance is the final confirmation, before delivery, that the system conforms to the client's requirements. This process is often followed (especially in the defense industry) by a formal test, which is actually not a test at all; it is a demonstration for the client that the system meets certain prescribed criteria and that the client should therefore accept the system and pay for it. Why is this not a test? Because the central purpose of testing is to find errors, and the last thing we want to find in formal testing is an error—but it does happen!

Two important data stores are included in Figure 7.3: DESIGN LIBRARY and TEST LIBRARY. These are repositories for reusable design and test elements. At the start of a project, they already contain all existing reusable elements, and more can be added in the course of development.

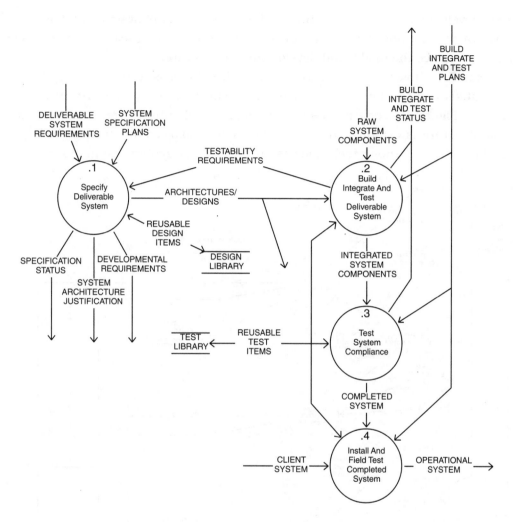

*Figure 7.3: DFD0, Develop System.*

How does Figure 7.3 relate to the process overview diagram in Chapter 5, Figure 5.1? That diagram expresses the overall concept of the development process without the rigor of the more formal requirements model. Roughly speaking, Process 1 in Figure 7.3 corresponds with the Deliverable System Development column of Figure 5.1, and Processes 2, 3, and 4 jointly correspond with the Integrate and Test Development column and the Technologies Implementation block.

Figure 7.4 is the DFD of Process 1: Specify Deliverable System, a process that represents the main topic of this book. Even though there are other parts of the system development process, a sound, well-structured set of system specifications provides a solid foundation for all aspects of the product life cycle, as we shall see when we enhance the model and develop the architecture.

Figure 7.4 shows three subprocesses within Process 1 that correspond to three subsets of the layers in Figure 5.1. The Specify System Architecture process in Figure 7.4 corresponds to the highest-level subset, where the system's overall structure is established and the major technologies are chosen, but specific allocations of those technologies to lower-level system elements are not

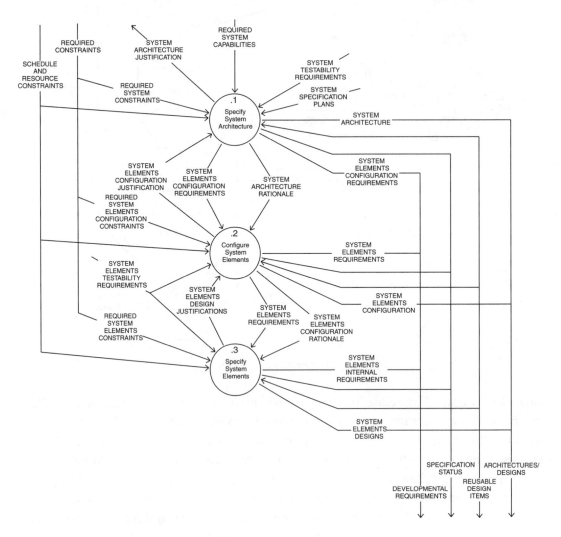

*Figure 7.4: DFD1, Specify Deliverable System.*

addressed. The Configure System Elements process in Figure 7.4 corresponds to an intermediate subset of layers in Figure 5.1, where the configuration and technologies of lower-level system elements, such as of computer hardware and software, are established. The Specify System Elements process in Figure 7.4 corresponds to the lowest-level subset of layers in Figure 5.1. Here, the technological details of the lower-level system elements are established, with each element incorporating one or more technologies, specified down to the level of detail necessary to build, integrate, and test. As always, conducting the processes in Figure 7.4, or equivalently, specifying the layers in Figure 5.1 does not necessarily proceed top-down—technological constraints in the detailed system elements, for example, often influence the overall system architecture in the higher levels, causing a bottom-up sequence.

## 7.4 THE ENHANCED DEVELOPMENT MODEL

It is time now to add some reality to our idealized essential model. Figure 7.4 clearly states the essential elements of system development, yet it makes unrealistic assumptions about interactions with the world outside the project. We know, for example, that clients do not simply hand off to developers complete, consistent, and correct deliverable system requirements. The manner in which such issues are dealt with is more or less company- and project-dependent. Figure 7.5 shows an enhanced version of DFD0 that allows us to screen the client's requirements and to add several other activities to the essential process.

Dealing first with the deliverable system requirements, we recognize in the enhanced model that they originate from several different sources, that they need to be screened and categorized in some manner (such as that described by the class diagram in Figure 2.9), and that they are likely to be mixed with non-developmental requirements that must be passed to other disciplines. Accordingly, two of the enhancement processes in Figure 7.5's Allocation (input processing) area are: Screen And Categorize Incoming Requirements, and Assign Project Requirements. These processes receive unscreened requirements as inputs from the client, from other system stakeholders, and from other disciplines. As outputs, the processes have the deliverable system requirements of the essential model, plus requirements for other disciplines in the organization. Note that if this assignment process were just a matter of splitting a group of requirements into parts that were clearly attributable to their assignees, then we could simply represent it with a branching flow. But what is assigned to whom is a more com-

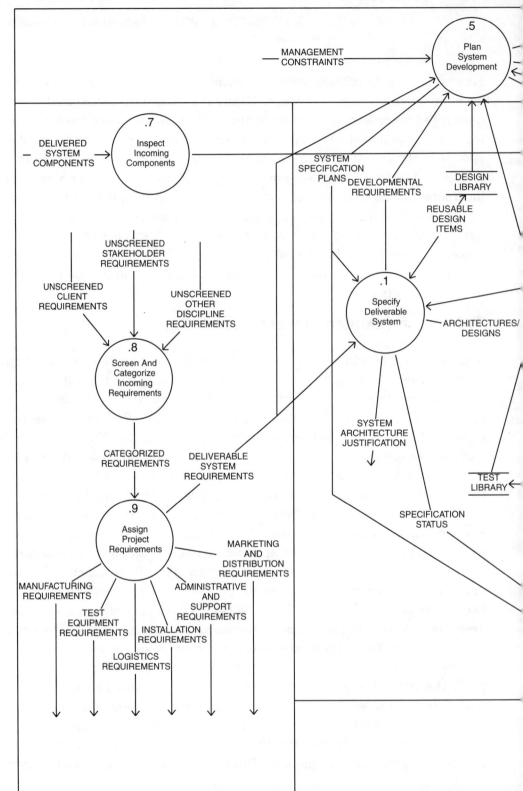

*Figure 7.5: EDFD0, Enhanced Develop System (Left Side).*

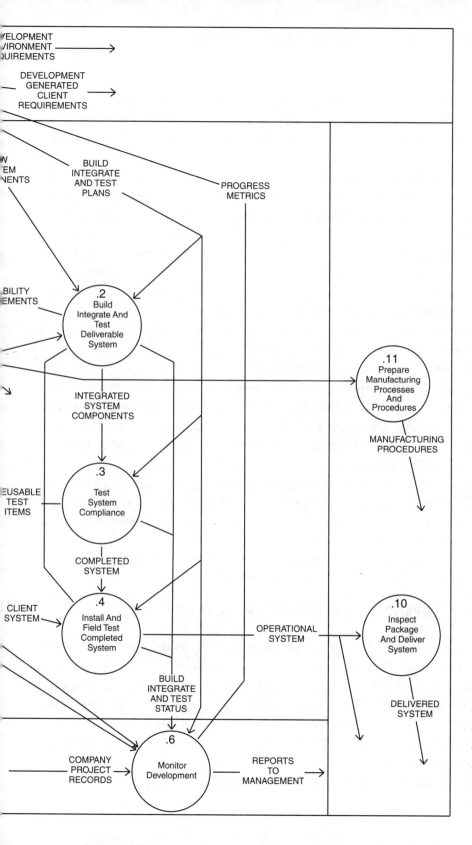

*Figure 7.5: EDFD0, Enhanced Develop System (Right Side).*

plex decision than that, so a process is needed instead. The third process in Figure 7.5's Allocation area is Inspect Incoming Components, which recognizes that we live in an imperfect world, and that not everything arriving at our door is perfect.

The Plan System Development process in Figure 7.5's Management/Control (User I/O) area recognizes that project plans do not come out of thin air, but must be developed within a defined scope for each project. This process receives as inputs MANAGEMENT CONSTRAINTS, DELIVERABLE SYSTEM REQUIREMENTS, DEVELOPMENTAL REQUIREMENTS, PROGRESS METRICS, DESIGN LIBRARY outputs, and TEST LIBRARY outputs. From these, it generates SYSTEM SPECIFICATION PLANS; BUILD, INTEGRATE AND TEST PLANS; DEVELOPMENT ENVIRONMENT REQUIREMENTS; and DEVELOPMENT GENERATED CLIENT REQUIREMENTS. This last item reflects the fact that client requirements are usually incorrect, inconsistent, and incomplete, and that we must resolve these issues with the client.

In Figure 7.5's Monitoring area, the Monitor Development process receives the project plans, status, and company records from earlier projects and converts them into PROGRESS METRICS and REPORTS TO MANAGEMENT. In the Deliverables Distribution area, we have two processes: Prepare Manufacturing Processes And Procedures—perhaps the most important process of the whole system—and Inspect Package And Deliver System.

We should emphasize that this set of enhancements is only one of many possible selections. You should decide what is right for your organization and your project. The essential model is useful in that it is the same for everyone, but it can be enhanced and architected as needed.

Next (or, rather, concurrently with the enhanced model), we must construct the project architecture (or organizational) context.

## 7.5 THE DEVELOPMENT ARCHITECTURE CONTEXT

You probably noticed that the enhanced development model has many more inputs and outputs than the essential model. All of these must have places to come from and go to, and if those places do not exist on the requirements context diagram, they must be added as new terminators on the architecture context diagrams, as shown in Figure 7.6. As we stated in Chapter 4, the architecture flow context diagram is the parent of EDFD0, and the model in Figure 7.6 further illustrates why: In addition to those in the requirements context diagram, new terminators are added to the AFCD to accommodate new flows in EDFD0.

We already discussed the terminators in the essential model's context diagram; the additional terminators in the AFCD represent other disciplines that make up a complete enterprise. There is a tendency in system development to pay too little attention to these other disciplines (even to despise them, in some cases), but they are all vital to the overall success of a product. In every case, we impose requirements on those disciplines, and they in turn impose requirements on us. *Every flow between these terminators and our development implies a concurrent, cooperative activity between ourselves and those disciplines.*

**Other External Stakeholders:** These are the external stakeholders, other than the client, that we referenced in Figure 5.1. They include management, regulatory authorities, and many others.

**Manufacturing:** It is of utmost importance that system development satisfies the needs of manufacturing—if a system works fine as an engineering prototype but is not manufacturable, it's worthless. This, of course, is the reason for classical concurrent engineering, in which manufacturing engineers are an integral part of the development team [SOCE].

**Design And Test Equipment:** Many organizations develop their own, customized design and test equipment, often combining it with off-the-shelf equipment to form a complete development and test environment.

**Logistics Support:** This activity—some, but not all, of which is derived from the development of the system—embraces field training, technical support, repairs, and maintenance, including all the field documentation that goes with them.

**Installation Design:** Often, especially in embedded systems, modifications to the host system are necessary to accommodate the system under development. An example is the mounting and cabling of a new navigation system into an existing aircraft.

**Administrative And Support Functions:** These functions include upper management, finance, accounting, human resources, train-

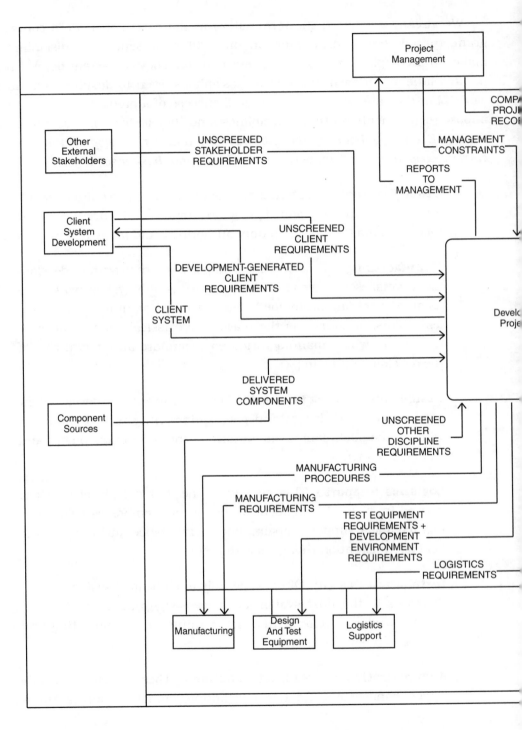

*Figure 7.6: Development Process Architecture Context (Left Side).*

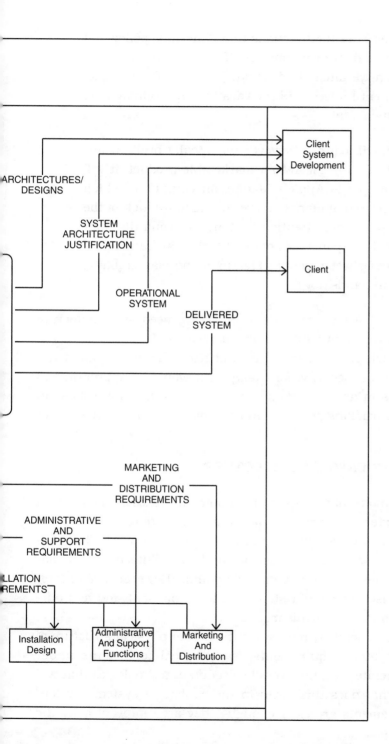

*Figure 7.6: Development Process Architecture Context (Right Side).*

ing, and others. These are the functions that determine policy and provide resources from their own domains. They influence the constraints under which we must conduct our projects—for example, the overall development budget, and the vacation and training time allotted for development staff.

**Marketing And Distribution:** However technically brilliant our system may be, if it does not lead to a marketable product, it will fail. (A classic example is Apple's Macintosh computer, which struggled against decreasing market share throughout much of the 1990's.) We must pay strict attention to marketing and distribution needs, even at the expanse of potential technical features. If there is ever a choice between technical features and marketability, the latter should win, hands down.

Having developed an AFCD, we face the question: Do we need an architecture interconnect context diagram to go with it? The answer is, It depends. If the channels by which the various flows travel to and from the development are unusual or have special needs (security, for example), it would be appropriate to specify these special needs in an AICD. Otherwise, if the channels are those in common use (mail, e-mail, trucking services, and so on), an AICD is probably not needed.

## 7.6 DEVELOPMENT PROCESS ARCHITECTURE

We now have an essential model of the system development process, an enhanced model with some typical external interfaces, and an architecture context diagram with all the terminators required for that particular set of interfaces. If we followed our usual course, we would now construct a child architecture flow diagram (and possibly its architecture interconnect diagram). However, before forging ahead with that exercise, we should step back for a moment and ask ourselves what such a diagram means for this model.

An architecture model, remember, represents the actual physical structure of a system, based on the system requirements, the physical constraints under which the system must operate, and the overall selection of technologies that will constitute the system. What does this mean in the context of system development? The system requirements are clear enough—they are represented by the requirements and enhanced requirements models we have already developed. The physical constraints are those of the organization and industry in which a project must work. The overall technologies selected are the disciplines needed for the project, the development procedures within the organization, and the types of tools (automated or otherwise) that will be used to support the project.

With this interpretation in mind, we can designate top-level architecture modules as disciplines and/or organizational entities. The requirements can then be allocated to those modules according to the assignment of responsibilities. Similarly, as we proceed through further levels of architectural detail, we can designate lower-level architecture modules as design tools and procedures.

Obviously, we are now in a realm that is almost entirely company- and project-specific, so we will go no further here than to identify some top-level architecture modules that are typical of most engineering organizations. Beyond the essential requirements, everything in this model should be scrutinized and redeveloped with respect to your own organization and project. Our goal here is to demonstrate how to do that. Figure 7.7 shows a typical set of architecture modules for an engineering organization.

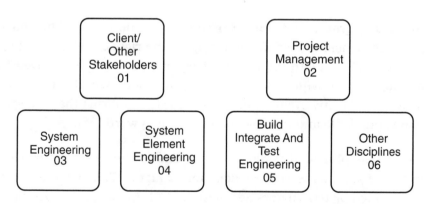

*Figure 7.7: Development Process Architecture Modules.*

Following is a description of each architecture module in Figure 7.7:

> **Client/Other Stakeholders:** Even though the entities in this module are outside the project, they have a strong influence on the development process, and we want them to be actively involved in it. This architecture module allows us to allocate tasks to them.

**Project Management:** Within the essential model, project management appears as a terminator; in the enhanced model it occupies the user-interface region of the template. Here, it requires its own architecture module so that its tasks can be properly allocated.

**System Engineering; System Element Engineering:** At this high architectural level, we choose to divide all development engineering between these two modules. System Engineering has prime responsibility for everything from the top-level system architecture to specifying the technological configuration in sufficient detail so that the separate disciplines can carry out their designs. System Element Engineering encompasses all other development disciplines—mechanical engineering, electrical engineering, hydraulic engineering, computer hardware engineering, and software engineering, to name but a few. At a level below that of Figure 7.7, these disciplines are separated into their own modules so that specific tasks can be assigned to them.

**Build, Integrate, And Test Engineering:** These disciplines have prime responsibility for the activities on the right-hand side of Figure 5.1. They, more than most disciplines, are deeply involved in development activities that extend beyond their own direct responsibilities. The involvement of these modules confirms that the system is buildable and testable; otherwise, it is worthless.

**Other Disciplines:** The disciplines in this module were not present in the requirements context diagram in Figure 7.2, but they were represented by terminators added to the AICD in Figure 7.6. As mentioned earlier, we model the involvement of everyone who sends anything to or receives anything from our project. The Other Disciplines architecture module is needed for task allocation and is divided at a lower level into a separate sub-module for each discipline.

## 7.7 DEVELOPMENT PROCESS TASK ALLOCATION

At this point, modeling the development process any further would require us to depart from our meta-model to investigate specific details of a particular organization or project. Instead, in this section, we simply offer some general guidelines for adapting the models to your own circumstances. Part II illustrates practical, detailed application of the methods.

The benefits of concurrent development will have a major effect on the next step in building our model of the development process. In effect, every process in EDFD0 (Figure 7.5) will be multiply allocated by several superbubbles, like some of the allocations in Figure 6.13 and like several examples in Part II. However, the lower-level modules (that is, the separate disciplines) will not all have responsibility for everything. Each detailed task will have one discipline with prime responsibility for it, but other disciplines will have responsibility to support it. By dividing the high-level processes among the disciplines, we can specify at lower levels the exact responsibilities of the prime and supporting disciplines. As a result, the supporting disciplines know right from the outset what is required of them, and they can schedule and budget their support accordingly.

Naturally, concurrency also applies to the planning process itself, so all disciplines must be involved in putting together the development process model for the project. For example, they must have a say in what is and is not allocated to them, and in what deliverables they exchange with other disciplines.

Everything else about the development process model follows the general rules and guidelines presented throughout Part I and illustrated in Part II.

## 7.8 VARIATIONS ON THE ARCHITECTURE TEMPLATE

We started this chapter by presenting in Figure 7.1 an architecture template for the overall system development process, and we have demonstrated the benefits of this variation. We now leave that meta-model, and present some further adaptations of the architecture template for specific parts of the development process. These examples show that the architecture template, in every development area, can serve as a very specific guide to the nature of the essential model and its enhancements. It is frequently a good idea to start with an adaptation of the template before attempting to enhance a model, or even before establishing the essential model.

The following development areas are illustrated in the cited figures by modified architecture templates:

- configuring and partitioning hardware and software (Figure 7.8)
- integrating a system (Figure 7.9)
- developing a customer specification (Figure 7.10)
- developing a system specification (Figure 7.11)
- developing a hardware specification (Figure 7.12)
- developing a software specification (Figure 7.13)

The templates for these areas in your company and project are almost certainly different from these examples, but the principles remain the same. Just as we have seen in the development process model in this chapter, the amount of work involved in applying these templates can be huge. Here, however, we are just presenting the templates as suggested starting points for that work.

**Objectives:** Create hardware/software modules and/or objects.

| | | |
|---|---|---|
| • Build detailed user documentation<br>• Manage building of hardware/software modules/objects | • Interface with manufacturing<br>• Interface with regulatory agencies | |
| • Partition and allocate responsibilities for building hardware/software modules<br>• Partition and allocate responsibilities for test equipment development<br>• Partition critical hardware/software segments for early/late implementation<br>• Partition separately high-level and low-level hardware/software | • Build hardware/software modules and/or objects<br>• Build prototypes, breadboards<br>• Build software drivers and stubs<br>• Build test equipment<br>• Build detailed user documentation | • Validate hardware modules with hardware specification<br>• Validate software modules with software specification<br>• Validate test scenarios for software/hardware modules<br>• Validate user documentation |
| | • Trace errors (in modules, algorithms, and so on) to origination point. Determine where errors were introduced and recommend improvement of implementation process.<br>• Collect data for tracking implementation | |

**Deliverables:** Hardware modules, software modules/objects, test equipment, user documentation.

*Figure 7.8: Hardware/Software Template.*

**Objectives:** Validate system versus system specification.

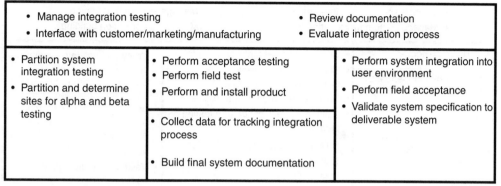

| | | |
|---|---|---|
| • Manage integration testing<br>• Interface with customer/marketing/manufacturing | | • Review documentation<br>• Evaluate integration process |
| • Partition system integration testing<br>• Partition and determine sites for alpha and beta testing | • Perform acceptance testing<br>• Perform field test<br>• Perform and install product<br><br>• Collect data for tracking integration process<br><br>• Build final system documentation | • Perform system integration into user environment<br>• Perform field acceptance<br>• Validate system specification to deliverable system |

**Deliverables:** Final system, installation documentation.

*Figure 7.9: System Integration Template.*

**Objectives:** Establish system purpose and customer specification.

| | | |
|---|---|---|
| • Identify schedules and scope<br>• Identify areas of evaluation/research | | • Determine project risks |
| • Model existing systems<br>• Gather user surveys<br>• Model existing environment<br>• Model user's perspective of system<br>• Interview customers<br>• Build operational scenarios | • Build blitz model of system<br>• Build blitz requirements model<br>• Build blitz architecture model<br>• Research available technology<br>• Build preliminary user documentation<br><br>• Determine state of technology<br>• Evaluate available parts/materials<br>• Evaluate production/manufacturing methods<br>• Evaluate testing methods | • Integrate blitz model with customer requirements<br>• Determine system feasibility<br>• Determine system manufacturability<br>• Define system testability |

**Deliverables:** Customer specification consisting of blitz models, preliminary user documentation, project plans, feasibility report, test plan, manufacturing plan, and development schedule.

*Figure 7.10: Customer Specification Template.*

**Objectives:** Prepare a detailed system specification.

| | | |
|---|---|---|
| • Manage specification integration<br>• Manage customer/marketing interface | | • Manage system partitioning<br>• Manage specification building |
| • Partition customer specification into technology-independent, technology-dependent, and implementation requirements<br>• Partition testing needs<br>• Partition manufacturing needs | • Build system requirements model<br>• Build system enhanced requirements model<br>• Build system architecture model<br>• Build test specification and testing plan<br>• Build manufacturing specification<br>• Build high-level user documentation | • Verify and validate system specification (for example, through walkthroughs, model balancing, identifying needs for further research, for prototyping, or for model simulation)<br>• Validate testing plan<br>• Validate manufacturing specification |
| | • Collect monitoring data for specification<br>• Perform planning and scheduling based on data collected | |

**Deliverables:** System specification consisting of requirements model, system enhanced requirements model, and system architecture model components; system acceptance testing plan; system manufacturing plan.

*Figure 7.11: System Specification Template.*

**Objectives:** Prepare a detailed hardware specification.

| | | |
|---|---|---|
| • Interface with component manufacturers<br>• Manage hardware design process | | • Contract and plan hardware component delivery<br>• Interface with hardware manufacturing |
| • Determine hardware/software partitioning<br>• Investigate available hardware parts (components or sub-assemblies)<br>• Partition hardware requirements: (build versus purchase versus reuse)<br>• Collect data for tracking hardware specification | • Build hardware requirements model<br>• Build detailed hardware architecture model (PC board layout, component selection, perform CAD/CAM, and so on)<br>• Build hardware test plan<br>• Build hardware manufacturing plan | • Validate hardware specification<br>• Integrate hardware/software specifications<br>• Integrate hardware specification<br>• Validate hardware testing plan and manufacturing plan<br>• Provide data to manufacturing |
| | • Determine effectiveness of process and recommendations for improving process | |

**Deliverables:** Hardware specification consisting of hardware architecture model, hardware testing plan, hardware manufacturing plan, and history (for future projects).

*Figure 7.12: Hardware Specification Template.*

**Objectives:** Prepare a detailed software specification.

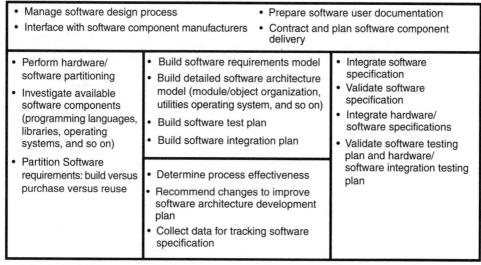

| | | |
|---|---|---|
| • Manage software design process | | • Prepare software user documentation |
| • Interface with software component manufacturers | | • Contract and plan software component delivery |

| | | |
|---|---|---|
| • Perform hardware/ software partitioning | • Build software requirements model | • Integrate software specification |
| • Investigate available software components (programming languages, libraries, operating systems, and so on) | • Build detailed software architecture model (module/object organization, utilities operating system, and so on) | • Validate software specification |
| | • Build software test plan | • Integrate hardware/ software specifications |
| | • Build software integration plan | • Validate software testing plan and hardware/ software integration testing plan |
| • Partition Software requirements: build versus purchase versus reuse | • Determine process effectiveness | |
| | • Recommend changes to improve software architecture development plan | |
| | • Collect data for tracking software specification | |

**Deliverables:** Software specification consisting of software architecture model, software testing plan, and hardware/software integration testing plan.

*Figure 7.13: Software Specification Template.*

# Part II

# Case Study: Groundwater Analysis System

# Chapter 8
## Initial Problem Statement

## 8.1 OVERVIEW

In this part of the book, we examine a fictitious system that is based on a real-world system developed with the Hatley/Hruschka/Pirbhai methods. Much of the original system, which automates the biomedical analysis of various body fluids, is proprietary, so with the kind consent of its owners, we illustrate similar principles using a system we dreamed up, in which samples of groundwater are analyzed for contamination by various pollutants.

The original system and the fictitious system are both remarkable for the diversity of technologies they employ—mechanical transports, hydraulics, pneumatics, chemistry, laser optics, electromechanical devices, computer hardware, and software—all in a relatively compact size. Systems just do not get much more multidisciplinary than this!

In this case study, a development shop receives a requirements specification in narrative form from the customer; as these requirements are analyzed and the development proceeds, further clarification and additional information are sought from the customer and other sources.

The customer requirements presented in the following paragraphs have already been divided into the categories described in earlier chapters. Actual customer requirements rarely arrive in such orderly form, so reaching even this point usually entails significant work.

## 8.2 Required Capabilities

Following are the required capabilities of the groundwater analysis system, as provided by the customer:

> A system is to be developed to analyze specimens of groundwater for numerous different pollutants, to display the results in real time as they are generated, to retain the results for future reference, and, upon request at later times, to display or print selected results or transmit them to a data processing center. A list to be updated periodically will identify the pollutants to detect.
>
> Since some specimens may be highly contaminated with dangerous toxins, all waste material from analysis and residual specimens must be disposed of according to EPA toxic waste regulations.
>
> For each specimen, the system must identify the source location, the source depth, the time of sampling, and the concentration of each pollutant in parts per million. In addition, the system must retain data on the acceptable level of each pollutant and highlight measurements that exceed these levels. The system must also retain data on valid test limits and flag as invalid any results that are outside those limits.
>
> The system must have a calibrate mode, in which the operator can load one or more reference specimens and adjust the analysis results for accuracy.
>
> The system must provide information to the operator on its operating status, including any malfunctions.
>
> The operator must be able to rerun the analysis of any selected specimen, either before it is removed from the system or after it has been reinserted. The normal purpose of a rerun is to check results that are invalid or beyond the acceptable level. For this purpose, the system must be capable of retaining at least twenty specimens, all available for initial or rerun analysis. When a rerun is requested, it must have priority over the running of other specimens.

## 8.3 REQUIRED PERFORMANCE

Following is what the customer initially provided regarding required performance. More performance information will eventually be needed:

- The specimens are to be analyzed at a rate of at least 40 per hour.
- The response time, from loading a given specimen to having its analysis available, must be no more than 5 minutes.
- Accuracy of the analysis must be within ±5% for each pollutant.

## 8.4 REQUIRED CONSTRAINTS

As usual, the customer places some significant constraints on the design choices available to us. These are listed in the following paragraphs.

### 8.4.1 Input/Output Constraints

Since the system's inputs and outputs are what the user sees most, it is very common to find constraints on these characteristics in the customer specification. This system is no exception.

- The specimens will be received in capped vials. The vials will be labeled with the specimen source location, source depth, and time of sampling. This information will be printed and bar coded. One operator will be available to load the vials into the system, to direct the system output, and to remove the used vials and specimens.
- The vials will be kept in refrigerated storage prior to being loaded into the system.
- The operator will enter data and control inputs through a standard computer keyboard.

### 8.4.2 Design Constraints

In addition to the input/output constraints, other constraints on the design are common. These often cause dismay among system developers, who tend to think that a customer has no business tinkering with the design. The fact is that there are often good business reasons for such constraints: A few of the many examples are economics, the availability of spare parts, and training. While developers may sometimes have a better solution, they should make sure they understand the business issues before challenging the constraints they are given.

Two constraints were identified, as follows:

> **Pollutant Analysis Technique:** This system will use the well-established techniques of adding reagents specifically developed to react with one or more pollutants, and of measuring the reaction through the diffraction and/or spectral dispersion of a light beam.
>
> The reagents and the specific measurements of their reactions with pollutants will be developed as part of the project.

> **Reuse of Existing Modules:** There is an existing integrated unit—which we shall call the Existing Sampling Module—for mixing the fluids, stabilizing their temperature and dilution, allowing the stabilized mixture to flow through a viewing chamber, and allowing a light beam to pass through the mixture for detection of its scatter and spectral dispersion. Because the Existing Sampling Module is still superior to competitive units, it will be reused in the system.
>
> The main system control and data analysis is to be carried out on a commercially available computer workstation.

An interesting facet of the original system from which ours is derived is that most of the revenue comes from selling the reagents after the system is installed, not from selling the system itself. The composition of the reagents is proprietary and is closely guarded as a company secret; the system is designed to work only with those reagents. This is a fine example of the importance of understanding the business model when developing a system. Without this understanding, the developers might just use an off-the-shelf reagent and end up with an unprofitable system. Of course, hand-in-hand with the insistence on proprietary reagents is the need for those reagents to provide some real benefit to the user, to justify the presumably higher cost. Marketing, management, system engineers, biomedical specialists, and probably others must work together to develop a model that makes good business and technical sense and also benefits the customer.

## 8.4.2.1 Other Design Constraints

Numerous other design constraints are usually included—indeed, they *must* be included—to ensure that a system will work reliably under all expected operating conditions. A particular subset of these constraints are loosely referred to as the "-ilities" of the system—with reliability, maintainability, testability, and safety among them. Other common constraints are: operating temperature range, size, shape, weight, power consumption, EMI (electromagnetic interference) generation, EMI susceptibility, vibration and shock, and design for future reuse (which is distinct from the constraint to reuse existing modules).

Each of these constraints has a profound influence on system design, and each involves a separate discipline or subdiscipline. Important though these constraints are, we shall not deal with them further in this book, beyond saying that the "-ilities" and other constraints must be taken into account and that most of them are included, directly or through derivation, in the architecture module specifications. In fact, it is very desirable to establish a standard format for AMSs that includes sections for all the constraints that are relevant to the particular type of systems under development.

The next chapter fits the above requirements into the various models described in this book.

# Chapter 9
## Modeling the Known Pieces

## 9.1 OVERVIEW

In this chapter, we build the pieces of the models that correspond to the requirements stated in Chapter 8. These pieces include the requirements context diagram, the system timing specification, the system entity model, and the architecture and requirements models for the Existing Sampling Module.

## 9.2 THE REQUIREMENTS CONTEXT

The requirements statements in Chapter 8 indicate that the central purpose of the system is to analyze groundwater, and that the external entities with which the system must interface are the operator, the specimen storage, the data processing center, and the toxic waste disposal. From these requirements, we can construct a context diagram, as shown in Figure 9.1.

Here, the main input flow is SPECIMEN; the main output flows are ANALYSIS RESULTS and SELECTED HISTORICAL RESULTS. By "main" flows, we mean flows that contribute directly to the central purpose of the system. VALID OPERATOR REQUEST is a supplementary input flow; SYSTEM STATUS, SYSTEM MODE, USED SPECIMENS, and WASTE are supplementary output flows. Many of the flows are defined in the dictionary at the end of Chapter 12. Everything in the context diagram that we

304

have described so far is derived fairly directly from the required multiplicities. We made an assumption—not included in the required multiplicities —that the operator will sometimes need to remove a specimen before it has been analyzed (if the wrong specimen had been loaded, for example, or if the analysis of another specimen is more urgent). This assumption results in SPECIMEN being a two-way flow.

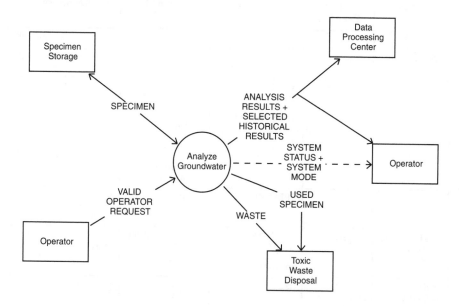

*Figure 9.1: Context Diagram.*

(Notice that the tool we used to construct these models uses the "+" symbol from the dictionary's BNF notation to gather multiple independent flows on a single flow vector.)

The essential model simply assumes that the reagents are present within the system as needed; therefore, they are not shown on the context diagram. Reagents are determined by the particular method chosen for the analysis, and their management is treated as an enhancement to the system.

## 9.3 THE SYSTEM TIMING SPECIFICATION

Figure 9.2 shows the top-level timing specification, or TSPEC. It includes all inputs and outputs at the context level. The customer specification only describes the overall throughput and delay of specimens and their analysis results, but there are several other system responses that need to be specified, as the TSPEC shows. Some are clearly noncritical, but others require discussion with the customer.

| Timing Specification: Analyze Groundwater | | | | |
|---|---|---|---|---|
| **Input Flow(s)** | **Input Event(s)** | **Output Flow(s)** | **Output Event(s)** | **Response Timing** |
| GROUND-WATER SPECIMEN | Entered | ANALYSIS RESULTS (all applicable components) | Corresponding output appears | ≤ 5 minutes for single event; ≥ 40 per hour continuous rate |
| REFERENCE SPECIMEN | Entered | ANALYSIS RESULTS (all applicable components) | Output appears with values matching, within specified tolerances, known specimen parameters | ≤ 5 minutes |
| N/A | | SPECIMEN | Removed from system | No critical timing; discretionary operator action |
| HISTORICAL RESULTS REQUEST | Entered | SELECTED HISTORICAL RESULTS (all components) | Corresponding output appears | Not critical; <30 seconds goal |
| MODE REQUEST | STANDBY requested when SYSTEM MODE = IDLE | SYSTEM MODE | Goes to STANDBY | Not critical; <30 seconds goal |
| | Other transitions | SYSTEM MODE | Goes to requested state | TBD |
| N/A | | SYSTEM STATUS | Value changes | No critical timing as long as it reflects actual system mode significantly faster than operator response time |
| SPECIAL ANALYSIS REQUEST; GROUND-WATER SPECIMEN | Both inputs entered with matching SPECIMEN ID | ANALYSIS RESULTS (all applicable components) | Corresponding output appears | ≤ 5 minutes |

*Figure 9.2: System Timing Specification (Continued).*

| Timing Specification: Analyze Groundwater | | | | |
|---|---|---|---|---|
| **Input Flow(s)** | **Input Event(s)** | **Output Flow(s)** | **Output Event(s)** | **Response Timing** |
| PARA-METER UPDATE REQUEST | Entered | ANALYSIS RESULTS (all applicable components) | Output appears with values corresponding to updated parameters | ≤ 5 minutes |
| RERUN REQUEST | Entered | ANALYSIS RESULTS (all applicable components) | Output appears with corresponding SPECIMEN ID | ≤ 5 minutes |
| SPECIMEN ANALYSIS COMPLETE | Entered | USED SPECIMEN | Ready for removal | Timing not critical as long as overall analysis flow rate of ≥ 40 per hour is maintained |
| ILLEGAL ENTRY | Entered | None | No response | None |
| N/A | | WASTE | Removed from system | Waste removal must be such that it can be accomplished while still maintaining the overall analysis flow rate of ≥ 40 per hour |

*Figure 9.2: System Timing Specification.*

## 9.4 THE ENTITY MODEL

In parallel with the functional analysis that we have already started, an information analysis using class diagrams is very useful. This analysis is frequently based on the requirements statement and discussions with the customer.

Figure 9.3 is a first-cut class diagram containing entities—Groundwater Specimen, Reference Specimen, Pollutant, Reagent, and Neutralizing Agent—that represent the principal items involved in the proposed system. The last two of these entities have been grouped together as members of the Agent set. The Groundwater Specimen and Pollutant have a Tested Pollutant Composition relationship, whereby after testing, a specimen is known to contain a certain concentration of certain pollutants. The Groundwater Specimen and Reagent have a Reagent Specimen Test Usage relationship, reflecting the selection of certain reagents for a given specimen.

The numerals and letters on the relationship lines show the multiplicities of the attached entities' involvements in their relationships. Some multiplicities are entered as question marks because their values are not clear from the requirements statement. For example, it is clear that many specimens will be used with a single reagent, but will more than one reagent be used with a single specimen?

Figure 9.4 shows a more complete (but not fully complete) class diagram, developed after further study of the requirements statement and discussion with the customer. Entities added to those in the first-cut diagram are Sampling Location, Pollutant Class, Toxic Pollutant, and EPA Toxic Waste Regulation.

The addition of Pollutant Class and its relationship with Pollutant reflects the fact that some pollutants are related and might share the same or similar reagents. In such cases, the reagent for one member of a pollutant set might be suitable as a backup reagent for another member. These are the kinds of useful discoveries that can be made through entity modeling.

Figure 9.3 and Figure 9.4 show the entities and relationships of the entity model, but not the attributes, which are defined in the entity and relationship specifications. We do not list them all here; instead, we illustrate them through one entity specification and one relationship specification.

The following specification is for Groundwater Specimen, a typical entity.

| Entity Name: | Groundwater Specimen |
|---|---|
| Alias: | None |
| Purpose (What/Why): | A sample of groundwater, taken at a known time, location, and depth and stored in a vial for the purpose of determining the concentration of pollutants that it contains. |
| Properties: | The container is a cylindrical vial, x mm in diameter, y mm long, with a leak-proof seal (see vial specification #ABCD). The vial is labeled with the sampling time, location, and depth in English and as a bar code (see label specification #EFGH). The vial is at least 3/4 full of groundwater when received by the system. |
| Attributes: | SPECIMEN ID<br><br>SAMPLE TIME<br><br>SAMPLING LOCATION<br><br>DEPTH OF SAMPLE |

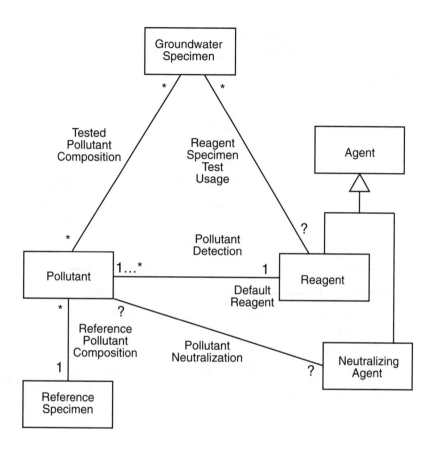

*Figure 9.3: Initial Entity Model.*

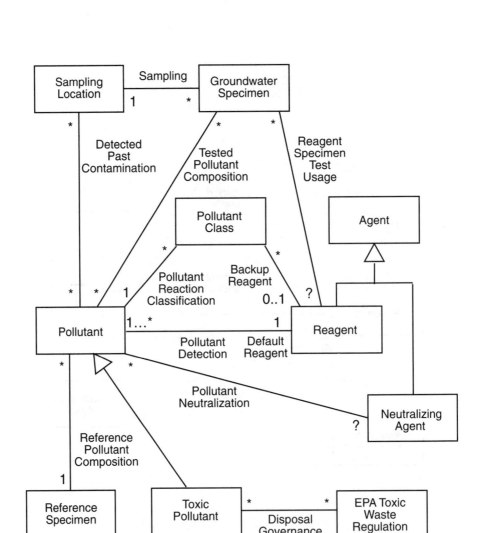

*Figure 9.4: Enlarged Entity Model.*

Consider this specification for Tested Pollutant Composition, a typical relationship:

| Relationship Name: | Tested Pollutant Composition |
|---|---|
| Alias: | None |
| Purpose (What/Why): | Relates groundwater specimens to pollutants and their concentrations in those specimens. |
| Participation: | Groundwater Specimen [Mandatory]<br>Pollutant [Optional] |
| Cardinalities: | For each Pollutant there are many Groundwater Specimens.<br>For each Groundwater Specimen there are many Pollutants. |
| Rules of Association: | The entities are associated if the Groundwater Specimen contains the Pollutant. |
| Attributes: | TESTED CONCENTRATION LEVEL |

These specifications, apart from providing the rigorous definitions that support the diagrams, also provide links to the other models. Usually, the attributes are also flows in the requirements model and therefore share the same requirements dictionary definitions.

Note also that the entities themselves can be flows. This last point highlights a strong distinction between software and systems. Within software, real physical objects can never exist, but in systems, they frequently do. Software gets around this through symbolic representations of real objects, or by using just their attributes. Unfortunately, this can lead to invalid assumptions about the properties or states of the objects.

Notice that Sampling Location, which was an attribute of Groundwater Specimen, has "grown up" to become an entity in the enlarged entity model shown in Figure 9.4. The modeling process revealed that Sampling Location has attributes of its own. However, it is still connected to Groundwater Specimen through a new relationship, Sampling.

## 9.5 THE EXISTING SAMPLING MODULE

In addition to satisfying the top-level essential requirements, we must reuse the Existing Sampling Module for which the requirements and architecture models are known. Figure 9.5 shows this module's complete enhanced requirements model, and Figure 9.6 shows a selection of the PSPECs for the processes in that model.

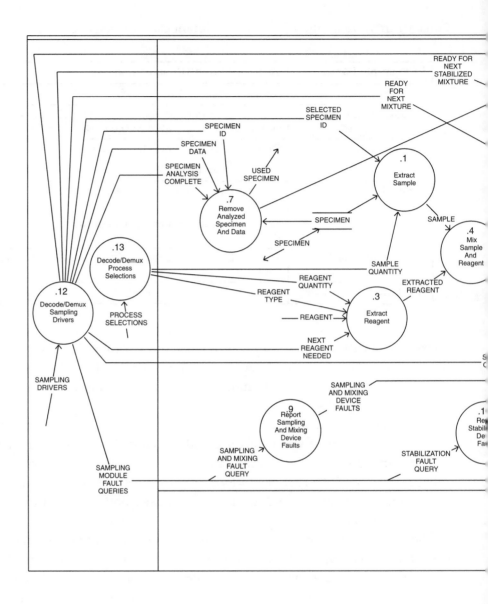

*Figure 9.5:*    *Enhanced Requirements Model, Existing*
*Sampling Module (Left Side).*

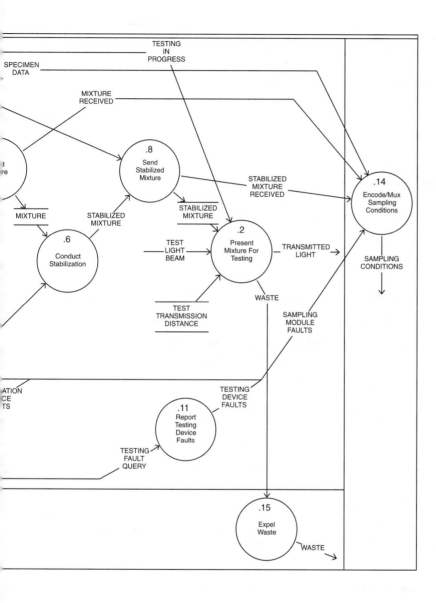

*Figure 9.5:  Enhanced Requirements Model, Existing*
*Sampling Module (Right Side).*

**PSPEC: Extract Sample**

Find the INPUT:SPECIMEN corresponding to INPUT:SELECTED_SPECIMEN_ID.

From that INPUT:SPECIMEN, extract a quantity INPUT:SAMPLE_QUANTITY to produce OUTPUT:SAMPLE.

**PSPEC: Extract Reagent**

Each time a INPUT:NEXT_REAGENT_NEEDED is received:

In the set INPUT:REAGENT, find INPUT:REAGENT_TYPE and extract a quantity INPUT:REAGENT_QUANTITY of the corresponding BIOLOGICAL_POLLUTANT_REAGENT or CHEMICAL_POLLUTANT_REAGENT to produce OUTPUT:EXTRACTED_REAGENT.

Each time a new INPUT:SAMPLE and INPUT:EXTRACTED_REAGENT are received:

Mix together INPUT:SAMPLE and INPUT:EXTRACTED_REAGENT to produce OUTPUT:MIXTURE.

**PSPEC: Send Mixture**

At start-up, set OUTPUT:MIXTURE_RECEIVED = FALSE.

Whenever INPUT:MIXTURE is received, set OUTPUT:MIXTURE_RECEIVED = TRUE.

Then, when INPUT:READY_FOR_NEXT_MIXTURE = TRUE, pass on INPUT:MIXTURE as

OUTPUT:MIXTURE and then set OUTPUT:MIXTURE_RECEIVED = FALSE.

**PSPEC: Conduct Stabilization**

Process each INPUT:MIXTURE received in accordance with the following components of INPUT:STABILIZATION_COEFFICIENTS:

Agitate in accordance with MIXING_PARAMETERS;

Increase temperature until it is within the range of DESIRED_TEMPERATURE;

Maintain the agitation and temperature for the duration of REACTION_TIME;

Then pass on INPUT:MIXTURE as OUTPUT:STABILIZED_MIXTURE.

*It is tempting to express the heating, mixing, and reaction as three different processes, but they must all be carried out together with one sample of test mixture.  Any separation of the processes is a design decision that does not belong here.*

**PSPEC: Present Mixture for Testing**

Each time a new INPUT:STABILIZED_MIXTURE is received:

Allow INPUT:TEST_LIGHT_BEAM to pass through it for a distance INPUT:TEST_TRANSMISSION_DISTANCE to produce OUTPUT:TRANSMITTED_LIGHT.

Then, when INPUT:TESTING_IN_PROGRESS = FALSE, remove INPUT:STABILIZED_MIXTURE as OUTPUT:WASTE.

*Figure 9.6: Selected PSPECs of Enhanced Existing Sampling Module.*

Since the module is a given, we do not need to spend time developing its models. The challenge instead is to blend the existing module into the overall system models.

We assume here that the existing module was originally developed using the H/H/P methods; otherwise, we would need to "reverse engineer" the models from the existing design and whatever specifications are available. This would entail examining the structure of the module to construct its architecture model, examining its functionality to construct its enhanced requirements model, and determining its core and enhanced functions to extract the essential requirements model. Depending on the size and complexity of the module, this reverse engineering can be a long and tedious process. Before embarking on it, we must judge how much detail we really need for the project at hand and tailor the work accordingly.

Figure 9.7 represents the Existing Sampling Module as a single, black-box architecture module. We only need to ensure that this module's capabilities and interfaces meet the needs of the overall system.

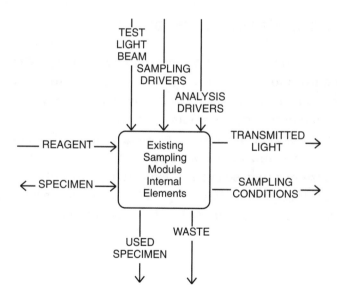

*Figure 9.7: Architecture Model for Existing Sampling Module.*

The next chapter in our case study builds upon the known pieces of the models that we have established in this chapter. We shall elaborate on both the architecture and requirements models.

# Chapter 10
## Building Upon the Known Pieces

## 10.1 TOP-LEVEL ESSENTIAL MODEL

Now that we have modeled the known pieces of the system, we can start to extend the model, upward and downward. In this way, we can complete the requirements and architecture models and specify the entire system.

The Level 1 diagram of the essential model, shown in Figure 10.1, reflects the basic functions required of the system: storing, sampling, mixing, stabilizing, and testing the specimens and reagents, and analyzing the results of the tests. In addition, the system must select the expected pollutants and their reagents, respond to operator requests, read the data included with each specimen, remove the analyzed specimens, and store the processing parameters.

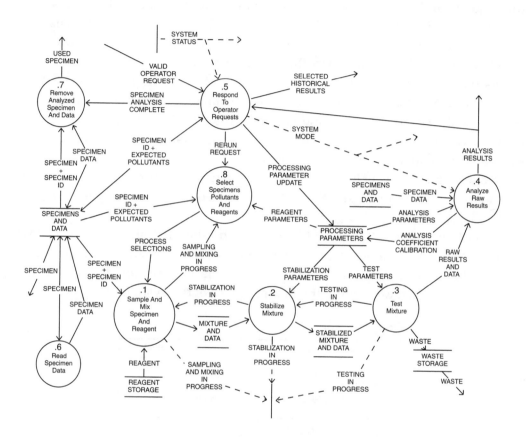

*Figure 10.1: DFD0, Analyze Groundwater.*

The requirements statements stipulate that the reagents and the specific measurements of their reactions must be developed as part of the project. How does this part of the project fit into the model? The answer is that the development of the reagents and of their reactions is accomplished by a chemical analysis that is not represented in the model. However, the model's dictionary definitions of the reagents and the details and parameters of the reactions will be derived from the results of the analysis. Although the chemical analysis is well beyond the scope of this book (and outside the technical domain of its authors), we mention it as just one of many trade-off studies that are customarily performed during system development. The architecture and requirements models may be used to compare different versions of the system, but the actual analyses that produce those versions are not represented within the models.

A CSPEC has been included in Figure 10.1 to determine the SYSTEM STATUS, and another, to determine SYSTEM MODE, is implied inside the Respond To Operator Requests process.

CSPEC0, in Figure 10.2, is a simple decision table that shows SYSTEM STATUS in the OPERATIONAL or RUNNING states, depending on whether any part of the process is in progress. This CSPEC will be elaborated considerably during enhancement, when we analyze the failure modes of the system.

| Input | | | Output |
|---|---|---|---|
| SAMPLING AND MIXING IN PROGRESS | STABILIZATION IN PROGRESS | TESTING IN PROGRESS | SYSTEM STATUS |
| FALSE | FALSE | FALSE | OPERATIONAL |
| TRUE | * | * | RUNNING |
| * | TRUE | * | RUNNING |
| * | * | TRUE | RUNNING |

*Figure 10.2: CSPEC0, Analyze Groundwater.*

Figure 10.3 through Figure 10.17 contain the descendent DFDs, PSPECs, and CSPECs of DFD0, each elaborating upon the information in that DFD. Note, in particular, that CSPEC5 establishes the system mode and controls the updates to the processing parameters, as shown in Figure 10.10.

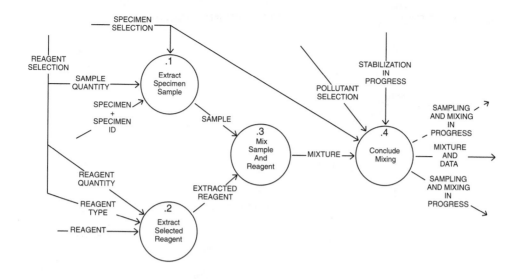

---

**PSPEC: Extract Specimen Sample**

Each time a new SAMPLE_QUANTITY is received:

Select the SPECIMEN whose SPECIMEN_ID matches
SPECIMEN_SELECTION;

from that SPECIMEN extract a quantity SAMPLE_QUANTITY to produce SAMPLE.

**PSPEC: Extract Selected Reagent**

Each time a new REAGENT_TYPE is received:

In the set REAGENT, find REAGENT_TYPE and extract a quantity REAGENT_QUANTITY of the
corresponding BIOLOGICAL_POLLUTANT_REAGENT or CHEMICAL_POLLUTANT_REAGENT to
produce EXTRACTED_REAGENT.

**PSPEC: Mix Sample And Reagent**

Each time a new SAMPLE and EXTRACTED_REAGENT are received:

Mix together SAMPLE and EXTRACTED_REAGENT to produce
MIXTURE.

**PSPEC: Conclude Mixing**

At start-up, set SAMPLING_AND_MIXING_IN_PROGRESS = FALSE.

Whenever a new POLLUTANT_SELECTION whose value is not "None" is received, set
SAMPLING_AND_MIXING_IN_PROGRESS = TRUE.

Then, when STABILIZATION_IN_PROGRESS = FALSE and MIXTURE is received, assemble
MIXTURE_AND_DATA using:

MIXTURE = MIXTURE;

POLLUTANT_TYPE = POLLUTANT_SELECTION;

SPECIMEN_ID = SPECIMEN_SELECTION;

then set SAMPLING_AND_MIXING_IN_PROGRESS = FALSE.

*Figure 10.3: DFD1, Sample And Mix Specimen And
Reagent, with Associated PSPECs.*

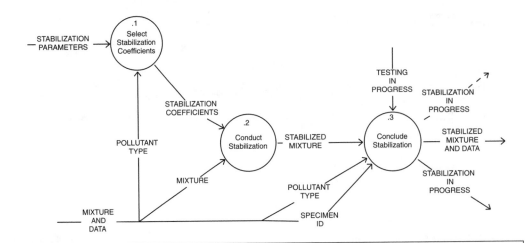

**PSPEC: Select Stabilization Coefficients**

Each time a new POLLUTANT_TYPE is received:

In the set STABILIZATION_PARAMETERS, find the item containing POLLUTANT_TYPE and set STABILIZATION_COEFFICIENTS to the corresponding STABILIZATION_COEFFICIENTS.

**PSPEC: Conduct Stabilization**

Process each MIXTURE received in accordance with the following components of STABILIZATION_COEFFICIENTS:

Agitate in accordance with MIXING_PARAMETERS;

increase temperature until it is within the range of DESIRED_TEMPERATURE;

maintain the agitation and temperature for the duration of REACTION_TIME;

then pass on MIXTURE as STABILIZED_MIXTURE.

**PSPEC: Conclude Stabilization**

At start-up, set STABILIZATION_IN_PROGRESS = FALSE.

Whenever a new POLLUTANT_TYPE is received, set STABILIZATION_IN_PROGRESS = TRUE.

Then, when STABILIZED_MIXTURE and TESTING_IN_PROGRESS = FALSE are both received:

Include STABILIZED_MIXTURE , POLLUTANT_TYPE, and SPECIMEN_ID as STABILIZED_MIXTURE_AND_DATA;

set STABILIZATION_IN_PROGRESS = FALSE.

*Figure 10.4: DFD2, Stabilize Mixture, with Associated PSPECs.*

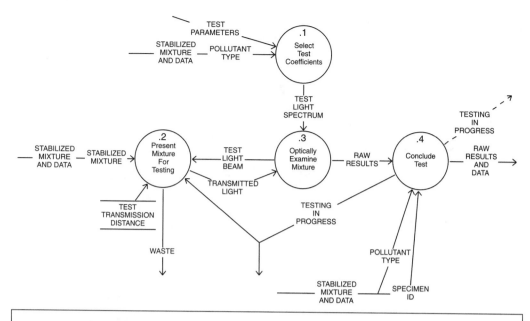

## PSPEC: Select Test Coefficients

Each time a new POLLUTANT_TYPE is received:

In the set TEST_PARAMETERS, find the item containing POLLUTANT_TYPE and set
TEST_LIGHT_SPECTRUM to the corresponding TEST_LIGHT_SPECTRUM.

## PSPEC: Present Mixture For Testing

Each time a new STABILIZED_MIXTURE is received:

Allow TEST_LIGHT_BEAM to pass through it for a distance TEST_TRANSMISSION_DISTANCE to
produce TRANSMITTED_LIGHT;
then, when TESTING_IN_PROGRESS = FALSE, remove STABILIZED_MIXTURE as WASTE.

## PSPEC: Optically Examine Mixture

While generating TEST_LIGHT_BEAM with the spectrum of TEST_LIGHT_SPECTRUM:
measure the spectral distribution of TRANSMITTED_LIGHT and enter it in RAW_RESULTS as
ACTUAL_SPECTRAL_DISTRIBUTION; measure the scatter distribution of TRANSMITTED_LIGHT and
enter it in RAW_RESULTS as ACTUAL_SCATTER_DISTRIBUTION.

*Include illustration of spectrum and scatter.*

## PSPEC: Conclude Test

At start-up, set TESTING_IN_PROGRESS = FALSE.

Whenever a new POLLUTANT_TYPE is received:
Set TESTING_IN_PROGRESS = TRUE.

Then, when RAW_RESULTS is received:

Include it with POLLUTANT_TYPE and SPECIMEN_ID to produce RAW_RESULTS_AND_DATA.

Set TESTING_IN_PROGRESS = FALSE.

*Figure 10.5: DFD3, Test Mixture, with Associated PSPECs.*

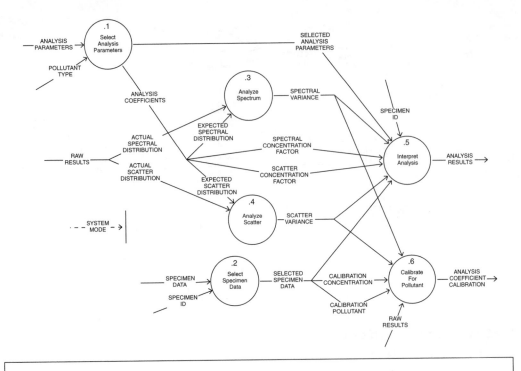

## PSPEC: Select Analysis Parameters

In the set ANALYSIS_PARAMETERS, find the item containing POLLUTANT_TYPE and set ANALYSIS_COEFFICIENTS and the components of SELECTED_ANALYSIS_PARAMETERS to the corresponding components of the selected item.

## PSPEC: Select Specimen Data

In the set SPECIMEN_DATA, find the item containing SPECIMEN_ID and set the elements of SELECTED_SPECIMEN_DATA equal to the corresponding elements in the selected SPECIMEN_DATA.

## CSPEC: Analyze Raw Results

## PSPEC: Analyze Spectrum

Calculate the cross-correlation function between ACTUAL_SPECTRAL_DISTRIBUTION and EXPECTED_SPECTRAL_DISTRIBUTION.

Then calculate the variance of the cross-correlation function as SPECTRAL_VARIANCE.

| Input | Output | |
|---|---|---|
| SYSTEM MODE | Interpret Analysis | Calibrate For Pollutant |
| NORMAL | Activate | |
| CALIBRATE | | Activate |
| STANDBY | | |
| IDLE | | |

## PSPEC: Analyze Scatter

Calculate the two-dimensional cross-correlation function between ACTUAL_SCATTER_DISTRIBUTION and EXPECTED_SCATTER_DISTRIBUTION.

Then calculate the variance of the cross-correlation function as SCATTER_VARIANCE.

*Figure 10.6:* DFD4, *Analyze Raw Results, with Associated* CSPEC, PSPECs.

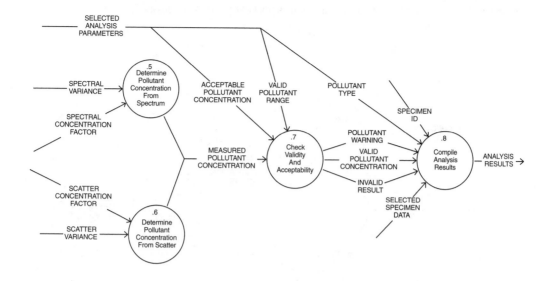

## PSPEC: Determine Pollutant Concentration From Spectrum

Set MEASURED_POLLUTANT_CONCENTRATION =
SPECTRAL_CONCENTRATION_FACTOR / SPECTRAL_VARIANCE.

## PSPEC: Determine Pollutant Concentration From Scatter

Set MEASURED_POLLUTANT_CONCENTRATION =
SCATTER_CONCENTRATION_FACTOR / SCATTER_VARIANCE.

## PSPEC: Check Validity And Acceptability

If MEASURED_POLLUTANT_CONCENTRATION is within the range of VALID_POLLUTANT_RANGE,
then set:

VALID_POLLUTANT_CONCENTRATION = MEASURED_POLLUTANT_CONCENTRATION

and set INVALID_RESULT = FALSE.

Otherwise, set INVALID_RESULT = TRUE.

If MEASURED_POLLUTANT_CONCENTRATION < ACCEPTABLE_POLLUTANT_CONCENTRATION
then set:

POLLUTANT_WARNING = FALSE.

Otherwise, set POLLUTANT_WARNING = TRUE.

## PSPEC: Compile Analysis Results

For each SPECIMEN_ID, gather the following into ANALYSIS_RESULTS :

SPECIMEN_ID = SPECIMEN_ID, SELECTED_SPECIMEN_DATA = SELECTED_SPECIMEN_DATA,

and for each POLLUTANT_TYPE that appears with the current SPECIMEN_ID,

either include INVALID_RESULT if it is TRUE or else include
POLLUTANT_CONCENTRATION = VALID_POLLUTANT_CONCENTRATION

and POLLUTANT_WARNING = POLLUTANT_WARNING.

*Figure 10.7:* DFD4.5, *Interpret Analysis, with Associated*
PSPECs.

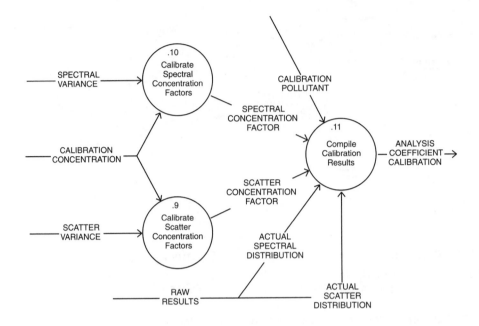

---

**PSPEC: Calibrate Scatter Concentration Factors**

Set SCATTER_CONCENTRATION_FACTOR =
CALIBRATION_CONCENTRATION * SCATTER_VARIANCE.

**PSPEC: Calibrate Spectral Concentration Factors**

Set SPECTRAL_CONCENTRATION_FACTOR =
CALIBRATION_CONCENTRATION * SPECTRAL_VARIANCE.

**PSPEC: Compile Calibration Results**

In ANALYSIS_COEFFICIENT_CALIBRATION, set:

POLLUTANT_TYPE = CALIBRATION_POLLUTANT

and the components of ANALYSIS_COEFFICIENTS to

EXPECTED SPECTRAL DISTRIBUTION = ACTUAL_SPECTRAL_DISTRIBUTION,

EXPECTED SCATTER DISTRIBUTION = ACTUAL_SCATTER_DISTRIBUTION,

SPECTRAL_CONCENTRATION_FACTOR = SPECTRAL_CONCENTRATION_FACTOR,

SCATTER_CONCENTRATION_FACTOR = SCATTER_CONCENTRATION_FACTOR.

*Figure 10.8: DFD4.6, Calibrate For Pollutant, with Associated PSPECs.*

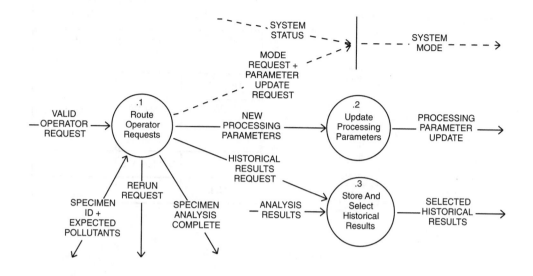

**PSPEC: Update Processing Parameters**

When activated, issue PROCESSING_PARAMETER_UPDATE = NEW_PROCESSING_PARAMETERS.

*Figure 10.9:*  DFD5, *Respond To Operator Requests, with Associated* PSPEC.

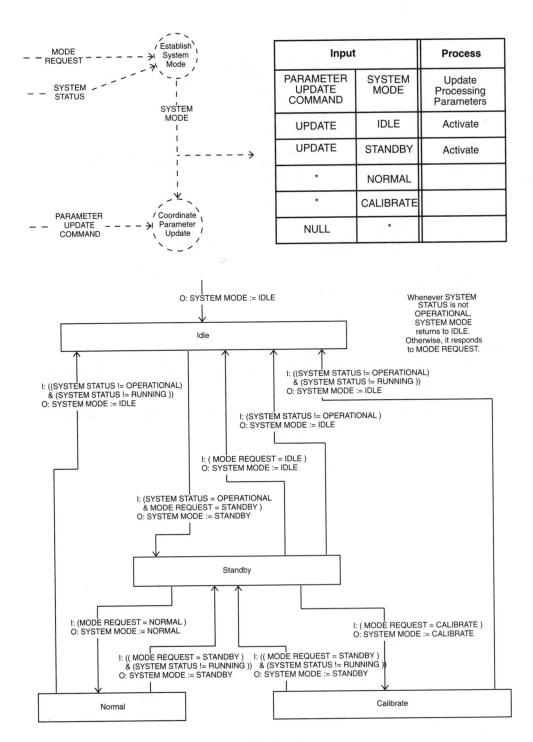

*Figure 10.10: CSPEC5, Respond To Operator Requests.*

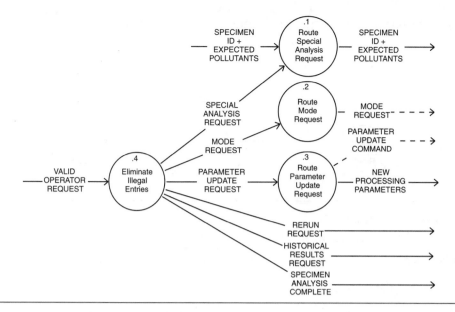

---

**PSPEC: Route Special Analysis Request**

Whenever SPECIAL_ANALYSIS_REQUEST arrives:

Match its SPECIMEN_ID with SPECIMEN_ID + EXPECTED_POLLUTANTS,
then update the corresponding EXPECTED_POLLUTANTS with the 1{POLLUTANT_TYPE} in
SPECIAL_ANALYSIS_REQUEST and set SPECIMEN_ID = SPECIMEN_ID.

**PSPEC: Route Mode Request**

Whenever MODE_REQUEST arrives, set MODE_REQUEST = MODE_REQUEST.

**PSPEC: Route Parameter Update Request**

Whenever PARAMETER_UPDATE_REQUEST arrives, send
PARAMETER_UPDATE_COMMAND and set
NEW_PROCESSING_PARAMETERS = PARAMETER_UPDATE_REQUEST.

**PSPEC: Eliminate Illegal Entries**

If VALID_OPERATOR_REQUEST is a SPECIAL_ANALYSIS_REQUEST, then set
SPECIAL_ANALYSIS_REQUEST = VALID_OPERATOR_REQUEST.

If VALID_OPERATOR_REQUEST is a MODE_REQUEST, then set
MODE REQUEST = VALID_OPERATOR_REQUEST.

If VALID_OPERATOR_REQUEST is a PARAMETER_UPDATE_REQUEST, then set
PARAMETER_UPDATE_REQUEST = VALID_OPERATOR_REQUEST.

If VALID_OPERATOR_REQUEST is a RERUN_REQUEST, then set
RERUN_REQUEST = VALID_OPERATOR_REQUEST.

If VALID_OPERATOR_REQUEST is a HISTORICAL_RESULTS_REQUEST, then set
HISTORICAL_RESULTS_REQUEST = VALID_OPERATOR_REQUEST.

If VALID_OPERATOR_REQUEST is a SPECIMEN_ANALYSIS_COMPLETE, then set
SPECIMEN_ANALYSIS_COMPLETE = VALID_OPERATOR_REQUEST.

Otherwise, (ILLEGAL_ENTRY) do nothing.

*Figure 10.11: DFD5.1, Route Operator Requests, with Associated PSPECs.*

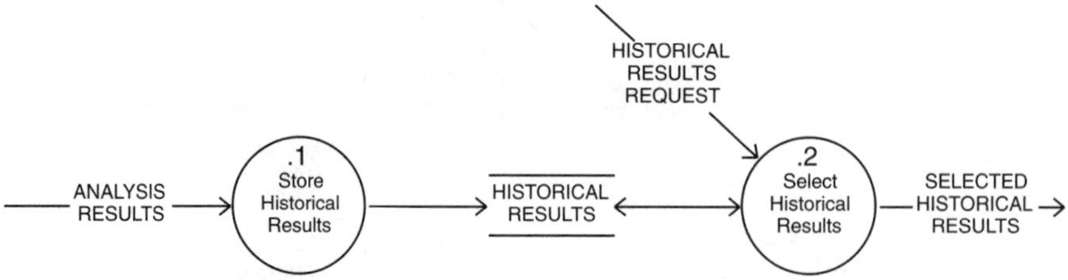

---

**PSPEC: Store Historical Results**

Set DATE_AND_TIME = the current date and time.

Then set HISTORICAL_RESULTS = ANALYSIS_RESULTS + DATE_AND_TIME.

**PSPEC: Select Historical Results**

Find all HISTORICAL_RESULTS whose
SPECIMEN_SOURCE_LOCATION matches the SPECIMEN_SOURCE_LOCATION (if any) in
HISTORICAL_RESULTS_REQUEST, and whose
SPECIMEN ID matches the SPECIMEN ID (if any) in HISTORICAL_RESULTS_REQUEST, and whose
POLLUTANT_WARNING matches the POLLUTANT_WARNING (if any) in
HISTORICAL_RESULTS_REQUEST, and whose
DATE_AND_TIME are within the DATE_AND_TIME_RANGE (if any) in
HISTORICAL_RESULTS_REQUEST.

If HISTORICAL_RESULTS_REQUEST contains DELETE_REQUEST, then delete the selected
HISTORICAL_RESULTS.

If HISTORICAL_RESULTS_REQUEST contains DISPLAY_REQUEST, then set
SELECTED_HISTORICAL_RESULTS to the selected HISTORICAL_RESULTS.

*Figure 10.12: DFD5.3, Store And Select Historical Results, with Associated PSPECs.*

---

**PSPEC: Read Specimen Data**

Read the bar code on SPECIMEN and return the result as SPECIMEN_DATA.

Return SPECIMEN as SPECIMEN.

*See specifications for specimen vials and bar codes for details of this process.*

**PSPEC: Remove Analyzed Specimen And Data**

Find SPECIMEN + SPECIMEN_ID matching
SPECIMEN_ANALYSIS_COMPLETE. Transfer SPECIMEN to
USED_SPECIMEN and UPDATE:SPECIMEN_DATA with that SPECIMEN_ID to clear.

*Figure 10.13: PSPEC6, Read Specimen Data; and PSPEC7, Remove Analyzed Specimen And Data.*

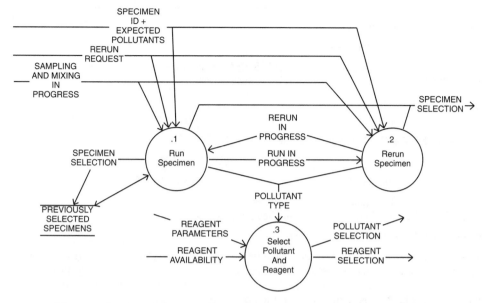

*Figure 10.14:* DFD8, *Select Specimens, Pollutants, And Reagents.*

---

**PSPEC: Run Specimen**

At start-up, clear PREVIOUSLY_SELECTED_SPECIMENS.

Then repeat the following indefinitely:

When SAMPLING_AND_MIXING_IN_PROGRESS = FALSE and
RERUN_REQUEST is not present and RERUN_IN_PROGRESS = UNSET,

set RUN_IN_PROGRESS.

Then find a SPECIMEN_ID (if any) that is not in PREVIOUSLY_SELECTED_SPECIMENS;

set SPECIMEN_SELECTION equal to the selected SPECIMEN_ID;

set POLLUTANT_TYPE equal to a member of EXPECTED_POLLUTANTS.

Thereafter, each time SAMPLING_AND_MIXING_IN_PROGRESS = FALSE, set POLLUTANT_TYPE
equal to another member of EXPECTED_POLLUTANTS until all members have been used.

Then unset RUN_IN_PROGRESS.

*This process takes each specimen that has not already been run and sequences through its set
of expected pollutants. If a rerun is requested or already in progress, this process waits until the
rerun is complete. Note that there is no requirement for the sequence in which the specimens
are selected, nor for the sequence in which the pollutants are tested.*

---

*Figure 10.15:* PSPEC8.1, *Run Specimen.*

**PSPEC: Rerun Specimen**

Repeat the following indefinitely:

When SAMPLING_AND_MIXING_IN_PROGRESS = FALSE and RERUN in RERUN_REQUEST is present and RUN_IN_PROGRESS = UNSET,

set RERUN_IN_PROGRESS;

then find the SPECIMEN_ID (if any) that matches the SPECIMEN_ID in RERUN_REQUEST;

set SPECIMEN_SELECTION equal to that SPECIMEN_ID;

set POLLUTANT_TYPE equal to a member of EXPECTED_POLLUTANTS.

Thereafter, each time SAMPLING_AND_MIXING_IN_PROGRESS = FALSE,

set POLLUTANT_TYPE equal to another member of EXPECTED_POLLUTANTS until all members have been used.

Then set RERUN_IN_PROGRESS = UNSET.

*This process takes each rerun request, finds the corresponding specimen (if it is present), and sequences through its set of expected pollutants. If a run is already in progress, this process waits until it is complete. Note that a rerun request takes precedence over a regular run, but there is no requirement for the sequence in which the pollutants are tested.*

*Figure 10.16: PSPEC8.2, Rerun Specimen.*

**PSPEC: Select Pollutant And Reagent**

Each time a new POLLUTANT_TYPE is received:

Find the member of REAGENT_PARAMETERS containing that POLLUTANT_TYPE and

select the associated REAGENT_SELECTION.

Then find the member of REAGENT_AVAILABILITY whose REAGENT_TYPE matches the selected REAGENT_SELECTION.

If the corresponding REAGENT_AVAILABLE = TRUE, then set

POLLUTANT_SELECTION = POLLUTANT_TYPE and set

REAGENT_SELECTION = REAGENT SELECTION.

Otherwise, set POLLUTANT_SELECTION = "None" and

REAGENT_SELECTION = "None".

*Figure 10.17: PSPEC8.3, Select Pollutant And Reagent.*

## 10.2 Enhancing the Essential Model

The top-level essential requirements model (DFD0, in Figure 10.1) assumes that the system inputs and outputs magically arrive at and leave the system in the required forms. We now must return to the real world and consider how to support the actual interfaces with the outside environment. Using the architecture template as a guide, we can enhance the essential requirements model with these interfaces. The following sections discuss this process for each of the enhancement regions of the template.

### 10.2.1 User-Interface Processing

The essential model in Figures 9.1 and 10.1 simply shows VALID OPERATOR REQUESTS from the operator, and ANALYSIS RESULTS, SELECTED HISTORICAL RESULTS, SYSTEM MODE, and SYSTEM STATUS to the operator. However, the actual operator requests consist of keystrokes that must be interpreted; similarly, the outputs must be formatted separately for display and for printing. To support these needs, we need to add processes in the template's user-interface region. Although the user requirements do not mention it, we almost certainly need to echo the operator inputs on the display. (For our purposes here, we assume that we can make a system-level decision to add this echo, or that we have already confirmed it with the customer.)

To meet these user-interface needs, we add five new processes, as shown in Figure 10.18: Get Operator Entries, Echo Operator Request, Display System Status And Mode, Display Results, and Print Results.

### 10.2.2 Input and Output Processing

The sole system input of the template's Input Processing variety is SPECIMEN, which the essential model shows arriving at the system as if by levitation! However, the specimens will have to be loaded and sometimes unloaded (in accordance with our assumption in the essential model), before they are analyzed. For this, a process called Load And Unload Specimens will be added in the Input Processing region of the template.

In the Output Processing region of the template, we must take into account the processing needed to transmit ANALYSIS RESULTS and SELECTED HISTORICAL RESULTS to the data-processing center. As shown in Figure 10.18, we add a process, Transmit Results, to deal with the formatting and handshaking required by the channel.

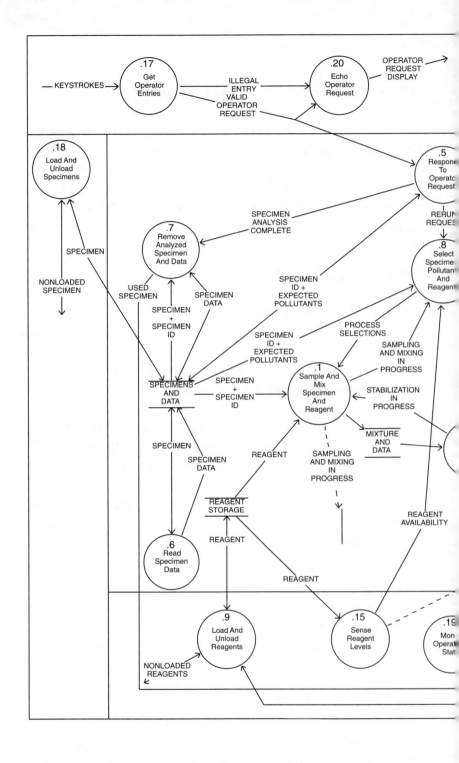

Figure 10.18: EDFD0, Enhanced Analyze Groundwater
(Left Side).

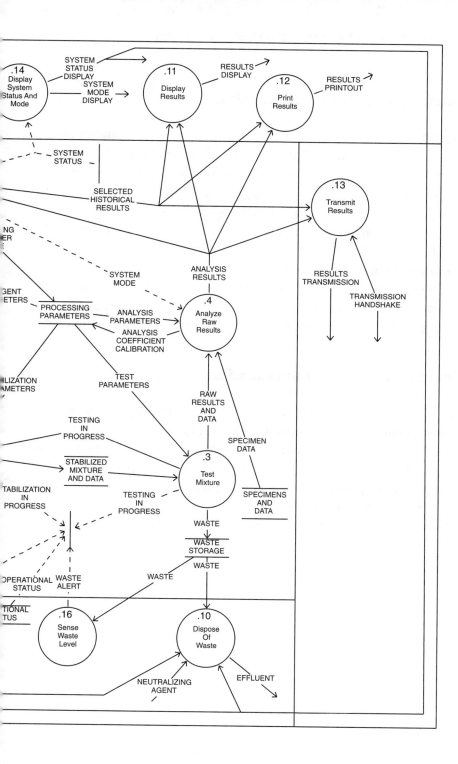

*Figure 10.18: EDFD0, Enhanced Analyze Groundwater (Right Side).*

### 10.2.3 Maintenance and Support Functions

Several necessary functions were deferred for consideration in the Maintenance and Support section of the template. For example, the reagents must be loaded and unloaded from time to time as the containers are emptied and as different reagents are needed. In accordance with the requirement that the system should display its status to the operator, the system must sense when reagents are getting low. The system must also sense when the waste container is getting full, and a means must be provided for removing the waste. Finally, a process is needed to monitor the system's operational status.

To meet these needs, five processes are added in the Maintenance region of the template, as shown in Figure 10.18: Load And Unload Reagents, Sense Reagent Level, Monitor Operational Status, Sense Waste Level, and Dispose Of Waste.

### 10.2.4 The Enhanced Requirements Model

Figure 10.18 shows the complete system-level enhanced requirements model. Figure 10.19 through Figure 10.26 contain the descendent DFDs and PSPECs of the enhancements. Figure 10.27 is the enhanced CSPEC0, showing the additional logic needed to control the enhancements of the DFD. This, remember, is the "technology nonspecific" model, in which real-world interface processing has been specified, but the actual technology it uses has not been chosen. That will be done in the architecture model, which we discuss in the next section.

**PSPEC: Load And Unload Reagents**

Ensure that every REAGENT_TYPE in REAGENT designated for the system has its CHEMICAL_POLLUTANT_REAGENT or BIOLOGICAL_POLLUTANT_REAGENT present by loading NONLOADED_REAGENTS as REAGENT.

Whenever SYSTEM_STATUS_DISPLAY = "Check Reagents and Waste", check if any CHEMICAL_POLLUTANT_REAGENT or BIOLOGICAL_POLLUTANT_REAGENT in REAGENT is below the LOW mark.  If so, when the current run is completed, remove that CHEMICAL_POLLUTANT_REAGENT or BIOLOGICAL_POLLUTANT_REAGENT and replace it with a full one of the same REAGENT_TYPE from NONLOADED_REAGENTS.

Any time a CHEMICAL_POLLUTANT_REAGENT or BIOLOGICAL_POLLUTANT_REAGENT is not needed for the upcoming analyses, it may be removed and included with NONLOADED_REAGENTS for later use.

**PSPEC: Sense Reagent Levels**

For each REAGENT_TYPE in REAGENT:

Sense the level of CHEMICAL_POLLUTANT_REAGENT or BIOLOGICAL_POLLUTANT_REAGENT remaining.

If the level is above the LOW mark, then in the REAGENT_AVAILABILITY containing the current REAGENT_TYPE, set the REAGENT_AVAILABLE = TRUE.  Otherwise, set the REAGENT_AVAILABLE = FALSE.

*See specifications for reagents and containers for details on LOW and EMPTY levels.*

**PSPEC: Sense Waste Level**

Sense the level of WASTE remaining:

If the level is above the FULL mark, set WASTE_ALERT = WASTE FULL.  Otherwise, set WASTE_ALERT = WASTE OK.

*See specifications for waste and waste containers for details on reading the level.*

**PSPEC: Dispose Of Waste**

Whenever SYSTEM_STATUS_DISPLAY = "Check Reagents and Waste", do the following before any further system operation:

Check the waste container, and if it is full, mix USED_SPECIMEN and WASTE with NEUTRALIZING_AGENT in the proportion TBD, then remove the mixture as EFFLUENT.

*Figure 10.19: PSPECs in Maintenance and Support Region of EDFD0.*

---

**PSPEC: Load And Unload Specimens**

Whenever a NONLOADED_SPECIMEN is available and there is room for it in the system, load it into the system as SPECIMEN.

If for any reason a SPECIMEN is not needed in the system, remove and return it as NONLOADED_SPECIMEN.

*Refer to customer policies and procedures for more details on the criteria for loading and unloading specimens.*

---

*Figure 10.20: PSPEC in Input-Processing Region of EDFD0.*

---

**PSPEC: Echo Operator Request**

Whenever a VALID_OPERATOR_REQUEST appears, convert it to display format and send it as OPERATOR_REQUEST_DISPLAY.

Whenever an ILLEGAL_ENTRY appears, set OPERATOR_REQUEST_DISPLAY = "Illegal Entry".

*See system display specification for details on display format.*

**PSPEC: Display Results**

Whenever ANALYSIS_RESULTS appear, convert them to display format and send them as RESULTS_DISPLAY.

Whenever SELECTED_HISTORICAL_RESULTS appear, convert them to display format and send them as RESULTS_DISPLAY.

*See system display specification for details on display format.*

---

*Figure 10.21: PSPECs in User-Interface Region of EDFD0.*

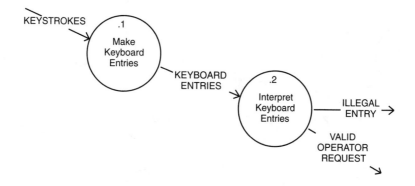

PSPEC: Make Keyboard Entries

Make KEYSTROKES in accordance with the customer's Required Input Specification to produce KEYBOARD_ENTRIES.

PSPEC: Interpret Keyboard Entries

Take each of the KEYBOARD_ENTRIES and compare it with each of the dictionary-defined elements of VALID_OPERATOR_REQUEST.

If a match is found, set VALID_OPERATOR_REQUEST = KEYBOARD_ENTRIES.

Otherwise, issue ILLEGAL_ENTRY.

*Figure 10.22:* DFD17, *Get Operator Entries, with Associated PSPECs.*

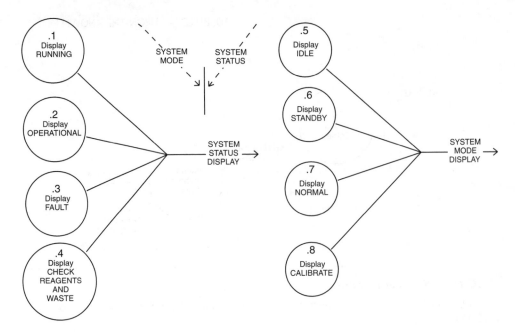

**CSPEC: Display System Status and Mode**

| Input | Process | | | |
|---|---|---|---|---|
| SYSTEM STATUS | Display RUNNING | Display OPERATIONAL | Display FAULT | Display CHECK REAGENTS AND WASTE |
| RUNNING | Activate | | | |
| OPERATIONAL | | Activate | | |
| FAULT | | | Activate | |
| NEEDS ATTENTION | | | | Activate |

| Input | Process | | | |
|---|---|---|---|---|
| SYSTEM MODE | Display IDLE | Display STANDBY | Display NORMAL | Display CALIBRATE |
| IDLE | Activate | | | |
| STANDBY | | Activate | | |
| NORMAL | | | Activate | |
| CALIBRATE | | | | Activate |

**PSPEC: Display RUNNING**

While activated, set SYSTEM_STATUS_DISPLAY = "Running".

**PSPEC: Display OPERATIONAL**

While activated, set SYSTEM_STATUS_DISPLAY = "Operational".

**PSPEC: Display FAULT**

While activated, set SYSTEM_STATUS_DISPLAY = "Fault".

**PSPEC: Display CHECK REAGENTS AND WASTE**

While activated, set SYSTEM_STATUS_DISPLAY = "Check Reagents and Waste".

Note: Remaining PSPECs are similar.

*Figure 10.23: DFD14, Display System Status And Mode, with Associated PSPECs, CSPEC.*

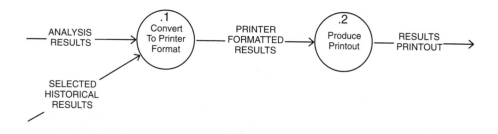

**PSPEC: Convert To Printer Format**

Convert ANALYSIS_RESULTS and SELECTED_HISTORICAL_RESULTS to the format required by the selected printer, producing PRINTER_FORMATTED_RESULTS.

*Details of formats are to be determined.*

**PSPEC: Produce Printout**

From the PRINTER_FORMATTED_RESULTS, produce printouts of the results as RESULTS_PRINTOUT.

*Details of formats are to be determined.*

*Figure 10.24: DFD12, Print Results, with Associated PSPECs.*

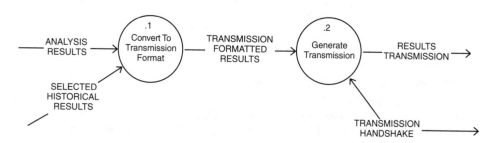

**PSPEC: Convert To Transmission Format**

Convert ANALYSIS_RESULTS and SELECTED_HISTORICAL_RESULTS to the format required by the selected transmitter, producing TRANSMISSION_FORMATTED_RESULTS.

*Details of formats are to be determined.*

**PSPEC: Generate Transmission**

Whenever TRANSMISSION_FORMATTED_RESULTS are received, send the TRANSMISSION_HANDSHAKE. Then, if and when the TRANSMISSION_HANDSHAKE response is received, send RESULTS_TRANSMISSION = TRANSMISSION_FORMATTED_RESULTS.

*Details of handshake and formats are to be determined.*

*Figure 10.25: DFD13, Transmit Results, with Associated PSPECs.*

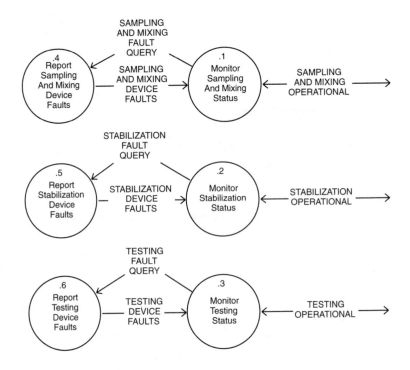

---

**PSPEC: Monitor Sampling And Mixing Status**

Every N seconds, issue a SAMPLING_AND_MIXING_FAULT_QUERY and UPDATE:SAMPLING_AND_MIXING_OPERATIONAL to TRUE or FALSE, according to whether SAMPLING_AND_MIXING_DEVICE_FAULTS becomes NO_FAULT or FAULT, respectively.

*N to be determined from characteristics of sampling and mixing device.*

**PSPEC: Report Sampling And Mixing Device Faults**

Each time SAMPLING_AND_MIXING_FAULT_QUERY is received, set SAMPLING_AND_MIXING_DEVICE_FAULTS to FAULT if a fault is present in the Sampling and Mixing Device; otherwise, to NO_FAULT.

*Detection of faults are to be determined from detailed design of sampling and mixing device.*

---

*Figure 10.26: DFD19, Monitor Operational Status, with Sample PSPECs.*

| Input | | | | | | | | Output |
|---|---|---|---|---|---|---|---|---|
| SAMPLING AND MIXING IN PROGRESS | STABILIZATION IN PROGRESS | TESTING IN PROGRESS | SAMPLING AND MIXING OPERATIONAL | STABILIZATION OPERATIONAL | TESTING OPERATIONAL | WASTE ALERT | REAGENT AVAILABLE | SYSTEM STATUS |
| * | * | * | FALSE | * | * | * | * | FAULT |
| * | * | * | * | FALSE | * | * | * | FAULT |
| * | * | * | * | * | FALSE | * | * | FAULT |
| * | * | * | TRUE | TRUE | TRUE | WASTE FULL | * | NEEDS ATTENTION |
| * | * | * | TRUE | TRUE | TRUE | * | FALSE | NEEDS ATTENTION |
| FALSE | FALSE | FALSE | TRUE | TRUE | TRUE | WASTE OK | TRUE | OPERATIONAL |
| TRUE | * | * | TRUE | TRUE | TRUE | WASTE OK | TRUE | RUNNING |
| * | TRUE | * | TRUE | TRUE | TRUE | WASTE OK | TRUE | RUNNING |
| * | * | TRUE | TRUE | TRUE | TRUE | WASTE OK | TRUE | RUNNING |

*Figure 10.27: Enhanced CSPEC0.*

## 10.3 ARCHITECTURE CONTEXT

Figure 10.28 and Figure 10.29 contain the architecture flow context diagram and the architecture interconnect context diagram, respectively. The terminators are the same as those in the requirements context diagram (Figure 9.1), with the addition of Reagent Storage, which interfaces with the reagent loading and unloading enhancement process that we added.

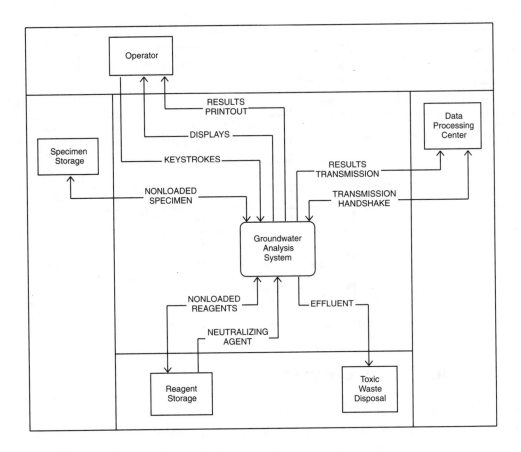

*Figure 10.28: Architecture Flow Context Diagram.*

Note that the AFCD balances with the *enhanced,* rather than the essential, requirements model. In the AICD, we have determined with the customer that the link with the data-processing center will be via Ethernet, and that toxic waste containers will be provided for disposal of waste. Other channels in Figure 10.29 might not be so familiar. For example, we treat the operator both as a terminator and as a channel. There is no inconsistency here. When acting as the source or sink of information or materials, the operator is a terminator; when acting as the vehicle for transferring those items to or from the system, the operator is a channel. The mechanism for transferring the displays to the operator is the Display Screen, and for transferring the printed output is the Printer Paper.

The notational convention used in Figure 10.29 is as follows: Heavy lines represent mechanical or physical interconnects; thin lines represent electrical data interconnects; zigzag lines represent optical interconnects.

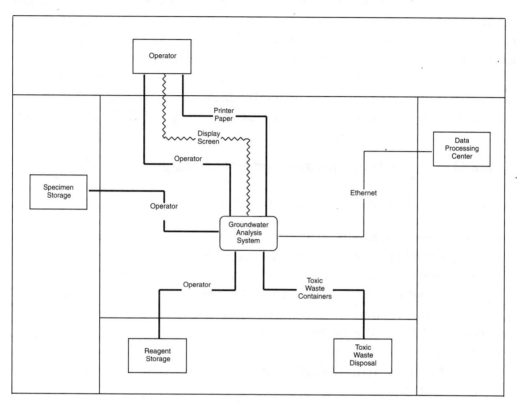

*Figure 10.29: Architecture Interconnect Context Diagram.*

## 10.4 BUILDING UP FROM THE EXISTING SAMPLING MODULE

In Figures 9.5 and 9.7, we saw the enhanced requirements and architecture interfaces for the Existing Sampling Module.

Examination of these figures shows that the module provides many of the core functions of the system, but not all of them: The module requires several inputs instructing it what to do and when to do it; it provides feedback information confirming that its tasks are proceeding; it must be provided with a light source and a destination to which the returned light must go; it must be provided with specimens and reagents; and it needs somewhere to send the waste.

## 10.4.1 An Intermediate Module

After examining the needs of the Existing Sampling Module, described above, and after trading off several design options, a decision was made to embed the module within a larger one that handles all the physical processes of the system. This higher-level module will be called the Sample Analyzer and will include, in addition to the Existing Sampling Module, an Optical Sensor, a Reagent Handler, and a Waste Handler. One more decision concerns whether to handle the Sample Analyzer's information processing in the Workstation (also a required module) or in a separate, local processor within the Sample Analyzer itself. In other words, should we use central or distributed processing?

## 10.4.2 Central versus Distributed Processing

This decision is based on numerous factors, including

- the processing load imposed by the Sample Analyzer
- the processing capacity of the Workstation and of microprocessors that might be available for the Sample Analyzer
- the channel capacities between the Sample Analyzer and the rest of the system, and those internal to the Sample Analyzer
- the reusability of the Sample Analyzer
- cost—both recurring and nonrecurring
- testability and maintainability of the Sample Analyzer and of the whole system

A trade-off study is needed to compare each of these factors and any others that are deemed important, for each possible configuration. The factors, after they have been weighted according to their perceived importance, can be used to calculate a figure of merit for each configuration. The configuration with the highest figure of merit wins—at least, in principle. In practice, political and organizational factors are often involved, and the decision is influenced by the personal preferences of the managers and groups in the organization.

In our case, we will assume that, by fair means or foul, the trade-off study led to a decision to make the whole Sample Analyzer reusable—not just the Existing Sampling Module—by including within it a local processor. Figure 10.30 shows the modules for the Sample Analyzer; the flows and interconnects cannot be added until the top-down and bottom-up pieces of the model have been reconciled.

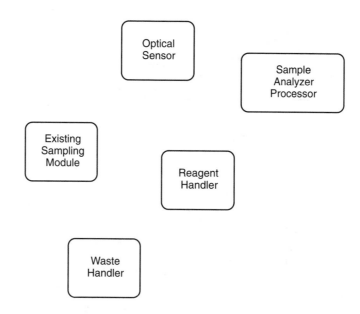

*Figure 10.30: Sample Analyzer Architecture Modules.*

## 10.4.3 Sample Analyzer Requirements

We deliberately started developing the Sample Analyzer architecture bottom-up because one of its components, the Existing Sampling Module, was a given. Of the modules in Figure 10.30, the Optical Sensor, Reagent Handler, and Waste Handler perform the simplest—though still vital—functions. Their requirements models are shown in Figure 10.31.

The requirements for the Sample Analyzer Processor are *not* simple, and in fact, would probably be constructed during the trade-off study described earlier. We shall develop those requirements in the following chapters as we put the rest of the model together.

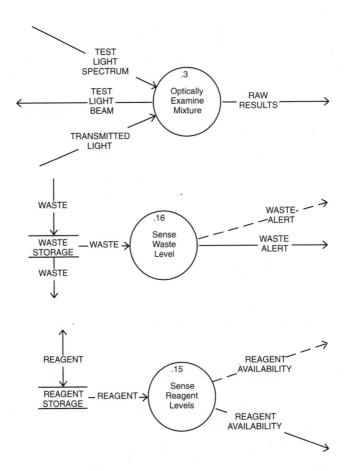

*Figure 10.31: Requirements for Optical Sensor, Waste Handler, and Reagent Handler.*

## 10.5 WHAT DO WE HAVE, AND WHAT IS MISSING?

We now have the top-level requirements model (including the TSPEC and the entity model), the enhanced requirements model, and the system architecture context diagrams. We also have embedded the Existing Sampling Module, with its existing requirements and architecture, into a newly created Sample Analyzer module.

We are illustrating here, as best we can, how the models can be populated in any sequence, and why a bottom-up approach is especially advantageous with reusable modules. What we would really like to illustrate is concurrency, whereby pieces of a model are put into place simultaneously by separate people or groups working cooperatively. However, this is quite difficult to achieve in a book, which is essentially a one-dimensional medium that starts at the beginning and proceeds sequentially to the end.

Concurrency commonly occurs in trade-off studies. For example, in the comparison between central and distributed processing, large parts of the requirements and architecture models for the whole system and for the Sample Analyzer module would have been constructed, at least tentatively, in order to support the final decision.

In this case study, what remains for us to construct are the pieces between the top-level model and the Sample Analyzer, the remainder of the system-level architecture, the allocation of requirements to the remaining architecture modules, and any further decompositions that are needed of those modules. We complete these elements in the following chapters.

# Chapter 11
## Filling In
## the Blanks

## 11.1 INTRODUCTION

We are now at a crossroads in the development of this system, where requirements and architecture intersect, and where bottom-up development intersects with top-down. At this point, we must simultaneously analyze architectures that will satisfy the enhanced requirements, determine how the enhanced requirements would be allocated to each of those architectures, and evaluate the reasonableness of the requirements themselves—changing them if necessary. These activities are at the very heart of system development. The trade-off studies that result from them determine both the technical and business success of the end product.

In the space of a single book, we cannot describe a complete set of trade-off studies, but in the following paragraphs, we discuss some of the key trade-off issues that affect this particular system.

## 11.2 ARCHITECTURE MODULES

The incomplete AFD in Figure 11.1 contains a set of architecture modules to serve tentatively as the top-level system structure. This set assumes that the Existing Sampling Module is contained within the Sample Analyzer module. There should be other candidate sets of modules, but we will restrict ourselves to this one and look next at the allocation of requirements to it.

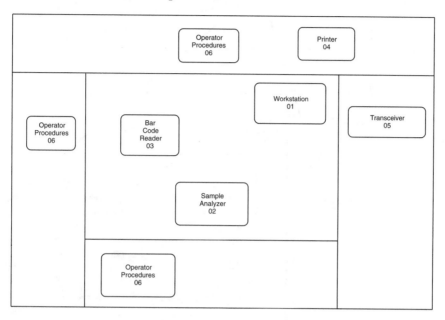

*Figure 11.1: Architecture Modules.*

Notice that Operator Procedures is treated as an architecture module. This is an effective way to indicate that some system functions can be allocated to the operator, and that those functions and the procedures that describe them are very much part of the system and its design.

It is interesting to note that we now have the operator serving three roles: terminator (when acting as a source or sink of information or materials, as in Figure 9.1), channel (when transferring information or materials to or from the system, as in Figure 10.29), and system module (when performing system functions defined in the Operator Procedures, as in Figure 11.1).

## 11.3 ALLOCATING THE ENHANCED REQUIREMENTS MODEL

Figure 11.2 shows superbubbles allocating the elements of EDFD0 (Figure 10.18) to the modules in Figure 11.1. The allocations are as follows: automated handling of the specimens and reagents is allocated to the Sample Analyzer module, information processing is allocated to the Workstation module, specimen data reading is allocated to the Bar Code Reader module, various manual operations are allo-

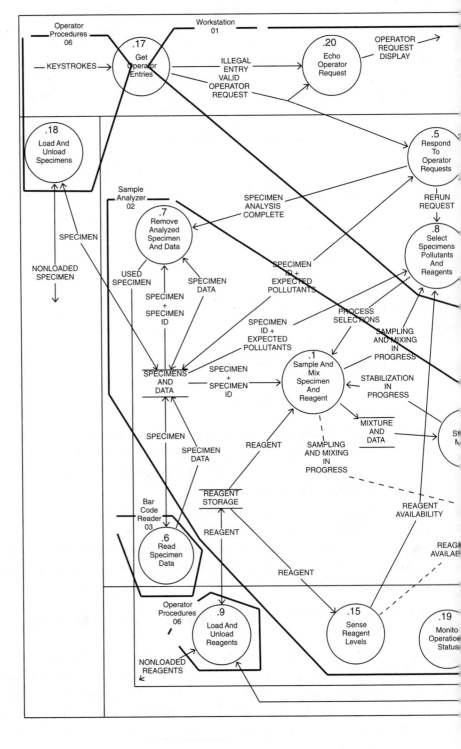

*Figure 11.2: Allocated EDFD0, Analyze Groundwater (Left Side).*

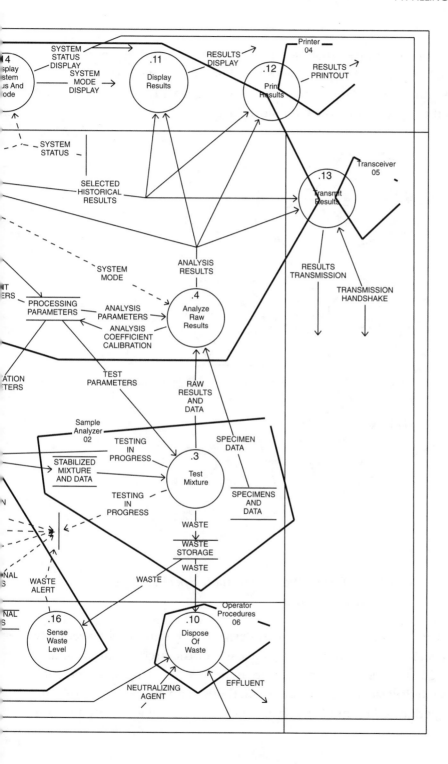

*Figure 11.2: Allocated EDFD0, Analyze Groundwater (Right Side).*

cated to the Operator Procedures module, and the Printer and Transceiver modules share some of their respective tasks with the Workstation module.

The processes that are split by superbubbles in Figure 11.2 have their child processes allocated to specific modules in Figure 11.3.

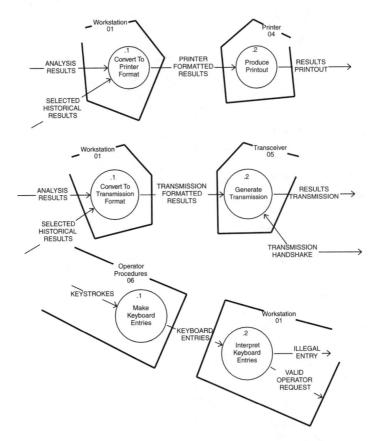

*Figure 11.3: DFDs of Split Processes, with Specific Super-bubble Allocation.*

From these enhanced, allocated DFDs, we can derive the system-level traceability matrix and the specific C/DFDs and CSPECs for each of the architecture modules in Figure 11.1 (a good CASE tool can be a great help for this task, which, like many tasks associated with these and other methods, can be very tedious and error-prone when performed manually). These diagrams are shown in Figure 11.4 through Figure 11.9.

| Requirements Component | Architecture Component | | | | | |
|---|---|---|---|---|---|---|
| | Work-station 01 | Printer 04 | Trans-ceiver 05 | Sample Analyzer 02 | Operator Proce-dures 06 | Bar Code Reader 03 |
| Analyze Raw Results | X | | | | | |
| Respond To Operator Requests | X | | | | | |
| Select Specimens Pollutants And Reagents | X | | | | | |
| Display Results | X | | | | | |
| Display System Status And Mode | X | | | | | |
| Echo Operator Request | X | | | | | |
| STORE: PROCESSING PARAMETERS | X | | | | | |
| CSPEC: Enhanced Analyze Groundwater | X | | | X | | |
| Convert To Printer Format | X | | | | | |
| Interpret Keyboard Entries | X | | | | | |
| Produce Printout | | X | | | | |
| Generate Transmission | | | X | | | |
| Sample And Mix Specimen And Reagent | | | | X | | |
| Stabilize Mixture | | | | X | | |
| Test Mixture | | | | X | | |
| Remove Analyzed Specimen And Data | | | | X | | |

*Figure 11.4: System-Level Traceability Matrix (Continued).*

| Requirements Component | Architecture Component | | | | | |
|---|---|---|---|---|---|---|
| | Work-station 01 | Printer 04 | Trans-ceiver 05 | Sample Analyzer 02 | Operator Proce-dures 06 | Bar Code Reader 03 |
| Sense Reagent Levels | | | | X | | |
| Sense Waste Level | | | | X | | |
| Monitor Operational Status | | | | X | | |
| STORE: REAGENT STORAGE | | | | X | | |
| STORE: WASTE STORAGE | | | | X | | |
| STORE: SPECIMENS AND DATA | | | | X | | |
| STORE: MIXTURE AND DATA | | | | X | | |
| STORE: STABILIZED MIXTURE AND DATA | | | | X | | |
| STORE: OPERATIONAL STATUS | | | | X | | |
| Load And Unload Specimens | | | | | X | |
| Load And Unload Reagents | | | | | X | |
| Dispose Of Waste | | | | | X | |
| Make Keyboard Entries | | | | | X | |
| Read Specimen Data | | | | | | X |

*Figure 11.4: System-Level Traceability Matrix.*

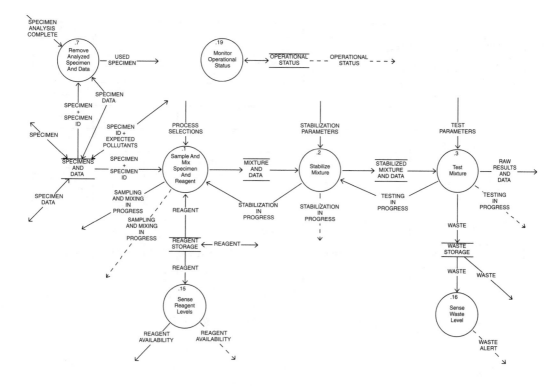

*Figure 11.5:* DFD, *Sample Analyzer 02.*

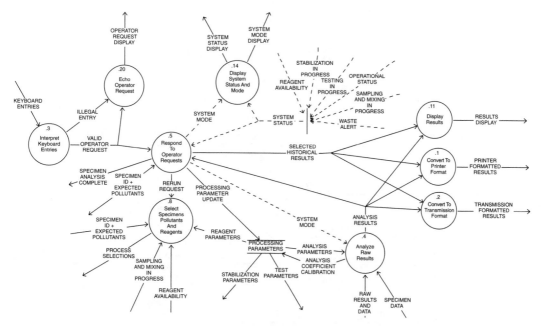

*Figure 11.6:* DFD, *Workstation 01.*

| Input | | | | | | | | Output |
|---|---|---|---|---|---|---|---|---|
| SAMPLING AND MIXING IN PROGRESS | STABILIZATION IN PROGRESS | TESTING IN PROGRESS | SAMPLING AND MIXING OPERATIONAL | STABILIZATION OPERATIONAL | TESTING OPERATIONAL | WASTE ALERT | REAGENT AVAILABLE | SYSTEM STATUS |
| * | * | * | FALSE | * | * | * | * | FAULT |
| * | * | * | * | FALSE | * | * | * | FAULT |
| * | * | * | * | * | FALSE | * | * | FAULT |
| * | * | * | TRUE | TRUE | TRUE | WASTE FULL | * | NEEDS ATTENTION |
| * | * | * | TRUE | TRUE | TRUE | * | FALSE | NEEDS ATTENTION |
| FALSE | FALSE | FALSE | TRUE | TRUE | TRUE | WASTE OK | TRUE | OPERATIONAL |
| TRUE | * | * | TRUE | TRUE | TRUE | WASTE OK | TRUE | RUNNING |
| * | TRUE | * | TRUE | TRUE | TRUE | WASTE OK | TRUE | RUNNING |
| * | * | TRUE | TRUE | TRUE | TRUE | WASTE OK | TRUE | RUNNING |

*Figure 11.7: CSPEC, Workstation 01.*

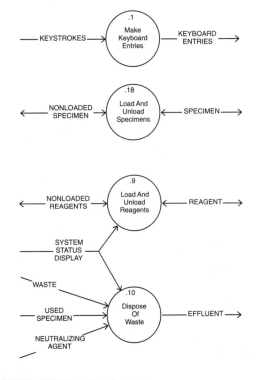

*Figure 11.8: DFD, Operator Procedures 06.*

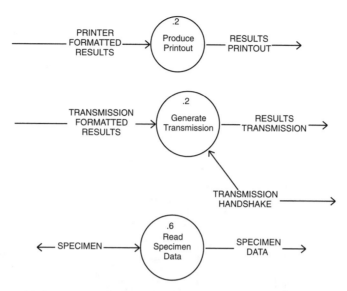

Figure 11.9:  *Figure 11.9:*  *DFDs for Printer 04, Transceiver 05, and Bar Code Reader 03.*

## 11.4 ENHANCING THE ALLOCATED MODELS

We now have a set of system-level architecture modules, each with its essential requirements allocated.  From this information, we can determine the routing of flows between modules.  However, these are still data flows, and before we can redefine them as architecture flows, we must perform another enhancement process to identify any additional processing that is needed to support the internal interfaces created by the new architecture modules.  In order to do so, we must have some idea what architecture channels we plan to use.  In fact, the enhancement process, the channel selection, and the creation of architecture flows must all be done concurrently.  We need to estimate the channel speed and capacity required by the inter-module flows, select channel types that seem to meet those needs, add any enhancements required to support those channels, check the accuracy of our assumptions about the channels, try other channels if necessary, and so on.

Once again, although we are describing these steps sequentially, please remember that in a real project, most development activities need some degree of concurrency.  This concurrency, and the multidisciplinary teams to support it, should be carefully planned into the project.

The enhanced DFDs for the system-level architecture modules are shown in Figure 11.10 through Figure 11.12.  Notice that some significant processing has been added to interface with an internal local bus, and the flows between the

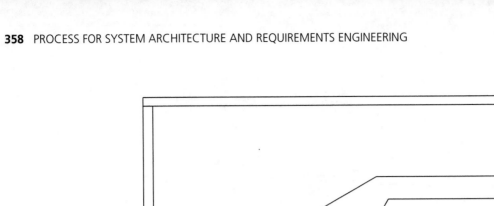

*Figure 11.10: EDFD, Sample Analyzer 02 (Left Side).*

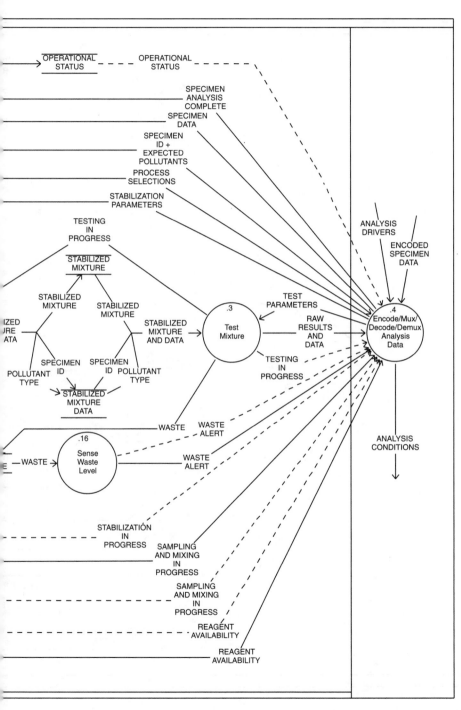

*Figure 11.10: EDFD, Sample Analyzer 02 (Right Side).*

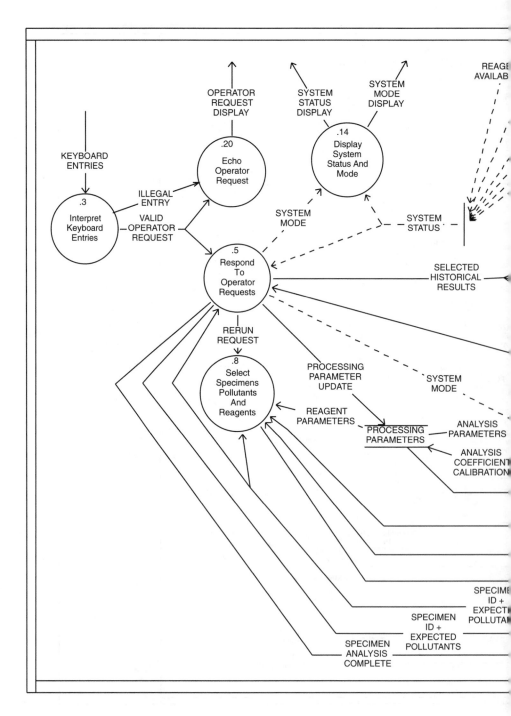

*Figure 11.11: EDFD, Workstation 01 (Left Side).*

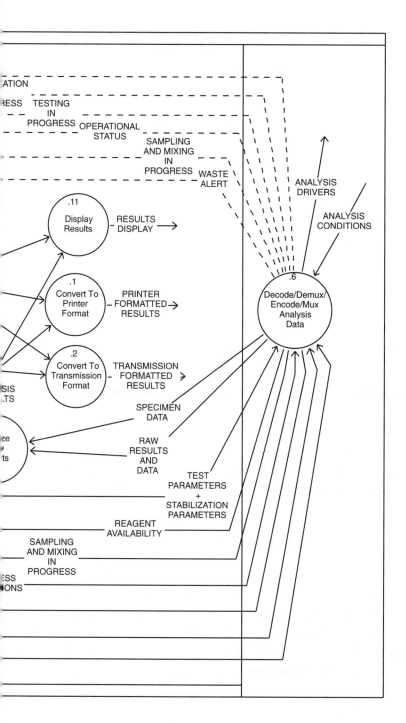

*Figure 11.11: EDFD, Workstation 01 (Right Side).*

Workstation and the Sample Analyzer have been grouped. The Operator Procedures, Printer, and Transceiver required no enhancement, since the inputs and outputs of their essential DFDs are already in the required form.

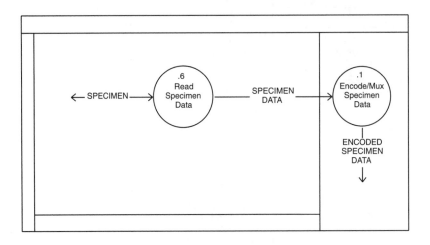

*Figure 11.12: EDFD, Bar Code Reader 03.*

## 11.5 ADDING THE ARCHITECTURE FLOWS AND INTERCONNECTS

Once the enhancements have been made to the DFDs of the system-level modules, it is a simple matter to add the architecture flows to the AFD. Figure 11.13 shows the complete system-level AFD. The system-level AID is shown in Figure 11.14, with the interconnects that were chosen through the channel configuration and capacity study.

## 11.6 FLOW-TO-INTERCONNECT ALLOCATIONS

To complete the architecture flow and interconnect specification, we must specify the allocations of flows to channels. In this system, generally, only one channel links a given pair of architecture modules, but in some systems, several such channels may exist. In such cases, the particular channel over which a given flow travels might not be obvious. To remove any ambiguity, all flow-to-channel allocations are recorded in the architecture dictionary, of which a sample is given in Section 12.6.

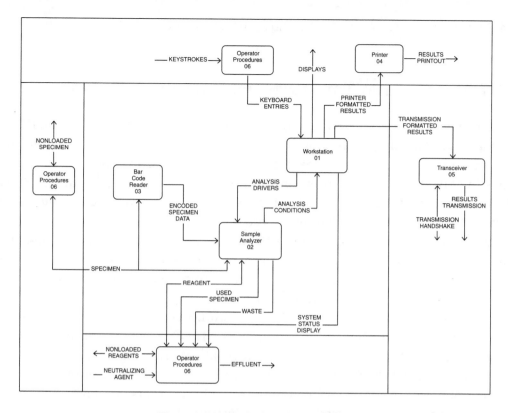

*Figure 11.13: System-Level* AFD.

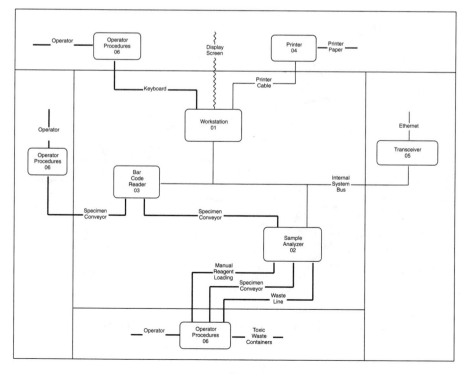

*Figure 11.14: System-Level* AID.

## 11.7 MERGING THE TOP-DOWN AND BOTTOM-UP PIECES

We now have EDFDs for the Sample Analyzer module (Figure 11.10) and the Existing Sampling Module (Figure 9.5); since we chose to embed the latter within the former, we must find a way to link them. An obvious starting point for this linking is the Mix Sample And Reagent process that appears in DFD1 (Figure 10.3)—a child of the Sample Analyzer EDFD—and in the Existing Sampling Module EDFD (Figure 9.5). In fact, DFD1 has other processes that are similar to the Extract Sample, Extract Reagent, and Send Mixture processes in the Existing Sampling Module EDFD. Comparing the PSPECs of these processes (in Figures 10.3 and 9.6 respectively), we see that those in the Existing Sampling Module are subsets of those in the enhanced Sample Analyzer.

It seems, then, that in order to link the two EDFDs, we need to split some of the processes in DFD1—but they are primitives. This is one of the situations, discussed in Chapter 2, that calls for derived requirements. Figure 11.15 shows a new version of DFD1, in which three of the processes are now non-primitives, split by superbubbles. Figure 11.16 contains the child diagrams and PSPECs of these newly split processes. We made a design decision that forced us to create new, derived requirements by splitting a primitive process.

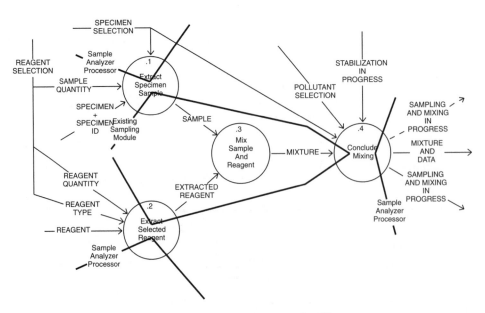

*Figure 11.15: Modified DFD1, with Allocations.*

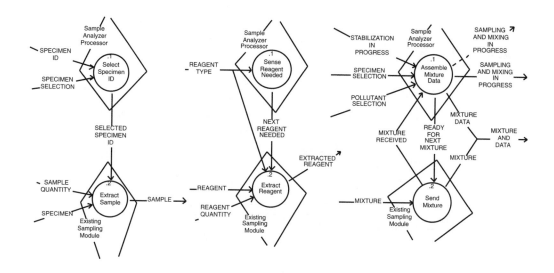

---

**PSPEC: Select Specimen ID**

Each time a new SAMPLE_QUANTITY is received:

Find the SPECIMEN_ID that matches SPECIMEN_SELECTION and send that SPECIMEN_ID as SELECTED_SPECIMEN_ID.

**PSPEC: Extract Sample**

Find the SPECIMEN corresponding to SELECTED_SPECIMEN_ID.

From that SPECIMEN, extract a quantity SAMPLE_QUANTITY to produce SAMPLE.

---

*Figure 11.16: Allocated Child Diagrams of DFD1, with Typical Associated PSPECs.*

In a similar way, the Conclude Stabilization process in DFD2 (in Figure 10.4) must be split to divide its function between the Existing Sampling Module and the Sample Analyzer Processor. This is shown in Figure 11.17 and Figure 11.18.

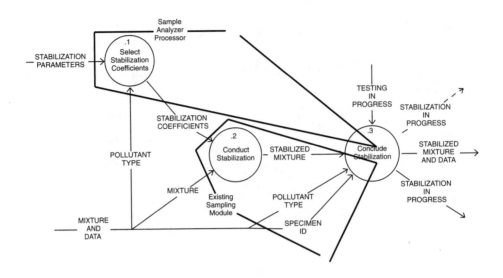

*Figure 11.17: DFD2, Stabilize Mixture, with Allocations.*

So, after comparing the top-level requirements model with the models for the Existing Sampling Module and the Sample Analyzer module, we have modified and fit them into one integrated model. This allows us to derive the traceability matrix and the requirements models for the remaining architecture modules of the Sample Analyzer. These are shown, with enhancements already in place, in Figure 11.19 through Figure 11.21.

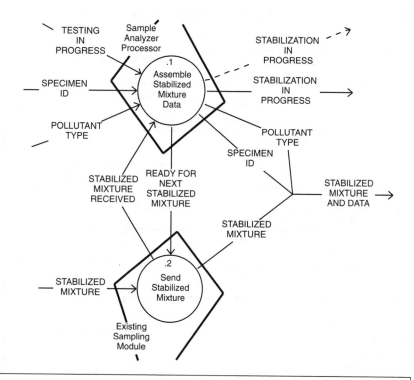

TESTING
IN
PROGRESS

Sample
Analyzer
Processor

STABILIZATION
IN
PROGRESS

SPECIMEN
ID

.1
Assemble
Stabilized
Mixture
Data

STABILIZATION
IN
PROGRESS

POLLUTANT
TYPE

POLLUTANT
TYPE

SPECIMEN
ID

STABILIZED
MIXTURE
RECEIVED

READY FOR
NEXT
STABILIZED
MIXTURE

STABILIZED
MIXTURE
AND DATA

STABILIZED
MIXTURE

.2
Send
Stabilized
Mixture

STABILIZED
MIXTURE

Existing
Sampling
Module

**PSPEC: Assemble Stabilized Mixture Data**

At start-up, set STABILIZATION_IN_PROGRESS = FALSE and
READY_FOR_NEXT_STABILIZED_MIXTURE = FALSE.

Whenever a new POLLUTANT_TYPE is received, set
STABILIZATION_IN_PROGRESS = TRUE.

Then, when TESTING_IN_PROGRESS = FALSE and
STABILIZED_MIXTURE_RECEIVED = TRUE, set

READY_FOR_NEXT_STABILIZED_MIXTURE = TRUE,

POLLUTANT_TYPE = POLLUTANT_TYPE, and

SPECIMEN_ID = SPECIMEN_ID.

Then, when STABILIZED_MIXTURE_RECEIVED = FALSE, set STABILIZATION_IN_PROGRESS = FALSE
and READY_FOR_NEXT_STABILIZED_MIXTURE = FALSE.

**PSPEC: Send Stabilized Mixture**

At start-up, set STABILIZED_MIXTURE_RECEIVED = FALSE.

Whenever STABILIZED_MIXTURE is received, set
STABILIZED_MIXTURE_RECEIVED = TRUE.

Then, when READY_FOR_NEXT_STABILIZED_MIXTURE = TRUE, pass on STABILIZED_MIXTURE as
STABILIZED_MIXTURE and then set STABILIZED_MIXTURE_RECEIVED = FALSE.

*Figure 11.18:* DFD2.3, *Conclude Stabilization, with Associated* PSPECs.

| Requirements Component | Architecture Component | | | | |
|---|---|---|---|---|---|
| | Existing Sampling Module | Sample Analyzer Processor | Optical Sensor | Waste Handler | Reagent Handler |
| Mix Sample And Reagent | X | | | | |
| Extract Sample | X | | | | |
| Extract Reagent | X | | | | |
| Send Mixture | X | | | | |
| Conduct Stabilization | X | | | | |
| Send Stabilized Mixture | X | | | | |
| Present Mixture For Testing | X | | | | |
| STORE: TEST TRANSMISSION DISTANCE | X | | | | |
| Report Sampling And Mixing Device Faults | X | | | | |
| Report Stabilization Device Faults | X | | | | |
| Report Testing Device Faults | X | | | | |
| STORE: SPECIMEN | X | | | | |
| Remove Analyzed Specimen And Data | X | | | | |
| STORE: MIXTURE | X | | | | |
| STORE: STABILIZED MIXTURE | X | | | | |
| Select Specimen ID | | X | | | |
| Assemble Mixture Data | | X | | | |
| Sense Reagent Needed | | X | | | |

*Figure 11.19: Sample Analyzer Traceability Matrix (Continued).*

| Requirements Component | Architecture Component | | | | |
|---|---|---|---|---|---|
| | Existing Sampling Module | Sample Analyzer Processor | Optical Sensor | Waste Handler | Reagent Handler |
| Select Stabilization Coefficients | | X | | | |
| Assemble Stabilized Mixture Data | | X | | | |
| Conclude Test | | X | | | |
| Select Test Coefficients | | X | | | |
| Monitor Sampling and Mixing Status | | X | | | |
| Monitor Stabilization Status | | X | | | |
| Monitor Testing Status | | X | | | |
| STORE: OPERATIONAL STATUS | | X | | | |
| Encode/Mux Decode/Demux Analysis Data | | X | | | |
| STORE: SPECIMEN DATA | | X | | | |
| STORE: MIXTURE DATA | | X | | | |
| STORE: STABILIZED MIXTURE DATA | | X | | | |
| Optically Examine Mixture | | | X | | |
| Sense Waste Level | | | | X | |
| STORE: WASTE STORAGE | | | | X | |
| Sense Reagent Levels | | | | | X |
| STORE: REAGENT STORAGE | | | | | X |

*Figure 11.19: Sample Analyzer Traceability Matrix.*

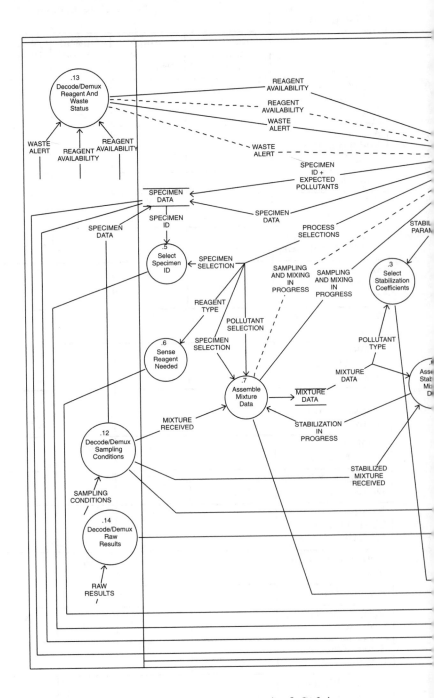

*Figure 11.20: EDFD, Sample Analyzer Processor (Left Side).*

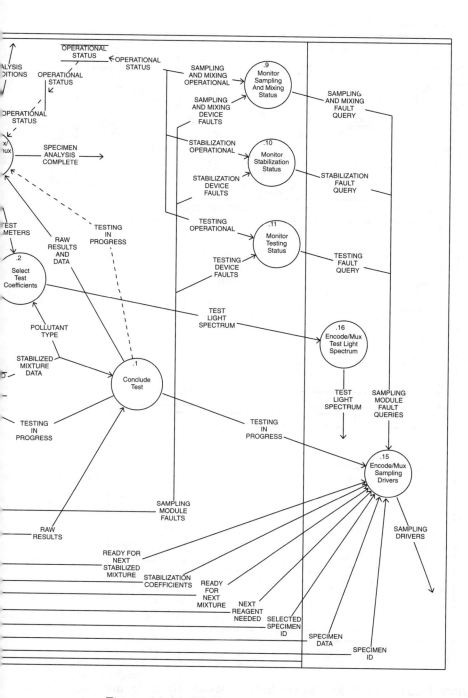

*Figure 11.20: EDFD, Sample Analyzer Processor (Right Side).*

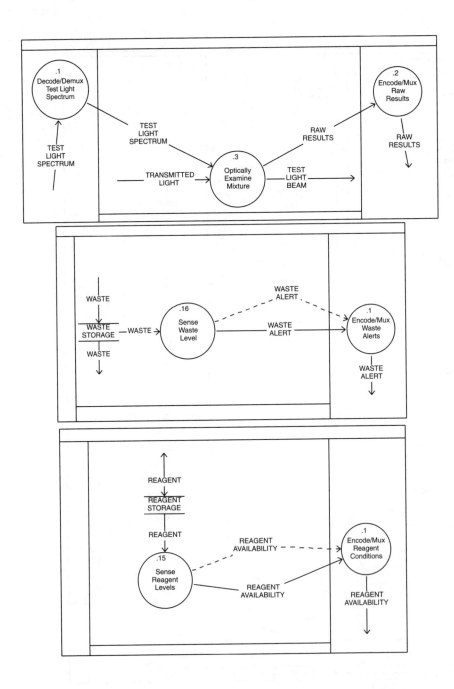

*Figure 11.21: EDFDs for Optical Sensor, Waste Handler, and Reagent Handler.*

The enhancements shown in Figures 11.19 through 11.21 are needed to establish the architecture flows in the corresponding AFD. This AFD and its AID are shown in Figure 11.22 and Figure 11.23.

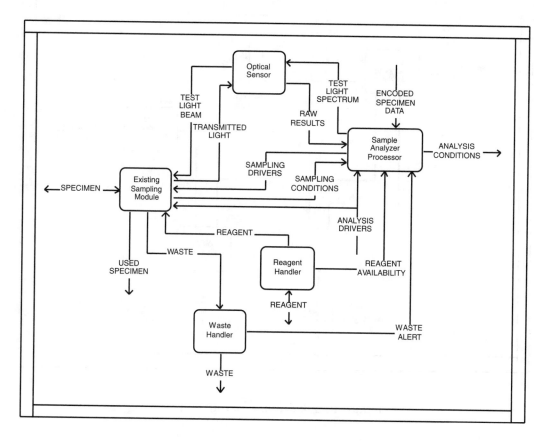

*Figure 11.22: Sample Analyzer AFD.*

Note the variety of technologies that come together in the Sample Analyzer module, as shown in the diversity of channels in the AID. We have the mechanical conveyor for the specimens, an optical channel for the test light and transmitted light, hydraulic lines for the reagents and waste, manual operations for loading and unloading reagents, and two kinds of data buses for information transfer.

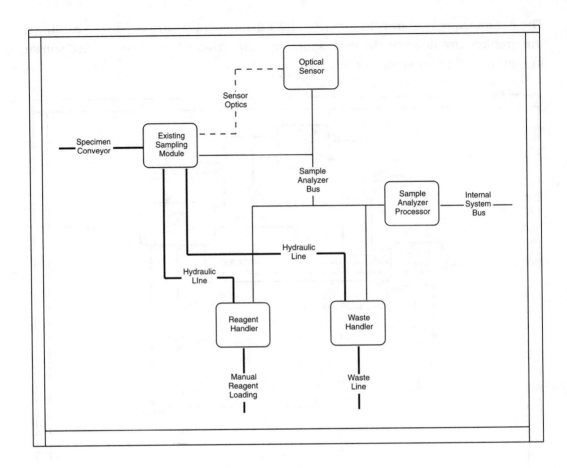

*Figure 11.23: Sample Analyzer AID.*

# Chapter 12
## Completing the Models

## 12.1 INTRODUCTION

We now have a fairly complete set of diagrams, but some very important model elements must be completed: the performance and timing requirements must be allocated to the sub-modules, and the architecture module specifications must be prepared.

The customer is most interested in the total system performance rather than in its various contributing elements. It is, therefore, very important to state this total performance in a single, easily accessible place—the top-level system module specification. It is here that the whole system performance budgeting strategy must be stated and then justified through analytical and test results.

## 12.2 ACCURACY ALLOCATION

The original customer requirements, stated in Chapter 8, call for an accuracy of ±5% in the analysis results. These results arise from several steps in the analysis process: taking measured samples of the specimen and reagent; stabilizing the mixture; optically testing the stabilized mixture; and analyzing the results of the test to produce a measured pollutant concentration. The overall five percent margin of error must be budgeted among all of these processes. The error-budgeting process in this case involves several disciplines and is beyond the scope of this book, but it would probably lead to specifications for

- required chemical consistency of the reagents
- accuracy of the sampling process
- stabilization parameters and their accuracy
- optical parameters and accuracies of the test light beam and optics
- word length and processing accuracies in the test analysis

These error budgets would be recorded in the PSPECs, the requirements and architecture dictionaries, and the module specifications, as appropriate.

## 12.3 TIMING ALLOCATION—CONCURRENT ARCHITECTURE MODULES

The original customer requirements also call for a throughput of at least forty specimens per hour and a response time of no more than five minutes. Since one fortieth of an hour is 1.5 minutes—much less than the required response time—there is room for some trade-offs here. If the sampling/stabilization/testing/analysis process takes 1.5 minutes or less, the throughput requirements will be met and the response time requirement will be exceeded. On the other hand, if the process takes more than 1.5 minutes, the situation gets more complicated.

Suppose we have carried out design analyses and trade-off studies and established that the fastest practical process speed with current technology is three minutes. This exceeds the response time requirement but will only give a throughput of twenty per hour—half of what is required.

One solution to this difficulty is to use, in each system, two Sample Analyzer modules that work concurrently. The combined throughput would then be forty per hour, as required. Of course, using two concurrent modules presents some system design problems: The mechanism for delivering specimens to the Sample Analyzers will be more complex, and the total number of concurrent processors in the system will increase to three, requiring additional coordination between them.

Another possibility might be to have the two Sample Analyzers share one processor. A trade-off involved in this decision is the additional complexity of managing two processes in one processor versus the cost of an additional Sample Analyzer Processor. Figure 12.1 and Figure 12.2 are the AFD and AID of a system with dual concurrent Sample Analyzer modules.

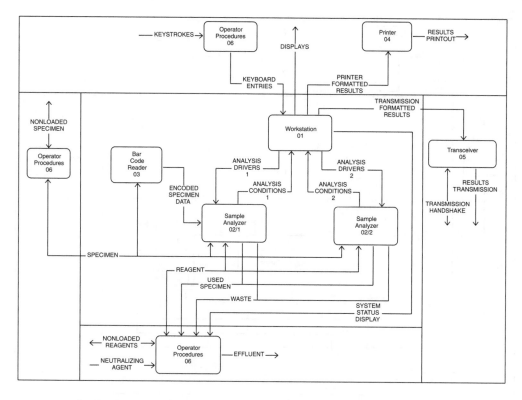

*Figure 12.1: Groundwater Analysis System AFD, with Dual Concurrent Sample Analyzer Modules.*

Let us assume that a decision has been made to use two concurrent Sample Analyzer modules, each with a response time of three minutes. Each architecture module is given its own timing specification, with response times allocated through the budgeting process.

Note that the timing specification must account for all system input and output flows and for timing requirements that arise apart from those given by the customer. All timing requirements must be budgeted among the architecture modules that are affected by them.

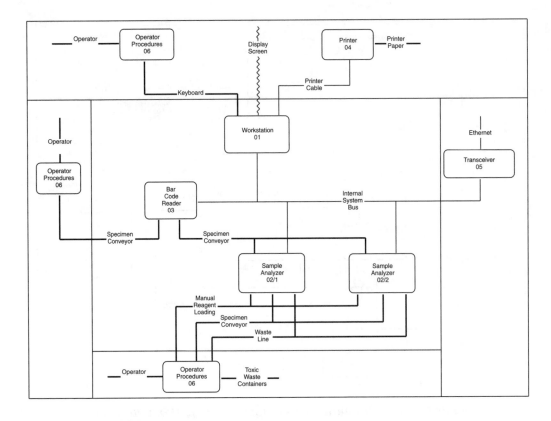

*Figure 12.2:* *Groundwater Analysis System AID, with Dual*
*Concurrent Sample Analyzer Modules.*

# 12.4 ARCHITECTURE MODULE SPECIFICATIONS

Every architecture module must have an architecture module specification. AMSs
are often quite lengthy and make numerous references to such things as trade-off
studies, company and industry standards, other systems in the same family, and
other specifications. Below, we outline the AMSs for the entire groundwater analysis system, and for the Sample Analyzer module.

## 12.4.1 Architecture Module Specification: Groundwater Analysis System

**Description:** The groundwater analysis system is designed to
meet the requirements of Customer Specification XYZ. Its primary

function is to analyze groundwater specimens to determine the concentration of various pollutants. It is a floor-standing unit consisting of a Sample Analyzer, a Workstation (a commercially available desktop computer), a Bar Code Reader, a Printer, and a Transceiver. The system requires an operator to run it, and the Operator Procedures provided with the system are an integral part of the system. The system receives groundwater specimens in capped vials, which are loaded by the operator. Reagents are mixed with samples taken from the specimens so that the mixture refracts and disperses a light beam into patterns that characterize the type of pollutant and its concentration. The samples and used specimens are disposed of in accordance with the EPA's toxic waste disposal regulations.

Through the Workstation, the operator is able to control the operation of the system and to monitor its status. Other operator functions include loading reagents according to what pollutants are expected, replacing pollutant containers when they are empty, and disposing of the waste after adding toxicity-neutralizing agents if necessary.

**Design Rationale:** Some of the design was predetermined, as listed below:

- the use of reagents and transmitted light for pollutant detection
- the use of an Existing Sampling Module (of type ESM32)
- the use of a commercially available computer workstation

Given these constraints, the following design decisions were made

- to embed the Existing Sampling Module in a more comprehensive Sample Analyzer module so that the larger module would itself be reusable in future systems (see Trade Study Report TSR57)
- to use a RISC-based workstation with 300Mhz clock and 128M RAM (see Report WS29)
- *(numerous other design decisions would be listed here, with rationales for their choice or references to documents that give these rationales)*

**Design Justification:** The system will meet the functionality and performance criteria called for in Customer Specification XYZ, as demonstrated in the following reports listed below.

- *Functionality:* The system will perform all the functions required of it, including interacting with a single operator without overloading the operator. See Operational Characteristics Report OC37 and Functional Analysis Report FA63 for more details.
- *Throughput and Response Time:* The required rate of at least forty specimens per hour, and the required response time of no more than five minutes from insertion to results of any given sample, are achieved with two parallel Sample Analyzer modules, each capable of twenty specimens per hour with no more than three minutes from insertion to results. This response time betters the requirement by two minutes. See Report TPT91 for more details.
- *Accuracy:* The accuracy required of ±5% in the measured pollutant concentration is achieved with 99.5% confidence, subject to calibrating the system at least once per week. See Report ACC73 for more details.

**Required Constraints:** *(References to reports on all the "-ilities," on any other constraints that apply to the system, and on how the design will meet them would be listed here.)*

**Functionality and Cross-Reference:** The complete functionality of the system is specified in EDFD0 and its descendent diagrams and specifications. The allocations of these functions to the system-level modules is shown in the traceability matrix for AFD0.

## 12.4.2 Architecture Module Specification: Sample Analyzer

**Description:** The Sample Analyzer performs all the physical operations of the groundwater analysis system and meets the requirements allocated to it by the top-level design of that system. It is designed to be reused in future systems with similar requirements.

The Sample Analyzer consists of an Existing Sampling Module, an Optical Sensor, a Sample Analyzer Processor, a Reagent Handler, and a Waste Handler. See the Sample Analyzer AFD and AID for the interconnecting flows and channels of this module.

**Design Rationale:** The reuse of the Existing Sampling Module was prescribed, but a decision was made to build it into a more comprehensive, reusable unit that would form the foundation for this line of products for years to come. See Report SA15 for details of this decision and for the selected modules in the Sample Analyzer.

**Design Justification:** The Sample Analyzer will meet the functionality and performance requirements allocated to it as described below.

- *Functionality:* The Sample Analyzer will perform all the functions allocated to it and represented in the Sample Analyzer EDFD. See Report SA15 for further details.
- *Throughput and Response Time:* The timing specifications allocated to the Sample Analyzer call for a throughput of twenty specimens per hour and a response time of no more than 2.5 minutes from receipt of a specimen by the Sample Analyzer to output of that specimen's raw results. The sub-modules of the Sample Analyzer were designed to meet this performance. See Report SA15 for further details.
- *Accuracy:* The accuracy allocated to the Sample Analyzer was ±5% in the measured pollutant concentration. This will be achieved with 99.5% confidence, subject to calibrating the system at least once per week. See Report ACC73 for more details.

**Required Constraints:** *(References to reports on all the "-ilities," on any other constraints that apply to the system, and on how the design will meet them would be listed here.)*

**Functionality and Cross-Reference:** The complete functionality of the Sample Analyzer is specified in the Sample Analyzer EDFD and its descendent diagrams and specifications. The allocations of these functions to the sub-modules is shown in the Sample Analyzer traceability matrix.

## 12.5 ARCHITECTURE INTERCONNECT SPECIFICATIONS

Our comments in Section 12.4 on the need for and the nature of architecture module specifications apply equally to this section. Like architecture modules, each architecture interconnect must have its own specification. Architecture interconnect specifications can be as lengthy as AMSs, and both may contain numerous references to trade-off studies, company and industry standards, other systems in the same family, and other specifications.

While architecture modules clearly present major design challenges and can even spawn major subprojects, the fact that interconnects can present similar challenges may be less obvious. For example, in a geographically distributed system, the need for a long-range, high-speed interconnect may spawn the development of an entirely new radio link.

Below, we sketch the typical content of the Local Bus AIS in the groundwater analysis system.

### 12.5.1 Architecture Interconnect Specification: Local Bus

**Description:** The Local Bus is an internal company-standard 16-bit parallel bus. See Specification BUS74 for more details.

**Design Rationale:** The bus was chosen for commonality with other company products, and it provides a parallel, multiplexed channel that is suitable for communications between the Workstation, the Sample Analyzer, the Bar Code Reader, and the Transceiver.

**Design Justification:** See Report CAP33 for an analysis of how this channel meets the capacity and throughput needs of the system.

**Required Constraints:** Specification BUS74 shows that this bus meets all the physical and environmental requirements of this system.

# 12.6 REQUIREMENTS AND ARCHITECTURE DICTIONARIES

Below are the requirements dictionary definitions for some of the data and control flows. Also below are the architecture dictionary definitions, physical descriptions, types, sources, destinations, and channel assignments for some of the architecture flows.

| Name | Definition | Type |
|---|---|---|
| ACCEPTABLE POLLUTANT CONCENTRATION | *Pollutant concentration in parts per million below which a given pollutant is acceptable* | Data |
| ACTUAL SCATTER DISTRIBUTION | *A set of points, each with an associated luminous intensity, in a two-dimensional plane representing the actual scatter of a white light beam passing through a mixture of a reagent and water that possibly contains a specified pollutant. [Include diagram here.]* | Data |
| ACTUAL SPECTRAL DISTRIBUTION | *A function of luminous intensity versus wavelength over the full visible spectrum, representing the actual spectral distribution of white light after passing through a mixture of a reagent and water that possibly contains a specified pollutant. [Include diagram or reference here.]* | Data |
| ANALYSIS COEFFICIENT CALIBRATION | POLLUTANT TYPE + ANALYSIS COEFFICIENTS<br><br>*An update to the ANALYSIS COEFFICIENTS for a given POLLUTANT TYPE arising from a calibration run.* | Data |
| ANALYSIS COEFFICIENTS | [ EXPECTED SPECTRAL DISTRIBUTION + SPECTRAL CONCENTRATION FACTOR \| EXPECTED SCATTER DISTRIBUTION + SCATTER CONCENTRATION FACTOR ]<br><br>*The expected properties of the light transmitted through a solution of a given pollutant. The spectral items are present only for chemical pollutants; the scatter items only for biological pollutants.* | Data |
| ANALYSIS CONDITIONS | RAW RESULTS AND DATA + SPECIMEN ID + EXPECTED POLLUTANTS + SPECIMEN DATA + REAGENT AVAILABILITY + WASTE ALERT + SAMPLING AND MIXING IN PROGRESS + STABILIZATION IN PROGRESS + TESTING IN PROGRESS + OPERATIONAL STATUS | Data |
| ANALYSIS DRIVERS | STABILIZATION PARAMETERS + TEST PARAMETERS + PROCESS SELECTIONS + SPECIMEN ID + EXPECTED POLLUTANTS + SPECIMEN ANALYSIS COMPLETE | Data |
| ANALYSIS PARAMETER CORRECTIONS | *Corrections to parameters in analysis algorithms in response to calibration results.* | Data |

*Figure 12.3: Requirements Dictionary (Continued).*

| Name | Definition | Type |
|------|-----------|------|
| ANALYSIS PARAMETERS | 1{POLLUTANT TYPE + ANALYSIS COEFFICIENTS + ACCEPTABLE POLLUTANT CONCENTRATION + VALID POLLUTANT RANGE}<br><br>*A list of the ANALYSIS COEFFICIENTS and ACCEPTABLE POLLUTANT LEVEL to be used with each POLLUTANT TYPE.* | Data |
| ANALYSIS RESULTS | SPECIMEN ID + SELECTED SPECIMEN DATA + 1{ POLLUTANT TYPE + [ POLLUTANT CONCENTRATION + POLLUTANT WARNING \| INVALID RESULT ] } | Data |
| CALIBRATION POLLUTANT | *Physical description of pollutant to be calibrated.* | Data |
| DATE AND TIME | *A calendar date and time of day.*<br><br>DOMAIN: Real | Data |
| DISPLAYS | SYSTEM STATUS DISPLAY + SYSTEM MODE DISPLAY + RESULTS DISPLAY + OPERATOR REQUEST DISPLAY | Data |
| EXPECTED POLLUTANTS | 1{POLLUTANT TYPE}<br><br>*The pollutants expected in a given groundwater specimen.* | Data |
| EXPECTED SCATTER DISTRIBUTION | *A set of points, each with an associated luminous intensity, in a two-dimensional plane representing the expected scatter of a white light beam passing through a mixture of a reagent and water that contains a specified pollutant with a specified concentration. [Include diagram or reference here.]* | Data |
| EXPECTED SPECTRAL DISTRIBUTION | *A function of luminous intensity versus wavelength over the full visible spectrum, representing the expected spectral distribution of white light after it passes through a mixture of a reagent and water that contains a specified pollutant with a specified concentration. [Include diagram or reference here.]* | Data |
| GROUNDWATER SPECIMEN | *A specimen of groundwater contained in a capped vial with data pertaining to the specimen imprinted on it both in narrative form and as a bar code. See specification for specimen vials and bar codes for further details.* | Data |
| HISTORICAL RESULTS | {ANALYSIS RESULTS + DATE AND TIME} | Data |
| HISTORICAL RESULTS REQUEST | (SPECIMEN SOURCE LOCATION) + (SPECIMEN ID) + (DATE AND TIME RANGE) + (POLLUTANT WARNING) + [ DELETE REQUEST \| DISPLAY REQUEST ] | Data |
| ILLEGAL ENTRY | *An indication that an operator keyboard entry does not match any of the specified forms.*<br><br>DOMAIN: [ Present \| Not Present ] | Data |
| INVALID RESULT | *Analysis result that is outside reasonable limits and therefore subject to rejection and possible specimen rerun.* | Data |

*Figure 12.3: Requirements Dictionary (Concluded).*

| Name | Definition/Physical Description | Type | Source | Destination | Channel |
|---|---|---|---|---|---|
| ANALYSIS CONDITIONS | RAW RESULTS AND DATA + SPECIMEN ID + EXPECTED POLLUTANTS + SPECIMEN DATA + REAGENT AVAILABILITY + WASTE ALERT + SAMPLING AND MIXING IN PROGRESS + STABILIZATION IN PROGRESS + TESTING IN PROGRESS + OPERATIONAL STATUS | Data | Sample Analyzer | Work-station | Internal System Bus |
| ANALYSIS DRIVERS | STABILIZATION PARAMETERS + TEST PARAMETERS + PROCESS SELECTIONS + SPECIMEN ID + EXPECTED POLLUTANTS + SPECIMEN ANALYSIS COMPLETE | Data | Work-station | Sample Analyzer | Internal System Bus |
| ENCODED SPECIMEN DATA | TBD | Data | Bar Code Reader | Sample Analyzer | Internal System Bus |
| KEYBOARD ENTRIES | *Groups of keystroke entries, separated by the chosen delimiters, for conversion into operator requests.*/See COTS Workstation specification for keyboard characteristics. | Data | Operator Procedures | Work-station | Keyboard |
| PRINTER FORMATTED RESULTS | TBD | Data | Worktation | Printer | Printer Cable |
| REAGENT | {[CHEMICAL POLLUTANT REAGENT \| BIOLOGICAL POLLUTANT REAGENT] + REAGENT TYPE} + REAGENT STORAGE | Data | Operator Procedures<br><br>Sample Analyzer | Sample Analyzer<br><br>Operator Procedures | Manual Reagent Loading<br><br>Manual Reagent Loading |
| SPECIMEN | [GROUNDWATER SPECIMEN \| REFERENCE SPECIMEN] | Data | Operator Procedures<br><br>Sample Analyzer<br><br>Bar Code Reader<br><br>Sample Analyzer<br><br>Operator Procedures<br><br>Bar Code Reader | Sample Analyzer<br><br>Operator Procedures<br><br>Sample Analyzer<br><br>Bar Code Reader<br><br>Bar Code Reader<br><br>Operator Procedures | Specimen Conveyor<br><br>Specimen Conveyor<br><br>Specimen Conveyor<br><br>Specimen Conveyor<br><br>Specimen Conveyor<br><br>Specimen Conveyor |

*Figure 12.4: Architecture Dictionary (Continued).*

| Name | Definition/Physical Description | Type | Source | Destination | Channel |
|---|---|---|---|---|---|
| SYSTEM STATUS DISPLAY | *Display of system status in accordance with system display specification.*/See COTS Workstation specification for display characteristics.<br><br>DOMAIN: [ "Fault" \| "Check Reagents and Waste" \| "Operational" \| "Running" ] | Data | Work-station | Operator Procedures | Display Screen |
| TRANS-MISSION FORMATTED RESULTS | TBD | Data | Work-station | Trans-ceiver | Internal System Bus |
| USED SPECIMEN | *A specimen that has been analyzed and is no longer needed by the system.*/ Residual specimen in original vial—see specimen and vial specifications. | Data | Sample Analyzer | Operator Procedures | Specimen Conveyor |
| WASTE | *Used test mixture.*/A mixture of groundwater and reagents for disposal in accordance with EPA regulations.<br><br>DOMAIN: Real | Data | Sample Analyzer<br><br>Sample Analyzer | <br><br>Operator Procedures | Waste Line |

*Figure 12.4: Architecture Dictionary (Concluded).*

# Chapter 13
# Groundwater Analysis System Summary

## 13.1 OVERVIEW

This completes the requirements and architecture models for the groundwater analysis system—at least, to the extent that can be described in a book. We started with some typically sketchy customer requirements, which included use of certain inputs and outputs, reuse of an Existing Sampling Module, and use of an off-the-shelf workstation.

The customer requirements were of all the types we described in Part I—required capabilities, required performance, and required constraints—and we fitted them into an incomplete model that served as a framework for the steps that followed. We built upon the incomplete model, pointing out the technical issues and trade-off studies that would typically arise in such a development. From the top-level essential model, we developed an enhanced model and an architecture context model. The Existing Sampling Module was embedded into a Sample Analyzer, which became one of the Level 1 modules of the system.

This combined bottom-up/top-down approach produced a partial model that allowed us to identify and insert the missing pieces. By choosing all the architecture modules, allocating the enhanced requirements model to them, further enhancing the allocated requirements, and allocating the resulting architecture flows to interconnects, we completed the system specification. Our system specification consists of the essential and enhanced requirements models for each architecture module, and the architecture model, which ties everything together. Details of the specification are contained in the PSPECs, CSPECs (if any), AMSs, AISs, and the requirements and architecture dictionaries. Traceability throughout is provided by the traceability matrices and by the structure of the model itself.

The system described in this case study is notable for the numerous different technologies it employs. The resulting system specification provides a cohesive source of requirements and top-level design for all of those technologies. Whether the technology specialists use our methods in their respective domains is an open decision, but regardless of their choice, the incoming requirements will be expressed in the same form and the impact of changes will be readily traced through all affected areas of the models.

# Appendix

# Changes, Improvements, and Misconceptions Since the Methods' Introduction

## A.1 A LEARNING EXPERIENCE

Since *Strategies for Real-Time System Specification* was published in 1987, the Hatley/Pirbhai methods—which, as we mentioned in Chapter 1, should now be called the Hatley/Hruschka/Pirbhai methods, or H/H/P—have been put to diverse use worldwide. We and many others have spent years training people in the system development process and in applying the requirements and architecture methods within that process. Simultaneously, many CASE tool developers have attempted to automate the methods in their products. Most importantly, many individuals, projects, and corporations have applied the process principles and the methods in their system development work. We have all learned a great deal throughout this process, and several changes and improvements have resulted. These changes and improvements are described throughout this book, but they are intermingled with the rest of the material wherever they best fit the general flow.

This Appendix identifies the changes and improvements, provides our rationale for making them, and references passages in the book that illustrate them. This information complements the information in *Strategies*, and together they will bring you completely up to date in the Hatley/Pirbhai methods.

Not surprisingly, several misconceptions about the methods have arisen over the years, some through the absence of information since *Strategies* was written, some through a lack of adequate training in the methods. This Appendix identifies the misconceptions—at least those of which we are aware—and explains how they came about and how to rectify them.

One of the founding principles of the methods is flexibility—the methods had to adapt to the varying needs of many users, and indeed they have. There are probably as many ways of using the methods as there are users. But some adaptations have been adopted almost universally, and it is these that are listed in this Appendix. We strongly recommend that, like everyone else who has used the methods, you should review and adapt the techniques in the context of your particular needs. Our only caveat is that you do this by design, not by accident, making sure that everyone involved agrees with the adaptations and uses them the same way. Otherwise, you will have chaos and disaster on your hands.

## A.2 CHANGES AND IMPROVEMENTS

The changes and improvements range from big hitters to minor details. In the following sections, we describe them in approximate order of descending significance.

### A.2.1 Superbubbles

The idea of superbubbles occurred to us almost immediately after *Strategies* was published—just too late, unfortunately, to get the message out to the world, though we immediately included them in our training. In *Strategies*, though, one figure—Figure 20.1: Partitioning between hardware and software—includes a rudimentary superbubble, but it is not identified as such. The principal means for representing the allocation of requirements to architecture modules was the traceability matrix, which provides a concise summary and is still very much a part of the methods but lacks the benefits of a graphical portrayal of the allocation. The matrix especially lacks a clear representation of processes that are split between multiple modules or allocated to multiple modules. Superbubbles on an enhanced DFD provide this graphical portrayal, and they have proved to be among the most powerful thinking tools for comparing and visualizing alternative system configurations. Superbubbles have become one of the most valuable and distinctive features of the methods.

Superbubbles are described and used extensively throughout this book. They are introduced in Section 4.5.2, and applied in the illustrations in Chapter 6 and in the case study in Part II.

## A.2.2 Addition of Object-Oriented Constructs

To say that object-orientation has taken the software world by storm would be a decided understatement. There are those in the OO world who would have us believe that everything that preceded OO is now worthless. In fact, OO, the requirements and architecture methods, and many other methods are all based upon many of the same principles. Object orientation adds to these fundamentals some extraordinarily powerful and valuable techniques for software development.

The requirements and architecture methods can be used in conjunction with these techniques. In fact, the architecture method was already remarkably similar to OO techniques, and the match becomes exact with the addition of a few constructs—which are introduced in Section 4.2 and will be kept up-to-date on the PSARE Website.

## A.2.3 The Total, Multileveled Methods Structure

Although it was implied in *Strategies* that the requirements and architecture models could be developed over multiple architectural levels, nowhere was this illustrated, and the ramifications of a multileveled model were not discussed. Constructing a multileveled model involves several structural issues—such as the number of requirements levels per architecture level, the introduction of derived requirements between levels, and the use of intermediate requirements and architecture context diagrams—that are not present in a single level.

The best overview of the multileveled structure is provided by Figure 6.1 and its accompanying text. Several of its ramifications are covered in other sections of this Appendix. The groundwater analysis system case study in Part II develops a multileveled architecture.

## A.2.4 Architecture Interconnect Context Diagram

In *Strategies*, we used architecture interconnect diagrams to represent the interconnects within the system, but we failed to illustrate their use in specifying the interconnects with the environment. Obviously, those external interconnects are at least as important as the internal ones. The architecture interconnect context diagram (AICD), which is simply a modified AID, shows the system module and its interconnects with the terminators. For clarity, what was in *Strategies* called the architecture context diagram is now referred to as the architecture flow context diagram (AFCD).

The AICD is introduced in Section 4.2.3 and used throughout the case study of Part II.

## A.2.5 Entity Model

In *Strategies*, the information model—now renamed the entity model—was discussed in a brief appendix, where it was given superficial coverage, at best. In systems that must store large volumes of data with complex interrelationships—that is, most modern systems—the entity model is essential. For consistency with object-oriented terminology, we also refer to the entity model as the entity class model. We introduce the entity model in depth in Section 4.3.2 after using it for illustration purposes in Section 2.2, and it is used throughout the book thereafter.

## A.2.6 Hardware/Software Interface

We modeled the hardware/software interface in *Strategies* by transitioning directly from a hardware/software module to separate hardware and software modules, but we did not address the specific interfaces that connect them. In this book, we cover the subject much more extensively, particularly in Section 6.4, detailing the various configurations and interconnects between hardware and software.

## A.2.7 Functions of Time in Data and Control Processes

In *Strategies*, we dealt very specifically with repetition rates of inputs and outputs—specified in the requirements dictionary—and with response times—specified in the timing specifications. A third, and equally important, facet of timing that we did not specifically address is functions of time in data and control processes. As discussed in Section 4.3.6, such functions frequently occur in real-world systems, and they have a significant impact on the interpretation of the requirements model.

## A.2.8 Extended Traceability

In *Strategies*, we covered traceability only through the traceability matrix, which covers traceability between the requirements and architecture within each architecture level. In fact, traceability is needed between many other elements of the models and between the model and external entities. All of these traceability links are equally important in obtaining complete assurance that all requirements have been satisfied and that every piece of architecture and design is fully justified. We cover this important topic in Section 5.3.4.

## A.2.9 Derived Requirements

We described in *Strategies* the enhanced requirements and the use of the architecture template to develop them, but we failed to address derived requirements, which are equally important. These requirements arise from architectural and design decisions that create new essential requirements in the architecture levels below. Derived requirements often change processes in the requirements model from primitive in one architecture level to non-primitive in the level below, leading to the formerly heretical construct of a process that has both a PSPEC and a child diagram.

Derived requirements are described in Sections 2.3 and 5.3.3, and they are illustrated in the case study of Part II.

## A.2.10 Special Cases of Architecture Flows and Interconnects

Conventionally, all architecture flows are allocated to architecture channels, and all architecture channels carry architecture flows. We said nothing to the contrary in *Strategies*. However, we find it is sometimes useful to have architecture flows without channels and architecture channels without flows.

In software development, architecture flow diagrams are customarily used without their corresponding interconnect diagrams. Software flows must, of course, travel by some medium or other between software modules, but the medium is invariably either memory or registers that are managed by the operating system and are not a direct concern of the architecture development.

In some systems—automobiles for example—such things as ground and power distribution are critical factors in system design. Architecture interconnects and their specifications can be used in such systems to define these distributions.

One might argue that the current flow through these interconnects should be represented as an architecture flow, but it is so elementary compared to other architecture flows that it can either be omitted or described in the interconnect specification.

We do not specifically address these special cases elsewhere in the book, but the examples given here illustrate circumstances in which they are useful and suggest other such uses that may apply to your systems.

## A.2.11 The Architecture Template as a Meta-Model

We introduced and used the architecture template in *Strategies* in the context of the methods. Later, we realized that the template represents a meta-model for system development and representation, regardless of the methods used. This theme is covered extensively in Section 3.4.2.

## A.2.12 PSPEC Guidelines

In *Strategies*, we covered the conventional structured English PSPECs described in the earlier literature, but we pointed out that other forms are acceptable—figures, diagrams, tables, equations, and so on—as long as they conform to the principles of balancing and data conservation. We emphasized that if a particular illustration would have been used in a traditional narrative specification (as they frequently are), then it should almost certainly be used in a structured specification, usually in a PSPEC. Unfortunately, this is one piece of advice that has rarely been followed by users of the methods, so—to paraphrase Yogi Berra—we reemphasize it all over again!

One more item needs to be mentioned here: Some users have embedded in PSPECs special languages that can be compiled and executed, thus linking the models directly to the software code. This is an excellent idea for lower-level applications of the methods, but beware of such approaches at the higher system levels, where specific computational algorithms are, by definition, not established.

## A.2.13 Extended Guidelines on Separation of Data and Control

We addressed the separation of data and control in *Strategies*, but it has remained a source of difficulty—unnecessarily, we believe. We have evolved several guidelines over the years, to help people deal with this problem. Here are some of them:

- If in doubt, make it data. The data model is simpler, and you can always change it later, if necessary.
- If you are really agonizing over whether to classify a flow or process as data or control, it probably doesn't matter much which one you choose. Many functions can be modeled either way—but remember the preceding guideline.
- The order of preference in constructing a model is: First, try no control (that is, use the process model only); if that is not possible, try combinational control; finally, if neither of the simpler approaches works, use sequential control. Apply this order of preference in every part of the model; you will minimize the extent and complexity of the control model and thereby simplify the entire model.

## A.2.14 Extended Guidelines for Architecture Module and Interconnect Specifications

The descriptions of architecture module and interconnect specifications in *Strategies* were quite scanty. Since these specifications are the foundation of the system architecture and design, we quickly developed more comprehensive guidelines for them. The actual content and format of AMSs and AISs are very specific to particular companies and projects, but there are some fundamental features they all must cover. Extended guidelines for AMSs and AISs are provided in Sections 4.2.5 and 4.2.6.

## A.2.15 Data Flows from CSPECs

In *Strategies*, we included data conditions (control flows that emanate from PSPECs) and process activators (CSPEC outputs that control processes in the process model), and we allowed flows to be categorized as data flows, control flows, or both. However, we did not provide any means for a CSPEC to have a data flow for an output, and it turns out that many systems need this. Consequently, we now allow CSPEC bars to appear on DFDs and to have data flows emanating from them.

It remains true that control flows cannot enter PSPECs. However, since a flow can be categorized as both a control and a data flow, it can enter a PSPEC as the latter. You might ask, Why have this rule at all? It is simply for clarity, to remind us of the purpose for which a particular flow is used in the model.

## A.2.16 Use of State Charts in CSPECs

While we were developing the requirements and architecture methods introduced in *Strategies,* David Harel at the Weismann Institute in Israel was developing state charts—an extremely elegant and powerful set of extensions to conventional state transition diagrams. Their only deficiency is that they can become quite complex and difficult to read when they have many states and transitions. State charts can be used very effectively to fulfill the main purpose of CSPECs: activating and deactivating processes. In Section 4.3.4, therefore, we extend the CSPEC tool set to include state charts.

## A.2.17 Elimination of Sequential and One-Shot Decision Tables and Process Activation Tables

In *Strategies,* we included the concepts of sequential and one-shot activation of processes in decision and process activation tables, but these ideas turned out to be fraught with possible ambiguities and other hazards. Instead, we now recommend using state transition diagrams or state charts for sequential and one-shot process activation, even if it means adding more states or introducing a whole new sequential machine. The benefits in clarity far outweigh the costs.

## A.2.18 Manual (Human) Subsystems

We did not emphasize sufficiently in *Strategies* the importance of representing human agents—operators, users, maintenance technicians, and so on—as intrinsic parts of a system. In many systems, operator and other human procedures are essential parts of system operation. They should be included as modules within the architecture model structure, subject to all the checks and balances of the methods. The difference is that instead of ending up as hardware and software, such modules become user or operator manuals. This idea is illustrated in the groundwater analysis case study in Part II.

## A.2.19 Primitive Process Notation

Some CASE tools use a special notation, often a double circle, for primitive processes. We have no objection to this notation when the tool itself can keep track of it and change it automatically when the model changes. When the meth ods are applied manually, this notation becomes just one more thing to remember to check.

## A.2.20 Stores Shown on Multiple Levels

Following the nonredundancy principle on which the methods are based, we recommended in *Strategies* that a store should only be shown on one diagram—generally, the diagram at the highest level in which it is used by more than one process. The store's flows then travel up and down through child diagrams in the usual way. Some people prefer to repeat the store symbol on every diagram as a reminder of where the flows came from. Like the primitive process notation, this approach presents no hazards when carried out by an automated tool; however, in manual applications, it can lead to errors, especially when the store name is changed in one place and not in another.

## A.2.21 Descriptions of Data Flow Diagrams

Structured Analysis purists contend that descriptions should not be added to a DFD—that the diagram alone must convey the message and any additional information can introduce ambiguities. While their argument is valid, and descriptive text should not extend or contradict the information the diagram *does* convey, the diagram does *not* convey some information that is well worth recording. That information includes the reasons that the diagram exists at all and that its particular form was chosen over all others. For the author and anyone else who has to work on the diagram in the future, this information can be extremely valuable as a historical record.

As we discussed earlier, some processes require both a PSPEC and a child diagram, and the former serves as a useful description of the latter.

## A.3 MISCONCEPTIONS ABOUT THE METHODS

The titles of the following sections spell out the misconceptions they address. Each section discusses how a misconception arose and how to correct it.

## A.3.1 The Methods Are Mostly for Real-Time and Embedded Applications

This misconception is a direct result of the title of the first book, *Strategies for Real-Time System Specification* [Hatley 88]. That title was chosen because the methods were first applied to a real-time embedded system—a flight management system for a commercial aircraft—and the real-time embedded market was considered the primary audience of the book. It was true from the outset, however, that the methods apply to all systems. If the methods are especially suited for any particular class of system, that would be large, complex systems—a very broad category encompassing most of today's systems, anyway.

## A.3.2 The Requirements Method Is More Important Than the Architecture Method

This misconception largely arose because the CASE tools that originally sought to support the methods in fact supported only the requirements method. As we emphasize in this book, the single greatest benefit of the architecture and requirements methods is the synergy between them, and neither one is more important than the other.

## A.3.3 The Most Significant Feature of the Requirements Model Is the Control Model

This and the following three misconceptions are closely related. The control model is certainly the most significant addition to basic SA, but the process model is a self-sufficient subset of the requirements model. In other words, the process model can be used alone, wherever it satisfactorily represents the requirements. Moreover, it should be used alone in those circumstances, because it is the simplest and most understandable model.

## A.3.4 Everything Involving Control Must Use the Control Model

The name of the control model clearly leads to this misconception, so we must accept full responsibility for any confusion. The control model was introduced for the specific purpose of representing major changes in the system's mode of operation, especially those involving major changes in system functionality. It does this by turning high-level processes in the process model on and off—an action that is not possible in basic SA. However, many engineering systems involve control without these major changes of functionality. The most notable example, perhaps, is a servo system, which includes a controller subsystem. Servo systems can usually be represented using the process model alone.

The key criterion for determining the need for the control model is that major changes of functionality are needed in different modes of operation; it is not that the word "control" is used to describe the system. The need for the control model is much more a facet of the method than of the system being specified.

## A.3.5 Everything Involved in Control Must Involve Control Flows

This misconception stems directly from the previous one, and the arguments against it are the same.

## A.3.6 All Discrete-Valued Flows Must Be Control Flows

This, too, is closely related to the preceding misconceptions, but it adds the flawed assumption that continuous-valued flows are normally data flows while discrete-valued flows are normally control flows. In fact, however, the data flows in a model can have any mix of continuous and discrete values, and in many systems, most of them are discrete. Control flows must be discrete-valued, but the converse is not true.

## A.3.7 The Methods Employ a Strictly Top-Down Decomposition Approach

This misconception is shared by all methods that have roots in SA and SD. It is beautifully countered by Parnas and Clemens in [Parnas 86], who point out that although completed models built with these approaches may appear to have been constructed through top-down decomposition, they can be and usually are constructed in whatever sequence best suits the system under development.

## A.3.8 The Methods Are Little Different from Basic Structured Analysis

This misconception is usually held by those who have only used the requirements model, which in turn is often due to the deficiencies of the earlier CASE tools (see A.3.2). Although the process model is almost identical to basic SA, the control model embodies a capability that is not available with SA, and the combined use of the architecture and requirements models extends the modeling scope beyond SA to the full, multidisciplinary system domain.

## A.3.9 The Methods Mostly Apply to Software

Structured Analysis has been applied mostly to software, and that is probably the cause of this misconception. The response is the same as for the previous item.

## A.3.10 The Methods Are Incompatible with Object-Orientation

We show in this book that with the addition of a modest number of new symbols, the architecture model and OO seem as if they were made for each other. Object orientation works best in the abstract world of software, in conjunction with more concrete methods at the higher system levels. For more details, see Section A.2.2 and its references.

## A.3.11 PSPECs Must Contain Sufficient Detail for Detailed Design

Having design-level detail in PSPECs was the usual practice in the early days of SA. However, when the requirements and architecture methods are used together, as they are today, the requirements model is divided into one sub-model for each architecture module. Within these sub-models, the PSPECs should only contain the level of detail appropriate for that architecture level. At the top levels of a large, complex system, the appropriate level of detail is far removed from that needed for detailed design. This issue, which involves the generation of derived requirements, is discussed in detail in Part I.

## A.3.12 The Models Should Be Executable

This misconception is closely related to the previous one. Executability implies that detailed system functions are known, but this is impossible at the higher system levels. Certainly, when the whole model set for a system is complete, it could be executed to produce a fairly accurate simulation of the real system. However, that degree of completion is usually not reached until late in a project. Any attempt to execute a model of the entire system without this degree of completion would require major assumptions about detailed system functions, and would therefore be of questionable value.

The execution or simulation of a system is certainly valuable, especially for verification of critical parts of a system early in development and for checking the functionality of the whole system later in development. However, the early, non-executable models are an essential part of development.

# Glossary

## INTRODUCTION

This Glossary provides an alphabetical list of system development words, phrases, acronyms, and abbreviations—with their definitions—that places particular emphasis on the Hatley/Hruschka/Pirbhai architecture and requirements methods and associated books and workshops. All of these terms are in common use among system developers and take on special meanings in the field of system engineering. Terms whose usage is consistent with standard dictionary definitions are not included here. This Glossary is not intended as an industry standard; nor is it meant to usurp such standards.

Items shown in *italics* in the definitions are defined elsewhere in the Glossary. Abbreviations are expanded without further definition; the expanded form is listed separately and defined there.

# GLOSSARY

**abstract, abstraction**  Expression of a statement in a more brief and generalized form.  In the *H/H/P methods*, the expression of a *data* or *control flow diagram* as a *parent process*.

**abstraction/detailing**  Characterization of a *layered structure* in which a given *layer* is an *abstraction* of the *layer* below, or a more *detailed* expression of the *layer* above.  A *layered set* of *DFDs* is an abstraction/detailing structure.

**ACD**    See **architecture context diagram**.

**action**  An activity resulting from a *transition* in a *sequential machine;* represented in an *STD* by the second label on a *transition*.

**activate**  Enable a *process* to carry out its *function*.  Performed by a *process activator* in the *H/H/P methods*.

**activator**  See **process activator**.

**AD**    See **architecture dictionary**.

**ADARTS**  A variation of *DARTS* focused on the Ada programming language.  The *architecture model* can transition to ADARTS at the level appropriate for detailed software design.

**AFCD**    See **architecture flow context diagram**.

**AFD**    See **architecture flow diagram**.

**aggregate, aggregation**  The assembling together of component parts.  In the *H/H/P* methods, the assembly of the *modules* in an *AFD* into its *parent module*, or the aggregation *relationship* in a *class diagram*.  Symbol: in a *class diagram*, a diamond symbol attached to the aggregate *entity*.

**aggregation/decomposition**  Characterization of a *layered structure* in which a given layer is an *aggregation* of elements from the *layer* below, or a *decomposition* of elements from the *layer* above.  A *layered set* of *AFDs* is an aggregation/decomposition structure.

**AICD**    See **architecture interconnect context diagram**.

**AID**    See **architecture interconnect diagram**.

**AIS**    See **architecture interconnect specification**.

**allocate, allocation**  Assignment of one *model's* elements to the elements of another—for example, the assignment of *requirements model* elements to *architecture modules* and *interconnects*.

**AMCD**    See **architecture message context diagram**.

**AMD**    See **architecture message diagram**.

**AMS**    See **architecture module specification**.

**analog**  Characterized by continuously varying values, as, for example, in a conventional audio amplifier.  Converse of *digital*.  The fundamental paradigm of the *process model* is analog.  (See also *continuous-valued*.)

**ancestor**  In a *layered structure*, any *layer* (or element within a *layer*) above the current layer.

**architect, architecting**  Someone who develops *architectures;* the act of developing *architectures*.

**architecture**  The major physical properties, style, structure, interactions, and purpose of a *system*. *Design* starts at the point at which architecture ends (but the boundary is fuzzy).

**architecture channel**  See **architecture interconnect**.

**architecture communication model**  A *layered set* of AFDs and/or AMDs with an AFCD and/or an AMCD at the highest *level*, *primitive modules* at the lowest *level* in each *vertical thread*, AMSs for all *modules*, and an AD.

**architecture context diagram (ACD)**  The highest of a *layered set* of *architecture diagrams*, showing the *system* as a single *module*, the *terminators* with which the *system* must interact, and the links between the two.  See AFCD, AICD, AMCD.

**architecture diagram**  Any of the diagrams in the *architecture model*.

**architecture dictionary (AD)**  A list or database of definitions of *architecture flows*, their physical descriptions, their *allocations* to *architecture interconnects*, and their source and destination *modules*.

**architecture flow**  *Information*, material, or energy that travels in or between *architecture modules* and/or *terminators*.  Symbol: a solid vector with horizontal and vertical segments marked with the *flow* name.

**architecture flow context diagram (AFCD)**  An ACD whose links between the *system module* and the *terminators* are *architecture flows*.  Special case of an AFD.

**architecture flow diagram (AFD)**  A diagram comprising *architecture modules* and *architecture flows*, or in an AFCD, one *module*, *terminators*, and *architecture flows*.

**architecture inheritance model**  A set of MIDs associated with the other *architecture diagrams* wherever *inheritance* is needed.

**architecture interconnect**  A physical medium over which *architecture flows* travel.  Examples are mechanical linkages, electrical buses, optical fibers, and radio waves.  Symbol: any of a wide variety of nondirectional line types, with horizontal and vertical segments, marked with the interconnect name.  Note the distinction between *interconnect* and *interface*.

**architecture interconnect context diagram (AICD)**  An ACD whose links between the *system module* and the *terminators* are *architecture interconnects*.  Special case of an AID.

**architecture interconnect diagram (AID)**  A diagram comprising *architecture modules* and *architecture interconnects*, or in an AICD, one *module*, *terminators*, and *interconnects*.

**architecture interconnect model**  A *layered set* of AIDs with an AICD at the highest *level*, *primitive modules* at the lowest *level* in each *vertical thread*, AISs for all *interconnects*, and an AD.

**architecture interconnect specification (AIS)**  A *specification*, usually narrative but with graphical illustrations as needed, defining the physical properties of an *architecture interconnect* together with its *rationale* and *justification*.

**architecture message context diagram (AMCD)**  An ACD whose links between the *system module* and the *terminators* are *messages*.  Special case of an AMD.

**architecture message diagram (AMD)**  A diagram comprising *modules* with *messages* passing between them and labeled with any *data* and *control information* associated with the *messages*.  Or in an AMCD, one *module*, *terminators*, and *messages*.  AMDs come in two styles—network style and hierarchy style.

**architecture method** The notation, syntax, semantics, guidelines, and heuristics that produce the *architecture model*.

**architecture model** The combination of the *architecture communication, interconnect,* and *inheritance models*. It represents the complete physical properties, structure, interactions, and purpose of a *system*. This is a *technology-dependent model*.

**architecture module** Anything from an entire *system* to any physically identified part of it. Symbol: a rounded rectangle *(bubtangle)*, marked with the module name and number.

**architecture module specification (AMS)** A *specification*, usually narrative but with graphical illustrations as needed, defining the physical properties of an *architecture module* together with its *rationale, justification,* and the elements *allocated* to it from the *requirements model*.

**architecture template** A graphical guide to *enhancing* the *essential model*, in which a region representing *core processing* is surrounded by four regions representing *user-interface processing, input processing, output processing,* and *support processing*.

**attribute** A property of an *entity* or *relationship* in an *entity model*, or of any element in a physical *model*.

**attribute specification** A *specification*, usually narrative but with graphical illustrations as needed, defining an *attribute* in an *entity model*.

**automated tool** A software-based tool automating a defined *method*.

**Axiom/Sys** An *automated tool* supporting the *H/H/P methods*, developed by STG.

**Backus-Naur form (BNF)** A notation used to define the structure of concatenated symbol strings in the *requirements* and *architecture dictionaries*.

**balance, balancing** *Consistency* between the inputs and outputs of *parent* and *child* diagrams or other model elements; the act of making these elements consistent.

**behavior, behavioral** The ability of a *system* to exhibit different *modes* of operation. Changes in *functionality* depending on internal or external *states*. Represented in the *H/H/P methods* by the *control model* acting on the *process model*.

**black box** An element in a *model* or *system* constructed so that other elements do not need to "see inside" it. Its overall *function* and its interfaces are known to the other elements, but how it implements them is not.

**block diagram** See *engineering block diagram*.

**BNF** See *Backus-Naur form*.

**Boolean (equation, logic)** A mathematical representation of *discrete-valued functions*. Named after its originator, George Boole.

**bubble** A *process* in a *DFD* or *CFD*.

**bubble chart, bubble diagram** See *data flow diagram*.

**bubtangle** A rounded rectangle used as the *architecture module* symbol. Derived from *bubble* + rectangle.

**C/DFD** See *control/data flow diagram*.

**capability** The ability of a *system* to perform one of its *required capabilities*. Note the distinction between capability and *required capability*.

**Capability Maturity Model (CMM)** A *model* for assessing the maturity of an organization's *development process*. It recognizes five maturity levels from 1 (initial or chaotic) to

5 (optimizing). Originally applied to software, but now extended to cover other disciplines including *systems*. Developed by the *SEI*.

**cardinality** See **multiplicity**.

**CASE (tool)** Originally, computer-aided software engineering (tool). Now also applies to *system* tools and to tools for both *systems* and software.

**CCD** See **control context diagram**.

**CFD** See **control flow diagram**.

**channel** See **interconnect**.

**child, grandchild, and subsequent "generations"** In a *layered structure*, the first, second, or subsequent *layer* below the current *layer*.

**class** See **entity class**.

**class diagram** A graphical representation, with supporting narrative *specifications*, of *entities* and *entity classes* and the *relationships* between them. The narrative *specifications* contain definitions of the *attributes* of the *entities*, *classes*, and *relationships*.

**class specification** A *specification* of the identifier, description, and *attributes* of a *class* in an *entity model*.

**client** A *customer*; an organization or person that pays for a *system*. For example, in the case of a commercial avionics system, it is the airframe manufacturer. (See also *operator, user.*)

**CMM** See **Capability Maturity Model**.

**CODARTS** See **Concurrent Design Approach for Real-Time Systems**.

**cohesion** A measure of the connectedness or commonality of purpose of the elements of a *subsystem, module,* or *component*. High cohesion usually signifies good *black-box* design. (See also *coupling.*)

**combinational (machine)** A *finite-state machine* whose current output vector is entirely determined by its current input vector and its transfer function. Thus, it has no memory. Usually represented by a *decision table*.

**comment** Text or illustration that accompanies a part of a *specification* in order to provide background information on that part without actually specifying anything.

**commercial off-the-shelf system (COTS)** A *system, subsystem,* or *system component* that is commercially available and used as part of a *system* under development.

**component** A low-level *system* element from which *sub-subsystems* are constructed.

**Concurrent Design Approach for Real-Time Systems (CODARTS)** A variation of *DARTS* focused on concurrent processing. The *architecture model* can change to CODARTS at the level appropriate for detailed *software design*.

**concurrent engineering, concurrent development** Originally devised to ensure good manufacturability by involving manufacturing engineers in the hardware *development process*. The techniques are now extended to ensure good *system integration* by involving any mix of disciplines in teams as needed throughout *system* development.

**conservation of data** The principle that all *flows* in a *model* must come from somewhere and go to somewhere.

**consistency (check)** See **balancing**.

**constraint** See **required constraint**.

**context** See **environment**.

**context diagram** A diagram at the highest *layer* in a *layered model*. It shows the *system* or its *functionality* as a single item, the *terminators* with which the *system* must interact, and the links between them. In the *H/H/P methods*, the *DCD*, *CCD*, *AFCD*, *AICD*, and *AMCD* are context diagrams.

**context module** The single *architecture module* in an *ACD*.

**context process** The single *process* in a *DCD* or *CCD*.

**continuous-valued** Having an arbitrarily large number of possible values within a finite range. Characteristic of *analog signals*. Converse of *discrete-valued*. In the *H/H/P methods*, any part of the *process model* may be continuous-valued, but no part of the *control model* may be.

**control, control element** In the *H/H/P methods*, *discrete-valued information* (and conceivably material or energy) used in the *control model* to *activate/deactivate processes* in the *process model* or to represent the *state* or *mode* of the *system*.

**control/data flow diagram (C/DFD)** The combination of a *CFD* and its corresponding *DFD*.

**control/data store** See **data/control store**.

**control context diagram (CCD)** The highest-*level* diagram of a *layered set* of *control flow diagrams*, showing the *system function* as a single *process*, the *terminators* with which the *system* must interact, and the *control flows* between the two. Special case of a *CFD*.

**control couple** The term for a *control flow* in *SD* and in *architecture message diagrams*. Symbol: a line with an arrowhead on one end showing direction of travel, and a filled circle on the other end.

**control element** See **control**.

**control flow, control signal** The movement of *control signals* between *processes* or between *processes* and *terminators* in a *control flow diagram*. Symbol: a free-form dashed vector with the *flow* name.

**control flow diagram (CFD)** A diagram consisting of *processes*, *stores*, *CSPEC bars*, and *control flows*, or in a *CCD*, one *process*, *terminators*, and the *control flows* between them.

**controlling/controlled** Characterization of a *layered structure* in which elements in one *layer* control elements in the *layer* below, or are controlled by elements in the *layer* above. A *CSPEC* and its *DFD* are a controlling/controlled structure.

**control method** The notation, syntax, semantics, guidelines, and heuristics that produce the *control model*.

**control model** A *layered set* of *CFDs* with, optionally, a *CCD* at the highest *level*, and *CSPECs* at other *levels* as needed to *control processes* in the *process model* and to generate *control flows*. This also includes a *TSPEC* and an *RD*. It is an optional part of the *requirements model*.

**control process, control function** See **control specification**.

**control signal** A *discrete-valued* variable represented as a *control flow* in the *control model*.

**control specification (CSPEC)** A *specification* containing one or more *finite-state machines*, with *control flows* from the corresponding *CFD* as inputs, and as outputs at least one *control flow* to the corresponding *CFD* and/or at least one *process activator* to a *process* on the corresponding *DFD*.

**control store** A *store* that contains *control elements* only.

***core processing, core functions*** *Essential requirements* allocated to the central region of the *architecture template*.

***core requirement*** See ***essential requirement***.

**COTS** See ***commercial off-the-shelf system***.

***coupling*** A measure of the connectedness between elements within a *model, system,* or *component.* Low coupling usually indicates good *black-box* design. (See also *cohesion.)*

**CSPEC** See ***control specification***.

***CSPEC bar*** The interface between a *CFD* and its *CSPEC.* Symbol: a thick, solid line on a *CFD,* of any length and orientation, with *control flows* entering and/or leaving it.

***CSPEC guide*** A diagrammatic representation, contained within a *CSPEC,* of the elements and their interconnections in the remainder of the *CSPEC.* Usually used in large *CSPECs.*

***customer*** See ***client***.

**DARTS** See ***Design Approach for Real-Time Systems***.

***DARTS chart*** The diagram used in the *DARTS* method.

***data, data element*** *Information,* material, or energy used within a *system* or within the *models* representing it. Note that this term was inherited from *SA* and can cause confusion because of its broader meaning in the *H/H/P methods.*

***data/control store*** A *store* containing both *data* and *control elements.*

***data condition*** A *control flow* generated by testing a *data flow* against one or more thresholds. In the *requirements model,* data conditions provide the link from the *process model* to the *control model (process activators* provide the link in the opposite direction).

***data context diagram (DCD)*** The highest-*level* diagram of a *layered set* of *data flow diagrams,* showing the *system function* as a single *process,* the *terminators* with which the *system* must interact, and the *data flows* between the *system function* and the *terminator.* Special case of a *DFD.*

***data couple*** The name for a *data flow* in *SD* and in *architecture message diagrams.* Symbol: a line with an arrowhead on one end showing direction of travel, and an empty circle on the other end.

***data dictionary (DD)*** A list or database of *data flow* definitions used in standard *SA.* Replaced with the *RD* in the *H/H/P methods.*

***data flow*** The movement of *data elements* between *processes* or between *processes* and *terminators* in a *data flow diagram.* Symbol: a free-form solid vector, marked with the *flow* name.

***data flow diagram (DFD)*** A diagram consisting of *processes, stores,* and *data flows,* or in a *DCD,* one *process* and *terminators,* connected by *data flows* between them.

***data model*** See ***entity model***.

***data signal*** See ***data flow***.

***data store*** A *store* containing *data elements* only.

**DCD** See ***data context diagram***.

**DD** See ***data dictionary***.

***deactivate*** Prevent a *process* from carrying out its *function.* Performed by a *process activator* in the *H/H/P methods.*

**decision table (DT)** A tabular representation of a *combinational machine* having input columns on the left, output columns on the right, and input and output values in the body. Used in *CSPECs* and *PSPECs*.

**decompose, decomposition** To divide a *system, model,* or any part of either into its *component* pieces.

**demultiplex** The retrieval of the original separate signals from a *multiplexed* signal stream.

**demux** See **demultiplex**. (See also *mux.*)

**derived requirement** A *requirement* arising from a *design* decision rather than directly from a *stakeholder need*.

**descendant** In a *layered structure,* any *layer* (or element within a *layer)* below the current *layer*.

**design** A representation of the physical realization of a *system* or *component*. Design starts where *architecture* ends, but the boundary is fuzzy.

**Design Approach for Real-Time Systems (DARTS)** A *method* developed by the *Software Productivity Consortium (SPC)* (www.software.org) especially suitable for *real-time* software systems. The *architecture model* can transition to DARTS at the level appropriate for detailed software *design*.

**detail, detailing** Expression of a statement in a longer and more specific form. In the *H/H/P methods,* the expression of a *process* as a *child* diagram.

**development process** The entire activity of converting a set of *stakeholder* needs into a deliverable, working *system*.

**DFD** See **data flow diagram**.

**dictionary** A list or database of definitions.

**digital** Characterized by *discrete-valued* representations of all variables, regardless of whether they are *continuous-* or *discrete-valued* in the real world. Converse of *analog*.

**discrete-valued** Having a finite number of possible values. Can be used to represent *states* or *modes,* or to represent sampled values of *signals* whose physical form is *analog*. Converse of *continuous-valued*. In the *H/H/P methods,* the *control model* is entirely discrete-valued; elements of the *process* model may be any mix of *continuous-* or discrete-valued.

**DT** See **decision table**.

**dynamic allocation** *Allocation* of *requirements* to *architecture* or *design* that is determined (usually by software) during *system* operation, and may vary from time to time. (Compare to *static allocation.)*

**EC/DFD** See **enhanced control/data flow diagram**.

**ECBS** See **Engineering of Computer-Based Systems**.

**EDFD** See **enhanced data flow diagram**.

**embedded system** A *system* that is installed within a larger *system* and which, from the *user's* or *operator's* point of view, is part of the larger *system*.

**engineering block diagram** The traditional representation in engineering of a *system* or any part of it, in which rectangles stand for *system* elements and lines of various kinds stand for their *interfaces*. The diagrams are ad hoc and not formalized. The basis for the *architecture method*.

**Engineering of Computer-Based Systems (ECBS)** An IEEE Technical Committee of leaders in the software engineering and computer science fields. The committee studies the selection, interfacing, and integration of embedded computers and their software with their host systems. See www.ece.arizona.edu/department/ecbs/.

**enhance, enhancement** Produce *enhanced requirements*.

**enhanced control/data flow diagram (EC/DFD)** The combination of an ECFD with its corresponding *EDFD*.

**enhanced control flow diagram (ECFD)** A *CFD* that has had the *architecture template* applied to it, and has had any necessary *requirements* added in the *enhancement regions*. These *enhancements* may include additions to the associated *CSPEC* or the addition of a *CSPEC* where none existed.

**enhanced data flow diagram (EDFD)** A *DFD* that has had the *architecture template* applied to it, and has had any necessary *requirements* added in the *enhancement regions*.

**enhanced requirement** A *derived requirement* resulting from the introduction of new *interfaces* within a *system* as physical *partitioning* decisions are made.

**enhanced (requirements) model** A *requirements* model to which *enhanced requirements* have been added, making it suitable for *allocation* to the physical reality of an *architecture module*. This is a *technology-nonspecific* model.

**enhancement region** In the *architecture template*, any of the four regions, surrounding the central region, in which *enhanced requirements* are added.

**entity** An item of interest to a *user* or to the *system*, the item's properties therefore recorded in an *entity* model and stored within the *system*. Symbol: a rectangle with the *entity* name. (See also *entity class*.)

**entity class, class** A group of *entities* with some common *attributes* that characterize the group. Symbol: a rectangle with the class name.

**entity model** A *model* consisting of *class diagrams*, *class specifications*, *entity specifications*, and *relationship specifications*.

**entity specification** A *specification* of the identifier, description, and *attributes* of an *entity* in an *entity model*.

**environment** The elements outside of a *system* with which the *system* is required to interact.

**essential model, essential requirements** What a *system* is required to do regardless of the particular *implementation* chosen. The *requirements* that would be sufficient in a perfect world where everything is arbitrarily fast, has arbitrarily large capacity, can communicate telepathically, and is error-free. This is a *technology-independent* model.

**event** 1. An input that causes a *sequential machine* to perform a *transition*; represented by the first label on a *transition* in an *STD*. 2. An input stimulus to a system that causes it to carry out one or more of its *functions*; the output(s) that result from those *functions*.

**finite-state (machine) [FS(M)]** A *process* characterized by *discrete-valued* inputs, outputs, and a transfer function. In the *H/H/P methods*, a *CSPEC* is always finite-state; a *PSPEC* can be finite-state or *continuous-valued*. May be *combinational* or *sequential*. Basis for the *control model*.

**flow** The movement of *data* or *control elements* in a diagram; the notation representing this movement.

**flow diagram** Any diagram representing any kinds of *flows* between elements of a *system*. For example: *DFDs* and *AFDs*, but not *AIDs*, *class diagrams*, or *MIDs*.

**FSM** See *finite-state (machine)*.

**function, functional(ity)** An activity that a *system* or any part of it performs.

**functional decomposition** A term, often used erroneously, to describe a *layered set* of *DFDs*, which, in fact, is an *abstraction/detailing* structure.

**grandchild** See *child*.

**grandparent** See *parent*.

**H/H/P (methods)** See *Hatley/Hruschka/Pirbhai methods*

**H/P (methods)** See *Hatley/Pirbhai (methods)*.

**Hatley/Hruschka/Pirbhai methods (H/H/P methods)** The updated version of the *Hatley/Pirbhai* architecture and *requirements methods*, described in this book.

**Hatley/Pirbhai (methods) (H/P methods)** The *architecture* and *requirements methods* as described in *Strategies for Real-Time System Specification*. (See also *Hatley/Hruschka/Pirbhai methods*.)

**hierarchy** A *layered structure* in which a given *layer* is subordinate to the *layer* above and/or superior to the *layer* below (compare to *network*).

**implementation** The physical realization of a *system* or any part of it.

**INCOSE** See *International Council on Systems Engineering*.

**information hiding** The principle underlying *black-box design*, whereby the internal details of an element are not visible from outside the element.

**information model** See *class model*.

**information system (IS)** A *system* that deals only with information (as opposed to dealing also with material and energy).

**inherit, inheritance** The *allocation* of the *attributes* of one model element to another. A property of the *supertype/subtype relationship*. Symbol: in *MIDs*, a straight solid vector with an open arrow pointing at the *supertype module*; in *class diagrams*, a triangle pointing to the *supertype entity*.

**input processing** One of the *enhancement regions* of the *architecture template* in which inputs to the *core functions* are converted from their form in the world outside the corresponding *architecture module* to the form needed inside it.

**integration** The progressive physical linking together of the parts of a *system* or *component*.

**interconnect** See *architecture interconnect*. Note the distinction between interconnect and *interface*: An interconnect has at least two *interfaces*.

**interface** A boundary between two parts of a system. Note the distinction between *interconnect* and interface: An *interconnect* has at least two interfaces.

**International Council on Systems Engineering (INCOSE)** A volunteer organization dedicated to the *system engineering* discipline (www.incose.com).

**IS** See *information system*.

**is-a (relationship)** See **supertype/subtype (relationship)**. The *subtype* "is a" instance of the *supertype*.

**justification** A statement by *architect(s)* or designer(s) on why they believe their approach will meet the incoming *requirements*.

**layer** One of the groups of elements in a *layered model*.

**layered model, layered set, layered structure** A *model* or structure whose elements are arranged in ascending or descending groups (or *layers* or *levels*), the elements in the highest group being the most *abstract, aggregated, controlling*, or highest *supertype;* the elements in the lowest group being the most *detailed, decomposed, controlled*, or lowest *subtype*. The elements in the intermediate groups progress in sequence between these limits. Within each group, the elements usually form a *network*. (See also *abstraction/detailing; aggregation/decomposition; controlling/controlled; supertype/subtype*.)

**level** See **layer**.

**leveling** Constructing a *layered model*.

**life cycle** See **system life cycle**.

**Mealy model, Mealy machine** A *sequential machine* in which the *actions* are associated with the *transitions*. (See also *Moore model*.)

**message** A command passed from one *module* or *object* to another, possibly accompanied by *data* or *control information*, and possibly resulting in the return of *data* or *control information*.

**message specification** A *specification*, usually in narrative form but with graphical illustrations as needed, defining a *message* and its associated *data* and *control* transfers.

**meta-model** A *model* of a *model*. Often created by a *method* used to describe itself.

**method, structured method** An organized technique for performing a task more easily than would be the case without the method. A method comprises: a notation consisting of a set of symbols; a syntax that establishes the manner in which the symbols may be used together; semantics defining the meaning of the resulting diagrams; and guidelines and heuristics on how to use the symbols, syntax, and semantics. Examples: *H/H/P methods*, SA, SD, UML, and so on.

**MID** See **module inheritance diagram**.

**mini-spec** In standard SA, the *specification* of a *primitive process*. Replaced in the *H/H/P* methods by PSPEC.

**mode** The property of a *system* to exhibit different *functionalities* under different circumstances. Typical modes are normal operating mode and maintenance mode.

**model, modeling** A representation of one or more aspects of interest of a *system* with the intention that the representation is easier to understand and analyze than the whole *system*. The result of applying a *method*.

**module** See **architecture module**.

**module inheritance diagram (MID)** An *architecture diagram* with *modules* and *inheritance relationships* between them.

**module specification** See **architecture module specification**.

**Moore model, Moore machine** A *sequential machine* in which the *actions* are associated with the *states*. (See also *Mealy model*.)

***multiplex*** The combination of several signal sources into a common signal stream, typically for transmission over a signal bus. Multiplexing techniques include time-division, frequency-division, and many others.

***multiplicity (in a class diagram)*** The number of instances of an *entity* or *entity class* that participate in an instance of a *relationship*. Notation: N, for exactly N instances; M...N, for any number from M to N instances; *, for any number of instances, including zero. M and N are integers, with M ≥ 0; N ≥ 1.

***multiplicity (in an entity diagram)*** The number of instances of an *entity* that can participate in a single instance of a *relationship*. Shown as a number or range of numbers on the *relationship* linked with the *entities*. Also called *cardinality*.

***mux*** See ***multiplex***. (See also *demux*.)

***need*** Something that would benefit *stakeholder(s)*, and is therefore a candidate to become a *system requirement*.

***network (model)*** A collection of interconnected elements, all of which have similar status (compare to *layered model; hierarchy*).

***numbering*** The orderly assignment of numbers to the elements of a *model* in order to make it easier to navigate around the *model*.

***object*** Something in the real world that can be conveniently represented in software, together with its *attributes*, operations, and *data*, in such a way that the representation is as independent as possible from the rest of the software.

***object oriented, object orientation (OO)*** An approach to software development using *objects* as the principal construct.

***object-oriented analysis (OOA)*** Analysis of software *requirements* using an *object-oriented* approach.

***object-oriented design (OOD)*** *Design* of software using an *object-oriented* approach.

***OO*** See ***object oriented, object orientation***.

***OOA*** See ***object-oriented analysis***.

***OOD*** See ***object-oriented design***.

***operator*** An individual who directly operates a *system*. For example, for a commercial avionics system, it is the pilot. (See also *client, user*.)

***output processing*** One of the *enhancement regions* of the *architecture template* in which outputs from the *core functions* are converted from their form inside the corresponding *architecture module* to the form needed in the world outside it.

***parent, grandparent*** In a *layered structure*, the *layers* above the current *layer*.

***participation*** In a *class diagram*, an indication whether it is mandatory or optional that a *class* or *entity* take part in an instance of a *relationship*. Mandatory participation is indicated by a *multiplicity* that does not include zero; optional participation, by a *multiplicity* that does include zero.

***partitioning*** Division of an element in a model into its subsidiary or *child* elements.

***pass-through*** Allocation of a *requirement* to an *architecture module* in which the *requirement* passes through without alteration to a *module* in the *layer* below.

***PAT*** See ***process activation table***.

**performance** The actual accuracy, *timing*, and other measures with which a *system* performs its *required capabilities*. Note the distinction between performance and *required performance*.

**Pirbhai, Imtiaz (1954–1992)** One of the originators of the *H/P methods*.

**primitive** The lowest-*level* element of a *vertical thread* in a *layered model*.

**process** 1. An activity carried out by a *system* and shown on a *DFD*. Symbol: a circle containing the process name and number; *bubble*. 2. *Development process*.

**process activation table (PAT)** A *decision table* whose outputs are *process activators*.

**process activator** An output from a *CSPEC* that turns on and off a *process* in the corresponding *DFD*. Shown only in the *CSPEC*, not on the *DFD*. Process activators provide the link in the *requirements model* from the *control model* to the *process model* (*data conditions* provide the link in the other direction).

**process control** See *process activator*.

**Process for System Architecture and Requirements Engineering (PSARE)** The *system development process* described in this book, which may be supported by the *H/H/P* or other *methods*.

**process method** The notation, syntax, semantics, guidelines, and heuristics that produce the *process model*.

**process model** A *layered set* of *DFDs* with a *DCD* at the highest *level*, and a *PSPEC* at the lowest *level* of each *vertical thread*. Also includes a *TSPEC* and an *RD*. The process model is an essential part of the *requirements model*.

**process specification (PSPEC)** The *specification* of a *primitive process*.

**prototype** An early, usually incomplete, build of a *system* to investigate its operation prior to building the complete, fully operational *system*.

**PSARE** See *Process for System Architecture and Requirements Engineering*.

**PSPEC** See *process specification*.

**rationale** A record of the reasons why a particular *architecture* or *design* choice was made.

**RD** See *requirements dictionary*.

**real-time (RT)** Characterization of a *system* that must produce outputs within absolute time limits. Examples include aircraft weapon delivery systems and television broadcast control systems.

**real-time extensions** Additions to earlier *methods* providing *timing* and *control specifications*, making them suitable for representing *real-time systems*. The *control model* and *TSPEC* are real-time extensions of *SA*.

**relationship** A link in an *entity model* between two or more *classes* or *entities*, representing the association between them. Symbol: for a binary relationship, a line, with the relationship name, linking the two *classes* or *entities*; for ternary or greater relationships, a diamond, with the relationship name, connected by lines to the participating *classes* or *entities*. Some common relationship types have their own special symbols.

**relationship specification** A *specification* of the identifier, description, and *attributes* of a *relationship* in an *entity model*.

**required capability** Something a *system* is required to do; can usually be observed at the *system* outputs. Examples include producing the selected item from a vending machine and providing navigation for an aircraft. Note the distinction between required capability and *capability*.

**required constraint** A *requirement* that limits the *design* choices available to meet one or more *required capabilities*. Examples include thermal limits and cost limits.

**required performance** The required accuracy, *timing*, and other measures with which a *system* must meet its *required capabilities*. Note the distinction between required performance and *performance*.

**requirement** A characteristic a *system* must have in order to meet its *stakeholder needs*. Also known as a *required capability* or *required constraint*.

**requirements dictionary (RD)** A list or database of *data* and *control flow* definitions for a *requirements model*. Replaces the *DD* in basic *SA*.

**requirements method** The notation, syntax, semantics, guidelines, and heuristics that produce the *requirements model*.

**requirements model** The combination of a *process model* and, optionally, a *control model* into an integrated whole.

**role** In an *entity diagram*, a label on the link between an *entity* and a *relationship* indicating what purpose the *entity* serves when it participates in that *relationship*. Roles are mandatory with recursive *relationships*, optional elsewhere.

**RT** See *real-time*.

**SA** See *Structured Analysis*.

**SA/SD** A popular expression used to describe generically the early *methods* for structuring software.

**SD** See *Structured Design*.

**SEI** See *Software Engineering Institute*.

**sequential (machine)** A *finite-state machine* whose current output vector is determined by its current input vector, its transfer function, and past *events*. Thus, it has memory. Usually represented by an *STD*.

**signal** Any input or output of a *system*, any part of a *system*, or *models* thereof.

**Software Engineering Institute (SEI)** A government-funded department of Carnegie-Mellon University established to improve the state of US software technology. Source of the software *CMM*.

**specify, specification** To define the *requirements*, *architecture*, or *design* of a *system* or any part of a *system*; the document or *model* that results. The *architecture* and *requirements* models constitute specifications.

**stakeholder** Any person, group, or organization having a legitimate interest in a *system* to be developed. Stakeholders include *client*, *user*, *operator*, maintenance personnel, manufacturing, management, regulatory agencies, and many others. It is a *system engineering* responsibility to identify all the stakeholders and their *system needs*.

**starve your bubbles** A popular maxim for *SA*. Equivalent to minimizing *coupling* between *processes*.

**state**  A stable condition of a *sequential machine* in which it is waiting for the occurrence of one of a specified set of *events* that will cause it to make a *transition*. Symbol: a rectangle marked with the state name.

**state/event matrix**  An *STM* with the current *state* on one axis, *events* on the other.

**state/state matrix**  An *STM* with the "from" *state* on one axis and the "to" *state* on the other.

**state chart**  An extension to the *STD* in which *states* may have substates, sub-substates, and so on. Used in *CSPECs* and *PSPECs*.

**state transition**  A permitted change of *state* in a *sequential machine*. Usually, in a given machine, not all possible changes of *state* are permitted. Symbol: a vector between *states*, with horizontal and vertical segments, labeled with the associated *event* and, optionally, one or more resulting *actions*.

**state transition diagram (STD)**  A diagrammatic representation of a *sequential machine* comprising *states, transitions, events,* and *actions*. Used in *CSPECs* and *PSPECs*.

**state transition matrix (STM)**  A matrix representation of a *sequential machine*. There are two variants: the *state/state matrix* and the *state/event matrix*. Useful with machines that are too large or complex for an *STD*, *STMs* tend to encourage consideration of all combinations of the parameters on the axes. They are often quite sparse, and hence do not take up much space. Used in *CSPECs* and *PSPECs*.

**state transition table (STT)**  A tabular representation of a *sequential machine*. More compact than an *STM*, but does not encourage consideration of any parameter combinations. Used in *CSPECs* and *PSPECs*.

**static allocation**  *Allocation* of *requirements* to *architecture* or *design* that remains constant during *system* operation. (Compare to *dynamic allocation*.)

**STD**  See **state transition diagram**.

**STG**  See **Structured Technology Group**.

**STM**  See **state transition matrix**.

**store**  A representation of *data* or *control flow(s)* at rest, retained for later use. Symbol: a pair of parallel lines with the name of the store's contents.

**StructSoft**  The company that developed *Turbocase/Sys* (www.turbocase.com).

**structure chart**  The principal graphical tool of *SD*. Consists of *modules*, invocation vectors, *data couples, control couples, module specifications,* and a *dictionary*. Works well for single-thread software *processes*, but not for concurrent *processes*.

**Structured Analysis (SA)**  The original software *requirements* analysis *method* developed by DeMarco. The basis for the *process model*.

**Structured Design (SD)**  The original software *design method*, developed by Yourdon, Constantine, and others. The *architecture model* can transition to *SD* at the level appropriate for detailed software *design*. (See also *structure chart*.)

**structured English**  A constrained subset of the English language designed to make *process* and *module specifications* more rigorous, but still readable by the *stakeholder* community.

**structured method**  A popular but redundant expression for *method*.

**structured programming**  The original approach to improving software *implementation*. It placed constraints on the size and structure of individual software *modules*, but not on the interconnections between those *modules*.

***Structured Technology Group (STG)*** The company that developed *Axiom/Sys* (www.stg-case.com).

***STT*** See ***state transition table***.

***subsystem, sub-subsystem*** An identified part of a *system* that usually can be operated or *tested* independently of the *system*. (See also *component*.)

***subtype*** A *module, object, class,* or *entity* that *inherits* the *attributes* of other such item(s)— its *supertype(s)*.

***superbubble*** A heavy, free-form line, labeled with a *module* name, surrounding a subset of an *EDFD* (and possibly a subset of its *children*), showing that the subset(s) are *allocated* to the indicated *module*. Superbubbles may split a *process* (indicating different parts of the *process* are *allocated* to different *modules*), and more than one superbubble may surround a *process* (indicating *allocation* of an entire *process* to multiple *modules*). Thus, the *requirements* and *architecture models* are orthogonal—the structure of one does not constrain the structure of the other. This orthogonality, combined with the persistent links between the two models, is a key feature of the *H/H/P methods*.

***supertype*** A *module, object, class,* or *entity* whose *attributes* are *inherited* by other such item(s)—its *subtype(s)*.

***supertype/subtype*** Characterization of a *layered structure* in which elements in one *layer* are *supertypes* of elements in the *layer* below, or *subtypes* of elements in the *layer* above. Supertype/subtype *layers* are used in *MIDs, class diagrams,* and *OO* diagrams.

***support processing*** One of the *enhancement regions* of the *architecture template* in which *functions* are added to support the physical needs of the chosen *implementation*. Examples include built-in-test, redundancy management, and restocking supplies.

***system*** In *system engineering,* we are not involved with systems in general, but with people-made systems only, so our definition is restricted to these: People-made systems are organized sets of *components* that work together to provide some perceived benefit for people. This definition deliberately leaves open issues, such as: What constitutes an organized set? Who does the perceiving? Are the benefits real or imagined? and so on. These are issues to be resolved for each system by system engineers.

***system architecture*** See ***architecture***.

***system development process*** A *development process* applied at the *system level*.

***system engineering*** The discipline of applying engineering principles to the development of *systems*.

***system life cycle, life cycle*** The entire life of a *system* and its development, from initial *need* through development, deployment, and upgrade to retirement and/or replacement.

***system specification*** A complete description of the *requirements, architecture,* and *design* of a *system*. A complete *architecture* and *requirements model* constitutes a system specification.

**technology dependent (model)** That part of a *system model* that reflects the specific technology chosen for the *system*. In the *H/H/P methods*, the *architecture model*.

**technology independent (model)** That part of a *system model* that is invariant with technologies that might be chosen. In the *H/H/P methods*, the *essential requirements model* without *enhancements*.

**technology nonspecific (model)** That part of a *system model* that has made provision for supporting new *interfaces* introduced by *design* decisions, but has not allocated them to actual technologies. In the *H/H/P methods*, the *enhanced requirements model*.

**template** See **architecture template.**

**terminator** Something or someone external to the *system* with which the *system* must interact. Symbol: a rectangle with a name.

**test, testing** Examining a product of development in order to discover errors in it. The means of examination are virtually unlimited: They include, but are not limited to, operating, inspecting, reviewing, and analyzing. The products of development are similarly diverse: They include, but are not limited to, a *system, subsystem, component, model,* or *specification.* Errors are judged against prescribed criteria that the product of development is expected to meet. Note that the formal acceptance test, popular in military contracts, is *not* testing, because its goal is not to find errors. The *H/H/P methods* are not test methods, but testing benefits greatly from their organization and well-defined structure. (See also *verification, validation.)*

**time-continuous** Existing at all instants in time. Converse of *time-discrete.*

**time-discrete** Existing only at a finite number of instants within a finite period of time. Converse of *time-continuous.*

**timing** Any use of absolute or relative time within a *system* or a *model.* The *H/H/P methods* assume that all parts of the *models* have access to absolute and relative time. This greatly simplifies the *models* in many cases, but some *systems* with special timing *needs* must show timing as *flows.*

There are three types of timing: the rate at which inputs must be received or outputs generated, *specified* in the *RD* and *AD; functions* of time that the *system* must perform, *specified* in PSPECs and CSPECs; and input-to-output timing relationships, *specified* in TSPECs.

**timing specification (TSPEC)** A tabular *specification* listing input and output *events* of a *system* or *subsystem* and the required *timing relationships* between them.

**traceability** The ability to discover all pieces of *architecture* and *design* that were derived from a particular *requirement* (forward or downward traceability), and all *requirements* from which a particular piece of *architecture* or *design* was derived (upward, backward, or reverse traceability).

**traceability matrix** A matrix showing the *allocations* of elements of the *enhanced requirements model* to elements of the *architecture model.* An integral part of an *AMS.*

**trade-off study, trade study** Consideration of several potential *architectures* or *designs* to compare their pros and cons, and either to select one of them as the best candidate, or to look for other candidates. Trade-off study results are recorded in the *rationale* sections of *AMSs* and *AISs*.

**transaction center** A structure frequently found in *DFDs*, with multiple parallel *processes* all sharing one input or set of inputs, and all contributing to one output or set of outputs.

**transition** See **state transition**.

**truth table** See **decision table**.

**TSPEC** See **timing specification**.

**Turbocase/Sys** An *automated tool* supporting the *H/H/P methods*, developed by *StructSoft*.

**UML** See **Unified Modeling Language**.

**Unified Modeling Language** An *object-oriented* language developed by three of the leaders in the *OO* world—Booch, Jacobson, and Rumbaugh —in an attempt to bring unity to the many disparate *OO* approaches that existed earlier. See www.rational.com. The *architecture model* can transition to *UML* at the level appropriate for software *design*.

**use case** A description of an interaction between a *system* and its *users;* an operating scenario.

**use-case diagram** A *flow diagram* used in *UML* to represent a *use case*.

**user, end user** Something or someone that makes use of a *system* after *implementation*. For example, for a commercial avionics system, it is the airline. (See also *client, operator.*)

**user-interface processing** One of the *enhancement regions* of the *architecture template* in which the actual *user* I/O is interfaced with the *core functions*.

**validation, validation testing** *Testing* to determine if a set of *requirements*, and/or a *system* developed from them, fails to meet the original *stakeholder needs*.

**verification, verification testing** *Testing* to determine if a *system* or *component* fails to meet its *requirements*. Often, *requirements* are applied in addition to those from which the *system* was developed to check for operation beyond the specified limits.

**vertical thread** In a *layered structure*, a connected vertical set of elements. For example, in a set of *DFDs*, a *primitive process* and all its *ancestors*.

**white box** Part of a *system* whose internal details are accessible to other elements. Generally considered undesirable, but *testing* often entails white-box *testing*, even of *black boxes*.

# Bibliography

Boehm 86        Boehm, Barry W. "A Spiral Model of Software Development and
                Enhancement," *ACM SIGSOFT Software Engineering Notes*, Vol.
                11, No. 4 (August 1986), pp. 14–24.

Booch 94        Booch, Grady. *Object-Oriented Analysis and Design with Appli-
                cations*, 2nd ed. Redwood City, Calif.: Benjamin/Cummings,
                1994.

Booch 99        _____, James Rumbaugh, and Ivar Jacobson. *The Unified Mod-
                eling Language User Guide*. Reading, Mass.: Addison-Wesley,
                1999. The most recent information on this object-oriented pro-
                gramming language can be found on the Website of Rational
                Software Corporation: www.rational.com.

Brooks 87       Brooks, Frederick P., Jr. "No Silver Bullet: Essence and Acci-
                dents of Software Engineering," *Computer*, Vol. 20, No. 4 (April
                1987), pp. 10–19.

Chen 76         Chen, Peter. "The Entity-Relationship Model—Toward a Unified
                View of Data," *ACM Transactions on Database Systems*, Vol. 1,
                No. 1 (March 1976), pp. 9–36.

CMM

There is so much current activity on the Capability Maturity Model[SM] that anything we might reference here would be out of date before publication. Instead, we recommend visiting some of the key Websites for the latest status. The three most active sites are: www.incose.org, www.sei.cmu.edu, and www.software.org.

Coad 91

Coad, Peter, and Edward Yourdon. *Object-Oriented Design.* Englewood Cliffs, N.J.: Prentice-Hall, 1991.

Crosby 79

Crosby, Philip B. *Quality Is Free.* New York: McGraw-Hill, 1979.

DeMarco 78

DeMarco, Tom. *Structured Analysis and System Specification.* Englewood Cliffs, N.J.: Prentice-Hall, 1978.

Deming 86

Deming, W. Edwards. *Out of the Crisis.* Cambridge, Mass.: MIT Center for Advanced Engineering Study, 1986.

Eeles 98

Eeles, Peter, and Oliver Sims. *Building Business Objects.* New York: John Wiley & Sons, 1998.

Gomaa 93

Gomaa, Hassan. *Software Design Methods for Concurrent and Real-Time Systems.* Reading, Mass.: Addison-Wesley, 1993.

Gomaa 99

_____. "CODARTS: A Software Design Method for Concurrent and Real-Time Systems," *Proceedings of the Structured Technology Conference for Real-Time Systems.* Eindhoven, The Netherlands: Bergson Corporation, 1999. Visit www.bergson-tools.com.

Harel 87

Harel, David. "Statecharts: A Visual Formalism for Complex Systems," *Science of Computer Programming,* Vol. 8 (1987), pp. 231–74.

Hatley 88

Hatley, Derek, and Imtiaz Pirbhai. *Strategies for Real-Time System Specification,* Rev. ed. New York: Dorset House Publishing, 1988.

Hatley 94

Hatley, Derek. "Current System Development Practices Using the Hatley/Pirbhai Methods," *Systems Engineering: The Journal of the National Council on Systems Engineering,* Vol. 1, No. 1 (July/September 1994), pp. 31–38.

Hatley 97          _____, and Gary Rushton. "A Total Systems Approach to Automotive Development," *Proceedings of the Seventh Annual International Symposium of the International Council on Systems Engineering*, August 1997. Visit www.incose.org.

Jackson 83         Jackson, Michael. *System Development.* Englewood Cliffs, N.J.: Prentice-Hall, 1983.

Jacobson 92        Jacobson, Ivar, Magnus Christerson, Patrik Jonsson, and Gunnar Övergaard. *Object-Oriented Software Engineering: A Use Case Driven Approach.* Reading, Mass.: Addison-Wesley, 1992.

Jacobson 99        Jacobson, Ivar, Grady Booch, and James Rumbaugh. *The Unified Software Development Process.* Reading, Mass.: Addison-Wesley, 1999.

Maier 98           Maier, Mark, and Philippe Kruchten. "Tutorial: Systems and Software Architecture," *Eighth Annual International Symposium of the International Council on Systems Engineering*, July 1998. Visit www.incose.org.

McConnell 93       McConnell, Steve. *Code Complete.* Redmond, Wash.: Microsoft Press, 1993.

McMenamin 84       McMenamin, Stephen M., and John F. Palmer. *Essential Systems Analysis.* Englewood Cliffs, N.J.: Prentice-Hall, 1984.

Navabi 93          Navabi, Zainalabedin. *VHDL: Analysis and Modeling of Hardware.* New York: McGraw-Hill, 1993. A search for VHDL on the Web will produce numerous other references.

Page-Jones 88      Page-Jones, Meilir. *The Practical Guide to Structured Systems Design*, 2nd ed. Englewood Cliffs, N.J.: Prentice-Hall, 1988.

Page-Jones 95      _____. *What Every Programmer Should Know About Object-Oriented Design.* New York: Dorset House Publishing, 1995.

Parnas 71          Parnas, David. *On the Criteria to Be Used in Decomposing Systems into Modules.* Carnegie-Mellon University, Technical Report CMO-CS-71-101; AFOSR-TR-74-0095. Pittsburgh: 1971.

Parnas 86 _____, and Paul C. Clemens. "A Rational Design Process: How and Why to Fake It," *IEEE Transactions on Software Engineering*, Vol. SE-12, No. 2 (February 1986), pp. 251–57.

Pyle 93 Pyle, Ian, Peter Hruschka, Michel Lissandre, and Ken Jackson. *Real-Time Systems—Investigating Industrial Practice.* New York: John Wiley & Sons, 1993.

Rechtin 97 Rechtin, Eberhardt, and Mark Maier. *The Art of Systems Architecting.* Boca Raton, Fla.: CRC Press, 1997.

Robertson 98 Robertson, James, and Suzanne Robertson. *Complete Systems Analysis*, Rev. ed. New York: Dorset House Publishing, 1998.

Rumbaugh 91 Rumbaugh, James, Michael Blaha, William Premerlani, Frederick Eddy, and William Lorensen. *Object-Oriented Modeling and Design.* Englewood Cliffs, N.J.: Prentice-Hall, 1991.

Sheard 96 Sheard, Sarah. "Twelve Systems Engineering Roles," *Proceedings of the Sixth Annual International Symposium of the International Council on Systems Engineering* (July 1996), pp. 481–88. Visit www.incose.org.

Shenhar 97 Shenhar, Aaron J., and Zeev Bonen. "A New Taxonomy of Systems: Toward an Adaptive Systems Engineering Framework," *IEEE Transactions on Systems, Man, and Cybernetics*, Vol. 27, No. 2 (March 1997), pp. 137–45.

Shlaer 88 Shlaer, S., and S. Mellor. *Object-Oriented Systems Analysis.* Englewood Cliffs, N.J.: Prentice-Hall, 1988.

SOCE There is a large body of literature on concurrent engineering. There is also a professional society devoted to the subject: The Society of Concurrent Engineering. For information and references on this subject, visit their Website: www.soce.org.

Taylor 95 Taylor, David A. *Business Engineering with Object Technology.* Reading, Mass.: Addison-Wesley, 1995.

Weinberg 88 Weinberg, Gerald, and Daniela Weinberg. *General Principles of Systems Design.* New York: Dorset House Publishing, 1988.

Yourdon 75          Yourdon, Edward, and Larry Constantine. *Structured Design: Fundamentals of a Discipline of Computer Program and Systems Design.* Englewood Cliffs, N.J.: Prentice-Hall, 1975.

## TRAINING AND TOOLS

Training and consulting in the system development process and the architecture and requirements methods is available in the United States from System Strategies—2174 Rosewood Street, Jenison, Michigan 49428-8170, USA; Tel: (616) 669-9915; Fax: (616) 669-9916; E-mail: hatley@earthlink.net—and in Europe from the Atlantic Systems Guild, Langenbruchweg 71, D-52080 Aachen, Germany; Tel: (+49) 241-165670; Fax: (+49) 241-962150; E-mail: hruschka@system-bauhaus.de.

Also check the Websites www.ucce.edu/systemstrategies.html, www.systemsguild.com, and www.system-bauhaus.com for more details on training and consulting offerings. Automated tools that currently provide comprehensive support for the methods are Axiom/Sys (www.stgcase.com) and TurboCASE/Sys (www.turbocase.com). Review the ongoing case study that complements this book at www.psare.com.

# Index